CW00798218

First Nature

Fascinated by Fungi

Exploring the History, Mystery, Facts and Fiction of the Underworld Kingdom of Mushrooms

Pat O'Reilly

It's easy to see why the wood-rotting fungus *Fistulina hepatica* has been given the common name Beefsteak Fungus. In damp weather the illusion is further reinforced by droplets of blood-like liquid that seep from these bracket fungi when they are young and fresh.

for Sue

First published in the United Kingdom in 2011, reprinted in 2020

First Nature
Bwlchgwyn
Rhydlewis
Llandysul SA44 5RE
Wales, UK
email: enquiries@first-nature.com

ISBN13: 978-0-9560544-9-4

***Some fungi are deadly poisonous**, and even when they are correctly identified there are mushrooms that for most people are good edible species but which can cause allergic reactions or illness in others. The information in this book is accurate to the author's best knowledge, but neither the author nor the publishers can accept responsibility for incorrect identification of mushrooms or other fungi made as a result of the contents of this book.*

Featured cover pictures
Front: Porcelain Fungus *Mucidula mucida*
Back: Fluted Bird's Nest *Cyathus striatus*

Contents

Parasol mushrooms *Macrolepiota procera* sometimes grow in huge 'fairy rings' in unimproved grassland. Caps can be up to 40cm in diameter, making this one of the largest cap-and-stem fungi found in temperate parts of the world.

Acknowledgements

When the idea for a new book is born, it is like a newborn child: it makes little or no sense. As the idea for this book grew up I took advantage of the expert advice and guidance of many people, and I shall now try to remember to thank them all. And I shall fail, for sure, because so many people have been generous with suggestions for improving the plan and with donations of picture content as well as commenting on early drafts that have since been remoulded beyond recognition.

I am particularly indebted to Dr David Parker, Head of Science at the Countryside Council for Wales, for reviewing the scientific sections of the book. (If anything in the science section is still less than clear the fault is entirely mine, because David's guidance was both thorough and crystal clear.) The same is equally true of the scientific guidance provided by Dr Kevin Davies, chairman of the Orchid Study Group associated with the National Botanical Garden of Wales, to whom I am also indebted. Yet more invaluable advice was forthcoming from mycologists David Harries and Richard Shotbolt, who generously allowed me to draw upon their wealth of experience. Other collaborators whose encouragement and help have been invaluable include David Adamson, Vaisey Bramley, Brian Broad, Doug Collins, Dr Paul Digard, Andrew Dyer, Sigisfredo Garnica, Dr Nick Giles, Richard Haynes, Dr Sue Impey, Nigel Kent, Christine Kimpton, Gary Locket, Dr Nigel Reeve, Vincenzo Ricceri, Mike and Hilary Rose, Penny Turner, Tom Volk, Andrew Ward, Sandra Waring, Nathan Wilson and Ray Woods.

To borrow from (or should that be *plagiarise?*) American playwright Wilson Mizner (1876-1933), *'Copy from one, it's plagiarism; copy from many, it's research.'* Having come across no book that covered the scope I had in mind for *Fascinated by Fungi*, I did not have to resist the temptation to plagiarise, but I had a lot of help with my research. Inevitably, only a small part of this book is solely the result of my own observations while wandering through woodland and wayside, meadow and moorland in search of fungi. (The pictures for the most part *are*, of course, and some of the habitat and habit observations.) Having the opportunity to 'stand on the shoulders of giants' it would be arrogance and foolishness beyond measure to ignore the published works of past and present mycologists more perceptive, more thorough and far more expert than myself. I can only say a general 'thank you' to all whose work has enabled me to organise my own thoughts and observations in an attempt to build a small mound upon their mountainous achievements. I have included a bibliography (necessarily limited for reasons of space) at the back of this book; it includes works by several of my heroes, my favourite fungi folk. Many more are worthy of note, and so my thanks to you all, whether specifically noted herein or not.

Pat O'Reilly, West Wales, UK, 2011

***Pluteus aurantiorugosus*, a striking member of a group known as the 'shield' mushrooms, which grow on rotting timber. The diversity of colours and forms is one of the fascinations of exploring the fungal kingdom.**

Preface

A forty-year fascination with fungi has taught me that there is so much more to this subject than free food for the few who can separate the trustworthy and tasty from the treacherous and toxic. So much of modern life – food and drink production certainly, but also crucial processes in forestry, agriculture and horticulture, medicine, manufacturing and much more – depends upon fungi and their complex interactions with everything else in the living world. Some fungi are amazingly colourful, remarkably intricate and spectacularly beautiful; others are weird not only in their appearance but also in the ways (and the astonishing variety of places) that they grow. I might have written '*simply* weird', but simple is not a word I associate with fungi. For millennia their mysterious nature has intrigued the intrepid, while their fruits of field and forest have fed the fearless - and the (surprisingly few) resulting fatalities have fuelled myths and legends. Monks and murderers have turned mushrooms to their advantage; artists and authors have fallen for the fascination of fungi. Once enticed in to this quirky kingdom, the magical mix of majesty and mystery has enough power to captivate the interest for a lifetime

The downside of this multifaceted complexity is how difficult it is for newcomers to gain a broad view of this vast subject. Fortunately there are books. Forty years ago they were few and for the most part sparsely illustrated; today, with so many more people interested in fungi, there are hundreds of good books on the subject. My Fungi Bookshelf is bursting with books and journals on the subject. Many of these well-thumbed volumes are old friends frequently revisited. A few are on the science and ecology of fungi; many more are field guides from around the world. Even so, I eagerly snap up any new releases, because no book comes near to comprehensive coverage of the subject of fungi identification, and I still come across species that are not covered (as far as I can tell) in any of my existing books. And with several thousand large fungi known to exist in the UK and Northern Europe, and many more on other continents, there is still plenty of scope for yet more such publications.

So is this another field guide? Certainly not! However, newcomers to the subject should find lots of help to get started on identifying more than 400 of the most common, spectacular and distinctive fungi - species that can be sorted out in the field (or more often in the forest) with a high degree of confidence and without having to resort to a microscope or special chemical tests.

A scientific tome, then? Definitely not! The science of fungi is complex and still far from fully understood. There are one or two excellent books and several authoritative scientific journals, written and peer-reviewed by scientists for fellow professional mycologists (those who pursue the scientific study of fungi). This book contains only a layperson's introduction to the subject – but then it could only be so, because it is written by a layman.

So if it's neither a field guide nor a scientific treatise, what is this book? It is a broad, and I hope simple-to-follow, introduction to this complex subject. You might also say that it's a love story. Certainly a love of the subject has been my motivation for writing the book. In doing so I pay homage to one of the least understood kingdoms of the natural world by exploring some of the history, mystery, facts and fiction born out of the fascinating foibles of fungi. As just one of millions of people sharing this fascination, I urge you to join us in the search for a greater understanding of a crucial component of our life-support system. Welcome to the fascinating Kingdom of Fungi.

Preface to the Second Edition

In the five years since the first edition of this book was published, fungi have evolved... but so slightly that our technology is not refined enough to notice any change. Mycological knowledge – the science of fungi – has changed quite considerably, however. Molecular study (DNA analysis is the popular term) has, dare I say, mushroomed. Fungal DNA barcoding is helping to delineate species whose visible characteristics are not separable; it can also reveal the identity of fungi that reproduce asexually and make the very concept of a species problematic. This new science has collapsed some taxonomic groups to a fraction of their former species counts, while other accepted species and even genera have been shown to be complexes in need of separation. In this second edition I have updated the names of fungi whose classifications have been recently amended.

That is in no way justification for producing a second edition, but having been delighted at the popularity of the first edition of *Fascinated by Fungi*, I have seized the opportunity not only to make corrections (thankfully very few) but also, based on feedback from users of the first edition, to extend some sections and even to include a few new ones. In particular as high quality microscopy is now affordable to most amateur mycologists, I have extended the section on choosing, setting up and using a compound microscope. Chapter 10 now includes more details of the microscopic characters that help separate species, and examples of these features are illustrated by photomicrographs.

Having thanked people for their contributions and help with the first edition, I now have an even longer list of acknowledgements. Reiterating my gratitude to all listed on the original Acknowledgements page, I must now also thank many others. The Countryside Council for Wales (CCW) is no longer in existence, having been subsumed into a much larger multi-purpose Natural Resources Wales. Even when managed properly, such reorganisations can be disruptive and demoralising. Fortunately many of the staff that made CCW an effective conservation agency remain as committed as ever to the cause, and I can only reiterate my thanks and admiration to these resilient professionals. Thanks are due also to Rob Petley-Jones of Natural England; Dr Rosie Plummer and Dr Bruce Langridge of the National Botanic Garden of Wales; Dr Gareth Griffith of the Institute of Biological, Environmental and Rural Sciences, Aberystwyth University; and Dr Martyn Ainsworth of the Royal Botanical Gardens, Kew. Comments, suggestions and picture contributions from friends in many countries have been invaluable in the updating and extension of this book, and those to whom I am indebted include Patrea Anderson, Marco Barbanera, Zoran Bozovic, Geoff Dann, Rogerio Dias, Arnor Gullanger, Simon Harding, Alistair Hutchinson, David Kelly, James Langiewicz, David Lawman, Angelos Papadimitriou, Katherine Paterson, Bill Prince and Hugh Purvis.

So much of what we learn comes from being with fellow enthusiasts, and for me the forays and workshop sessions organised by the British Mycological Society are a continuing source of information and inspiration. I am deeply indebted to Penny Cullington, Alick Enrici, Shelly Evans, Caroline Hobart, Geoffrey Kibby, Peter Roberts, Peter Smith, Mario Tortelli and the many other BMS members who so generously make time to share their knowledge and expertise with others.

Pat O'Reilly, West Wales, UK, 2016

Chapter 1 - Kingdom of the Underworld

Exploring the Majesty, Mystery and Mythology of Mushrooms

Frisky dogs, slimy frogs, prickly hedgehogs – they are real living creatures: animals. A toddler could tell you that. Dogs bark and bite; dolls don't. Doggy needs real food; dolly's dinner is make-believe. Simple!

The Easter Cactus on granny's windowsill was real, too. Pretty, of course, but to a toddler not very exciting. It wasn't an animal; it was a plant – until granny became ill and we took over, lavishing upon it so much care (and water) that it collapsed and died.

This Easter Cactus may be pretty but it is hardly likely to do anything sudden and surprising; that's because it is a plant rather than an animal. In this respect fungi are more like plants than animals, but in many other respects they are more akin to animals, as we will see in the first two chapters of this book.

Animal, Vegetable or Mineral?

Plants and animals are living organisms, but the behaviour and needs of plants and of animals are so different that any visual similarities aren't likely to fool us for more than a moment. A stick insect isn't a stick, despite the amazing visual mimicry. Bees and nettles can sting, but even to a child the difference is immediately obvious: one is an animal, the other a plant - the living world neatly divided into these two realms, with everything else inert and lifeless conveniently classed as mineral. This simplistic view was not just for children; it was widely accepted by scientists until quite recent times. But we now know that Life on Earth is much more complex than that. There are at least six and possibly more groups of living things so different one from another that they justify the distinction of 'kingdoms'. Among these is the kingdom of fungi, one of the wackiest parts of our weird and wonderful world.

Spectacular Rustgills, scientific name *Gymnopilus junonius*. Conspicuous fungi such as these colourful woodland mushrooms are very much ethnic minorities in the largely hidden kingdom of fungi.

Learning about fungi is great fun, and if you join a fungus group you might even meet some fun guys. But in fact the origin of the name 'fungus' has no direct relationship with fun; it comes from the Greek word 'spoggos' meaning sponge – probably a reference to the spongy nature of the caps, gills and tubes that bear the reproductive parts of many of the larger and more conspicuous fungi.

The murky past of mushrooms

Mycology, the scientific study of fungi, has a limited and fragmentary history. The reason for this is mainly cultural. Because mushrooms were thought to be creations of the devil (or at least of evil spirits, wicked elves and powerful fairies capable of great mischief) few people were willing to get involved with the subject of fungi. To do so was considered (by The Church) sinful. Flowers, in contrast, have generally been associated with happiness and wellbeing, and as a result down through the centuries they have intrigued enquiring minds and provoked so much more serious study and informed debate.

Until the early 20th Century, the uniqueness of fungi was so little understood that they were considered to be inferior kinds of plants. They were lumped in with liverworts, mosses and the like and labelled 'lower plants' - for no better reason than their apparent habits of staying where they are born and not (at least overtly) preying on other organisms. Wrong on both counts, actually, as we shall see in Chapter 2, where we look at how evolution has equipped fungi to feed, breed and fight their corners in the modern world.

Right now let's consider just a few examples of the mystique, the magic and the many myths that mushrooms and other fungi have gathered in the last few thousand years of a history that, for some fungus-like organisms at least, stretches back perhaps as much as a million millennia.

Despite their sombre colours and contorted shapes, these Trumpet Chanterelles *Craterellus tubaeformis* (formerly referred to more often as *Cantharellus tubaeformis*) are delicious in sauces and casseroles. Fear of the unfamiliar still deters many people from sampling some of the finest and most abundant fruits of the forest.

Mycophobia and Mycophilia

A mycophobic culture is one in which most of the people have little interest in fungi (other than perhaps eating one or two species purchased in shops) and many have an irrational and sometimes intense fear of fungi. All too often that fear extends even to the cultivated button mushrooms that are sold in supermarkets. Serve any kind of mushrooms at a dinner party for new acquaintances and there's always a risk that someone will reject not just the mushrooms but the whole meal.

People born into mycophilic cultures are usually very familiar with wild fungi. They frequently see framed pictures of edible mushrooms, and poisonous ones too, decorating the walls of schools, offices and homes, and they eat a wide range of species. Collecting wild edible fungi for food is as common in mycophilic countries as blackberry picking is in Britain and Ireland, for example; however, familiarity and knowledge are not one and the same thing, and a little knowledge can be dangerous. Cases of fungus poisoning are far more common in mycophilic countries than in mycophobic countries.

Ethnomycology is the study of the historical uses of fungi and their impacts on societies. This branch of science grew up from an interest in psychoactive substances contained in fungi – notably psilocybin and psilocin - but it also encompasses medicinal, nutritional and other uses of fungi.

Robert G Wasson (1898 – 1986) became intrigued by this subject as a result of honeymooning with his Russian wife in the Catskill Mountains of the USA. Struck by the contrasting attitudes of people in Russia and in the USA towards fungi, Wasson wrote extensively on the topic. In 1957, after visiting Mexico and taking part in sacred mushroom rituals, the Wassons had an article published in *Life* magazine entitled *Seeking the Magic Mushroom.* It introduced the English-speaking world to psychoactive fungi just in time for the so-called 'beatnik' era.

Magic Mushrooms *Psilocybe semilanceata* are small grassland fungi with pixie-cap points; they contain the psychoactive compound psilocybin. In the UK psilocybin is a Class A drug, and possession of Magic Mushrooms is an offence under the Misuse of Drugs Act 2005.

Among his list of mycophobic countries Wasson included Britain, the USA and Canada as well as (rather more contentiously, perhaps) the Scandinavian countries. Much of southern Europe – most notably France and Italy – as well as the eastern European Slavic countries he categorised as mycophilic.

China, too, has a tradition of fungiphilia, with documentary evidence for this dating back at least 4000 years. (The degree of fungus interest or aversion varies, of course, within all countries.) It is clear from book sales and from membership of fungus groups that attitudes in many countries are now changing rapidly. Even in Britain, traditionally one of the most mycophobic of countries, the range of edible mushrooms available in supermarkets is far wider than it was thirty years ago; however, compared with, say, northern Italy or central France there is still a long way to go.

A roadside display of carved Ceps *Boletus edulis* in central France

One region of France has special reason to celebrate mushrooms; it is home to the world-famous Black Truffle *Tuber melanosporum*. Until recent times the only place these prized edible fungi were known to grow was among the roots of oaks in alkaline, limestone-rich soil in the Périgord region of southwest France. The Black Truffle is now cultivated in other countries, but it remains a very expensive delicacy. However, the harvest of Ceps *Boletus edulis* and other fine edible fungi in woods around Périgeaux and neighbouring towns greatly exceeds the truffle harvest, and local wild mushrooms of one sort or another are on the menu there during every month of the year.

Within the Périgord region, fungi of many kinds are gathered for food, and their importance to the community is overtly celebrated in many ways. For example, gigantic carved Ceps adorn roundabouts and civic gardens in several towns in this part of France. In many a café and restaurant the décor includes pictures, ceramics, carvings and numerous other artefacts made in the likeness of mushrooms of various shapes and colours. Some of the souvenir shops there are stocked almost exclusively with fungiform mementos that are as popular with locals as with visitors to the region.

One of many shelves of 'fungiphernalia' on display at a café in Villefranche-du-Périgord

Mushroom or toadstool?

There are no clear-cut definitions of the terms mushroom and toadstool. Both generally refer to fungi with caps and stems, rather than to bracket fungi, crusts, moulds and rusts or to the many microscopic fungi that so greatly outnumber those we can see. But what do people mean when they say either mushroom or toadstool? Are these terms truly interchangeable?

In English the name mushroom is often used when referring to edible fungi. The word may be a derivation from the French *mousseron*, one meaning of which is moss; hence it may simply be a reference to their often soft and sometimes fleecy moss-like texture. On the other hand there could be a habitat link: many mushrooms do indeed occur in mossy grassland and woodland areas. Other suggested origins include the French word *mouche* meaning fly, the Welsh *maes* meaning field, the Latin *mucus*, meaning slime.

Although for many people it has an altogether darker connotation than mushroom, the origin of the term toadstool is equally obscure. Possibly it is an association with toads and their poisonous warty skins, because toxins similar to those secreted by a toad's skin do occur in some poisonous fungi; or perhaps it comes from the German *todestolle*, meaning seat of death. Other than in posed situations, in a lifetime of walking in the countryside I have yet to come across a toad sitting on a toadstool (although I have seen many other small creatures sitting on fungi), but of course it could happen. If the first edible fungus seen by the world's first mycologist happened to have a toad sitting on it, surely the term toadstool would not now have anything at all to do with the edibility of fungi.

Toads are greatly misunderstood and so too are toadstools, but they have more in common than that. Toxins very similar to those secreted by the warty skin of a toad are also found in some kinds of toadstools.

The bufadienolide toxins (commonly called bufotoxins) secreted by the glands behind a toad's eyes and from the warts on its skin are part of its armour: a defence mechanism. They are the reason that toads can cause such discomfort to people who pick them up but then do not wash their hands right away. (Most predators that try to eat toads soon learn that they taste awful.) There is, however, no scientific basis for the belief that handling a toad can cause warts; warts are caused by viruses, and definitely not by toads.

Merely touching a poisonous mushroom poses little danger, as long as no bits of it get mixed up with food that you intend to eat (although it's advisable to avoid excessive handling of known toxic species). It is sad, therefore, that some people persistently kick over mushrooms in the mistaken belief that they are eradicating the fungi and hence reducing the risk of poisoning in future. In most instances they are merely depriving others of the pleasure of enjoying what are fascinating and in many cases very beautiful sights.

Briefly handling the deadly poisonous Lilac Fibrecap *Inocybe geophylla* var. *lilacina* is okay as long as none of it ends up in the mushroom risotto you are planning for that very special dinner party. It's wise, however, to wash hands before tucking in to a mid-foray picnic.

Nowadays the Field Mushrooms, Horse Mushrooms and others in the genus *Agaricus* are referred to by some fungi gatherers as the 'true mushrooms' or simply as 'mushrooms', with all other cap-and-stem fungi lumped together - the edible, the inedible and the poisonous – as 'toadstools.' The snag with this is that several *Agaricus* species are inedible (because they taste unpleasant) and a few are seriously poisonous.

The Yellow Stainer *Agaricus xanthodermus* can cause a very nasty stomach upset. Most other members of the genus *Agaricus* are edible and have the word Mushroom as part of their common name. (In this book 'mushroom' is used as a general term for any large fungal fruitbody of the cap-and-stem form.) When clarity is crucial, it is best to refer to all fungi simply as 'fungi' and to indicate a particular species by using its scientific name.

The Fungal Royal Family

The mushrooms that we see in grassland, on forest floors and sometimes on living trees are neither plants nor animals. They are not really organisms at all but merely parts of organisms. They are in fact the reproductive organs of fungi, organisms which lack the green pigment chlorophyll and are incapable of photosynthesising their own food. They are also unable to run, swim or fly away if danger threatens. If this sounds like the worst of both worlds (or should that be of both kingdoms?) you might wonder whether fungi have much of a future at all. If their past is anything to go by they will be around for at least as long as our planet supports plant and animal life. Recent research suggests that the first fungus-like organisms appeared on Earth something like 1,200 million years ago, whereas animal life is generally thought to stretch back a mere 600 million years and flowering plants perhaps no more than 130 million years.

Early fungi were microscopic. Indeed, the kingdom of fungi is today, as it always has been, dominated by vast numbers of species invisible to the naked eye. This book is not about the myriad microscopic mushrooms but about the flamboyant fungi, the (relatively) large ones that we see in woods and fields: the royal family of the vast fungal kingdom.

The diverse shapes and colours of fruitbodies are the visible evidence of a largely hidden kingdom of organisms that have evolved over hundreds of millions of years.

While a fungal organism (termed a mycelium) may take weeks, months or even years to grow to the stage where it is capable of reproducing, the sexual reproductive organs themselves - the mushrooms that mycologists generally refer to as fruitbodies - can go from non-existent to fully formed in just a few hours.

Murder by Mushrooms

The apparently magical ability of fungi to appear overnight and the fact some of them have been found to be deadly poisonous gave mushrooms rather a bad press. Clearly they were not animals, and yet they were so unlike most other 'plants' that, in some quarters at least, they hardly qualified as vegetables either.

Drawing extensively on earlier work by the physician Apollodorus, in the 2nd Century BC Nicander of Colophon, a Greek poet and physician with an interest in matters poisonous and in their antidotes, wrote of the *...evil ferment of the earth that men generally call fungi.* Even Pliny, the 1st Century Roman philosopher, who wrote in praise of truffles *...the most wonderful of all things is the fact that anything can spring up and live without a root*, seems to have had second thoughts. He later referred to them as *...imperfections of the earth* and questioned whether they were in fact alive at all. Despite all this uncertainty the Romans did eat some fungi. Indeed, if there is any truth in the tale then Claudius, the fourth emperor of Rome, who died in 54AD, was a victim of intentional mushroom poisoning. Those historians who feel the evidence for poisoning is convincing say that the emperor's wife Agrippina was involved in the murder plot.

Emperor Claudius (National Archaeological Museum of Naples)

A more recent case - one that excited great interest both in France and further afield - was that of Henri Girard. Around 1909 M. Girard, an insurance agent, lived in Montreuil-sous-Bois. Known as Gentleman Girard, he had many friends both locally and in Paris and was, by all accounts, well educated and very knowledgeable about literature, music, science and medicine. This latter interest proved to be particularly significant.

Henri Girard encouraged an acquaintance, M. Pernotte, to take out life insurance with two different companies for the total sum of 8,400 French francs. This money was to be paid to Girard in the event of M. Pernotte's death. Soon afterwards the whole Pernotte family went down with typhoid fever. As soon as they had recovered they took a holiday, but on their return M. Pernotte still felt unwell and Henri gave him a hypodermic injection – ostensibly medicine that would make him better. M. Pernotte died of poisoning and Henri received the insurance money, but police suspicions were raised when they found that, among other toxic substances, Girard had purchased cultures of the typhoid bacillus.

Girard came close to murdering at least two other men using typhoid organisms, but in each case they recovered. Undeterred, Henri switched his attention to poisonous fungi. His next victim was a M. Duroux, and true to form Girard had arranged insurance, this time without his victim's knowledge; as an insurance agent he could do this easily in those days. Amazingly, Duroux survived more than one poisoning attempt. Rather less fortunate was Madame Monin, a widow with whom Girard became rather more than friendly. Having taken out four life assurances on Mme Monin, Girard then poisoned her with a glass of wine reputedly laced with poison prepared from fungi. Shortly afterwards, the unfortunate Mme Monin collapsed in the street; she died a few hours later, a post-mortem examination suggesting mushroom poisoning as the cause of death. Girard almost certainly used Deathcaps *Amanita phalloides* in some of his poisoning potions.

By the time they were apprehended, Girard and two female accomplices had already claimed and received three of Mme Monin's life insurance payments. A fourth claim was met with suspicion and refusal by another insurer, and this ultimately led to Girard's arrest. Police investigations revealed a poisons laboratory in Girard's house and linked him and his accomplices to several other suspicious poisoning incidents, at least one of which had resulted in a death. Girard was set to appear before the criminal court in Paris, but in 1918, while in prison, he died of tuberculosis, thereby escaping the justice of the guillotine.

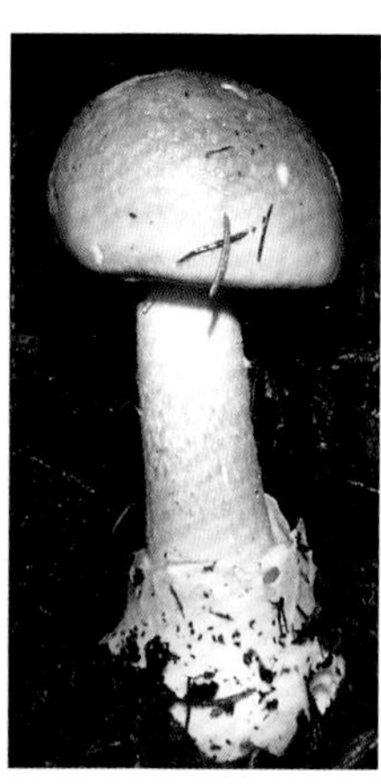

What's your poison, Monsieur Girard?

Henri Girard's wife and his mistress were convicted as accomplices to his dastardly crimes, and they received life sentences.

Murder by mushrooms may actually have been much less common than historical records suggest. It's likely that in the past, as now, any hint of uncertainty about the details of a celebrity's accidental death (or even a natural one) could do nothing but spark theories of conspiracy. Nevertheless, as fungi gained an increasingly bad reputation and with it the unenviable title 'excrescences of the earth' they were, in effect, being classed as minerals.

Accidental poisonings

The majority of victims of mushroom poisoning are very young children, and mercifully the species involved are rarely the Deathcap *Amanita phalloides,* but most often Brown Mottlegills *Panaeolina foenisecii* and occasionally other related little brown mushrooms that spring up in newly-mown lawns. The resulting sickness and discomfort are unpleasant but not usually life-threatening.

Brown Mottlegills
Panaeolina foenisecii

Mistaking poisonous fungi for edible ones is all too common. In 1994 two young men and a young woman ate some Deadly Webcaps *Cortinarius rubellus* having mistaken them for Chanterelles *Cantharellus cibarius*. They survived, but the two men had to have kidney transplants. In 2008 best-selling writer Nicholas Evans (of *The Horse Whisperer* fame) and members of his family made a similar mistake, with near-fatal consequences.

The Deathcap is the most common cause of death by accidental mushroom poisoning. This large pale mushroom is found throughout the world (it was reportedly introduced unintentionally to the Americas and Australasia along with imported oak tree species now cultivated there) and it is quite common and widespread in many countries. Although the fungi species involved are rarely stated, some horrifying statistics are published in countries where gathering wild fungi is a commonplace means of supplementing an otherwise scarce food supply. For example, in July 2000 the Ukraine Health Authority reported that at least 112 Ukrainians including 33 children, among whom was an entire family of seven people, had died that year of mushroom poisoning.

One-day Wonders

In *The Tempest*, William Shakespeare refers to Elves… *whose pastime is to make midnight mushrooms* - and in the 16th Century elves were definitely not considered trustworthy. At that time no one realised that mushrooms and other fungal fruitbodies are merely the reproductive parts of fungi that can live and grow unseen within soil, wood and many other kinds of organic material (including people, as anyone who has suffered from athlete's foot or from ring-worm can testify).

Human imagination fills knowledge vacuums with make believe which, despite a complete absence of evidence, becomes myth, folk lore and accepted truth. Pike, stealthy predator fish of weed-rich lakes and slow-flowing rivers, were once thought to come from the leaves of an aquatic plant known as pickerelweed (its scientific name is *Pontederia cordata*).

A pickerel, or young pike. In *The Compleat Angler* (first published in 1653), the bestselling fishing book of all time, Izaak Walton wrote:
…pickerel weed and glutinous matter, with the help of the sun's heat in some months, and some ponds apted for it by nature, do become pikes.

Since their seeds could not be found, it is hardly surprising that so many fictitious origins were also ascribed to fungi. Not until 1710 were fungal spores found and identified as such, as a result of the pioneering work of an Italian scientist Peter Anton Micheli (1679-1737). This discovery led to the realisation that fungal mycelia arose from a natural reproduction process rather than being the work of supernatural forces.

Although the fruitbodies of some kinds of wood-rotting fungi grow very slowly while periodically shedding spores over several years, many more fungi produce fruitbodies that last but a few days or perhaps a couple of weeks. A few are truly ephemeral, emerging, shedding their spores and then decaying and disappearing in a single day.

The Yellow Fieldcap *Bolbitius titubans* thrives on damp hay. Its bright-yellow toadstools appear overnight…

…but by mid afternoon they have faded to a dull fawn colour, and the following morning there is little or nothing left of them.

The Humongous Fungus Furore

While many fungi have but a few hours as visible fruitbodies and perhaps only a year as a living mycelium, others live and grow for hundreds and sometimes thousands of years, rivalling the oldest trees for longevity and even for size - of the mycelium mass, that is, not of an individual fruitbody as in some newspaper reports the discovery of the 'humongous fungus' was suggested to imply. The humongous fungus furore, as it came to be known, led to many claims and counter claims – promoted by the press, it should be said, not by the mycologists involved.

Honey Fungi can seriously damage forests.

It all started in 1992 with a huge group of Honey Fungi (*Armillaria* genus) reported from an oak forest near Crystal Falls, Michigan USA by scientists Myron Smith, Johann Bruhn and Jim Anderson.

DNA testing indicated that one of the mycelia extended over an area of 15 hectares (about 37 acres). It was estimated to be at least 1500 years old and to weigh around 100 tonnes. This would make it one of the world's largest living organisms.

Eight years after Smith and colleagues published their remarkable and very detailed findings, an even bigger Dark Honey Fungus *Armillaria ostoyae* was discovered in the Malheur National Forest in Oregon. This huge mushroom ring spanned some 890 hectares (2,200 acres), which would entitle it to the soubriquet 'the world's largest known living organism measured by area'. Its age has been estimated at nearly 2,500 years. Whether or not this is an individual organism is not entirely clear: unless all of the mycelium is interconnected it would have to be classed as a colony of several smaller individuals.

The largest single fruitbody so far recorded was a Giant Elm Bracket *Rigidoporus ulmarius*, at Kew Gardens in London. This parasite, which attacks deciduous broadleaf trees, grew to 1.7 metres x 1.4 metres and was half a metre thick; its weight was estimated at more than a quarter of a tonne. In comparison the largest mammals on the planet, blue whales, are much bigger, the record being held by a pregnant female some 33 metres long and estimated to weigh more than 170 tonnes.

Some trees grow even bigger and very much heavier than any of the animals. The General Sherman Tree (right), a Giant Redwood *Sequoiadendron giganteum* in Sequoia National Park, California is some 84 metres tall and is calculated to weigh well over 2000 tonnes. Coincidentally, its age is estimated at 2500 years, much the same as the age of the huge Dark Honey Fungus mentioned above.

Do Fungi hold the Secret of Eternal Life?

There is little doubt that individual mycelia can live for many hundreds and perhaps even a few thousands of years, rivalling in longevity the Bristlecone Pines *Pinus longaeva* in the White Mountains of California. The oldest of these, nicknamed Methusula, is still alive nearly 5000 years after its first tender shoot braved the windswept mountainside. But even this old pine is a mere youngster compared with the *real* Methusulas of the living world.

A research team led by Professor Eske Willerslev of Copenhagen University excavated bacteria which, despite being buried for half a million years in the permafrost of Canada, Siberia and Antarctica, were able to repair their DNA and to get on with life. This ability to repair the cell damage caused by ageing is the key to immortality, and if bacteria can do it then maybe somewhere there are species of fungi for which the grim reaper's harvest has failed. Perhaps in the end it all depends on what we mean by the term 'living organism'.

Fungal diversity

As soon as you take more than a passing interest in fungi, you cannot help but be struck by their amazing diversity. Smaller than the smallest plants, bigger than the biggest animals, in colours more varied than the rainbow and shapes quite unimaginable, fungi are constantly surprising the world of science and delighting all who marvel at the wonders of Nature. What's more, experts believe that the fungi so far identified, named and described represent just a tiny proportion of those in existence – probably no more than ten per cent.

Alder Bracket *Xanthoporia radiata* (until recently more generally known by the synonyms *Inonotus radiatus* and *Mensularia radiata*). Among the many wonders of the world of fungi is the tremendous diversity of shapes, colours and textures that fruitbodies adopt.

The Fungal Rainbow

The first time you come across a bright blue mushroom you could be forgiven for thinking that you have fallen victim to its arms-length hallucinatory powers. As with flowers, no colour within or outside the rainbow (including those illusory brown hues that are found everywhere *except* in rainbows) is beyond the realms of the kingdom of fungi.

Bright red caps of the Sickener *Russula emetica* stand out boldly against the green background of this mossy forest floor. The name says clearly 'not for lunch!'

The strongly-scented Aniseed Funnel *Clitocybe odora* is a woodland species. Its startling blue cap and stem gradually fade to dull fawn.

Golden Waxcaps *Hygrocybe chlorophana* can add a welcome splash of bright yellow to the green sward of old churchyards during late summer and autumn.

Greenish fruitbodies growing in moss or grass can be very hard to spot. This is a False Saffron Milkcap *Lactarius deterrimus*.

In damp woodland often in groups, under birch trees, the caps of the Orange Birch Bolete *Leccinum versipelle*, are easy to find.

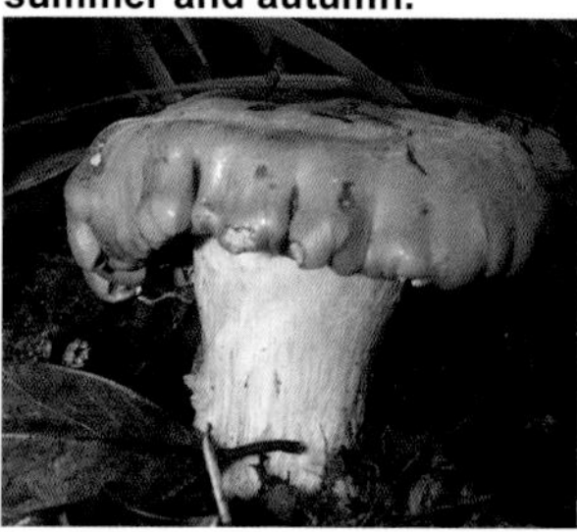

At the violet end of the spectrum are many toxic toadstools. This is the Mealy Bigfoot Webcap *Cortinarius caerulescens*.

The mushrooms purchased in greatest quantity in the UK are white cultivars derived from *Agaricus bisporus*, a brown-capped species that is still sold as Chestnut Mushrooms. (There are altogether too many brown-capped mushrooms, and because they are so difficult to identify most amateur fungiphiles steadfastly ignore the little brown mushrooms – LBMs, as they are unfondly termed.)

There are also multi-coloured mushrooms, some with spots, others with radial stripes or annular bands, and plenty that change colour dramatically over a period of just a few hours.

***Agaricus bisporus*, sold in shops as 'Chestnut Mushrooms'**

The shape of things to come (and go)

While a domed cap on a stem is the stereotypical mushroom or toadstool, fungi come in a great variety of other shapes and a vast range of sizes. Some are more or less spherical, others form neat cups or stemmed vases, and quite a number have inexplicably taken on forms remarkably similar to parts of the human body. The examples shown below are just a few of the many forms of fungi commonly encountered in fields and woods, on mountain tops and sea shores. If you can imagine a shape that you have never seen before, there's a very good chance that somewhere there is a fungus just like it!

The Yellow Swamp Brittlegill *Russula claroflava* is a typical stem-and-cap mushroom.

Earthstars often occur in very large colonies. This is the Daisy Earthstar *Geastrum floriforme*.

Scarlet Elfcups *Sarcoscypha austriaca* and many other kinds of cup fungi feed on rotting wood.

Bracket fungi like the Dryad's Saddle *Polyporus squamosus* have pores rather than gills on their fertile surface.

These fairy club fungi are known as Golden Spindles *Clavulinopsis fusiformis*, a species associated with unimproved grassland.

Red Cage *Clathrus ruber* has a lattice form and such a vivid red colour that on first sight it is hard to believe this really is a fungus.

When stumbled across in a churchyard, Dead Man's Fingers *Xylaria polymorpha* can give one quite a start!

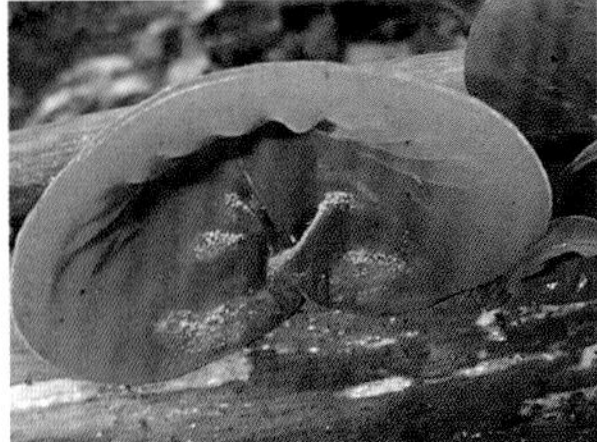

Jelly Ear Fungus *Auricularia auricula-judae* often has form, folds and texture very like a human ear.

The Victorians considered the physical appearance of the Stinkhorn *Phallus impudicus* to be offensive.

There are so many other shapes that fungi take. Some look like brains, others like buttons, leaves, ribbons, coral or worms. Fungi occur on soil, mud, sand and even concrete; on tree trunks, twigs, leaves and roots. Some fungi can even fruit under water or beneath snow.

Fungi – the Ultimate Shapeshifters

By the time a young bird leaves the nest it has a beak, legs, wings, feathers; it can feed and at least either hop, fly or swim; and in most respects it looks very much like one or other (or both) of its parents. Fungi are not generally like that. When fungal fruitbodies emerge from the substrate in which they are growing they may not look at all like the mushrooms or toadstools they are destined to become. This can make accurate identification of fungi more difficult in the early stages of their development; however, if you intend eating them then nothing less than certainty of identification will do.

Don't wait *too* long, however: fungi that we find good to eat are also attractive to insects, slugs and other creatures searching for a meal, and so the older mushrooms are quite likely to be half eaten or infested with maggots.

Freshly emerged from the forest floor and with its spherical cap closed so that the gills cannot be seen, this *Amanita rubescens*, commonly known as the Blusher because its flesh turns pink when bruised or cut, could easily be confused with several other kinds of woodland fungi that are poisonous.

The identity becomes much more obvious as the cap grows larger and becomes convex such that the gills beneath it can be examined easily.

Now the cap is fully expanded and the gills are busily releasing millions of fungal spores per hour. It would be best to leave this ageing one alone. While you would get more munch per mushroom by gathering mature specimens such as this, it is obvious from the damaged stem that 'someone else' has already taken a liking to it. They may still be inside and busily tucking in to a second helping.

Growing, growing...

In contrast with the gradual change in shape of *Amanita rubescens* and most other stem-and-cap mushrooms, some of the fungi whose fruitbodies develop as ball-like growths emerging from the underground mycelium go through a very sudden transition to maturity and an equally rapid demise.

The fruitbody of the Stinkhorn *Phallus impudicus* develops from an off-white egg-shaped ball that grows underground over a period of several weeks until it is about 6cm in diameter. At this stage the top of the ball often protrudes above the ground. A rubbery outer coating, known as the peridium, protects the developing fruitbody from damage as it expands and pushes against twigs on the woodland floor.

According to experts on such matters, at the ball stage (which has earned them the enticing name of witches' eggs) immature Stinkhorns are edible. Extensive research into the subject has so far failed to uncover any record of a fungus foray ending in a fight over these delicacies!

Within the egg is a compressed tapered stem covered at its upper end in an olive-coloured gelatinous gleba. Stinkhorns get their name from this smelly gleba, which contains the reproductive spores.

The white stem has a tough, sponge-like structure rather like expanded polystyrene, and as the tip breaks through the volva so the white stem grows upwards and outwards by incorporating expanding air bubbles.

Going, going...

Once the ball splits at the top, the stem expands fully in an hour or so. If you want to see Stinkhorns at this stage in their development you really need to get up early on a summer's morning before the air warms up and insects begin foraging for food.

And this is why...

With a vile smell (vile to our senses, that is) that is detectable up to a mile or more downwind of freshly-emerged Stinkhorns, it's hardly surprising that these fungi attract insects. Even in the darkest of forests, flies have no difficulty finding their way to the spore-bearing sticky gleba on the caps of Stinkhorn fungi.

...gone! Within a few minutes there is nothing more for the flies to eat, and they set off in search of another meal. Any spore-laden gleba attached to their feet is destined to end up in a potential new location for a Stinkhorn colony.

The universal veil

A protective casing known as the universal veil or peridium, enclosing the whole of the developing fruitbody, is a common feature of many, but by no means all, macrofungi.

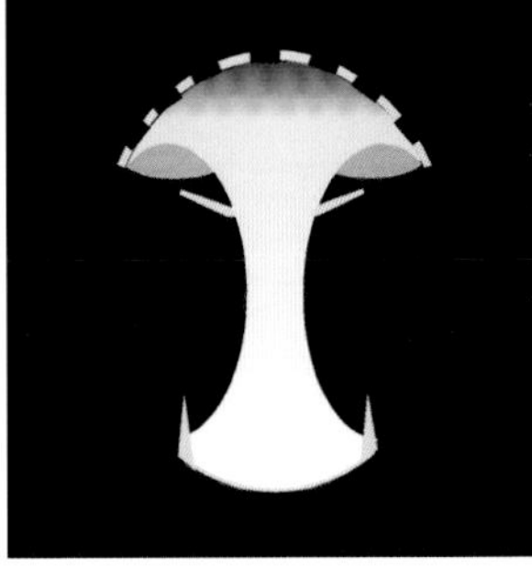

Initially (far left) the universal veil, shown here in pale blue, covers the entire embryonic mushroom. As the mushroom expands (near left) the veil ruptures, sometimes leaving fragments attached to the cap surface.

Fragments of the universal veil remain on the caps throughout the short life of some fruitbodies, serving as helpful identifying features. Sometimes buried out of sight, part of the universal veil may remain attached to the base, forming what is termed a volva.

This emerging Orange Grisette *Amanita crocea* has just pierced its universal veil, which remains as a bag-like volva at the base of the stem when the fruitbody is fully developed. In some species the volva shrinks to a narrow collar or rim around the base of the stem, while for many others there is no sign of universal veil remnants by the time the mushroom reaches maturity.

The developing fruitbodies of some mushrooms have chunks of the universal veil clinging to their caps only for a short while, whereas related species have caps that retain their veil fragments either in patches or as distinctive scale-like flakes.

When the universal veil is firmly attached to the young cap, expansion of the cap tears the veil into fragments that become increasingly more widely spaced on the surface of the mushroom cap. The veil fragments may be distributed regularly or randomly, they may be regular or irregular in shape, and they may lie flat on the cap surface or stick up like conical spikes; these features can be aids to identifying mushroom species.

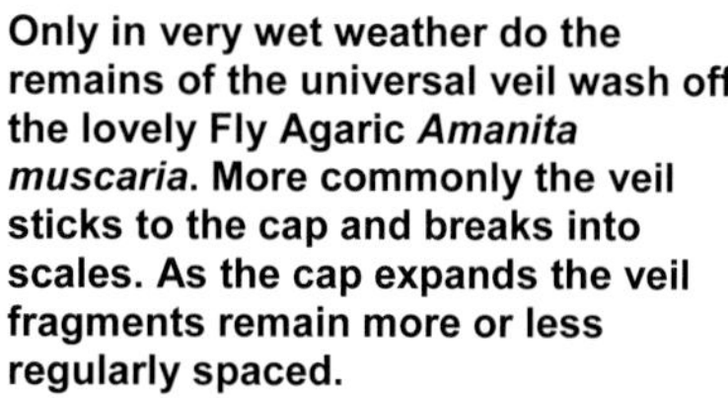

Only in very wet weather do the remains of the universal veil wash off the lovely Fly Agaric *Amanita muscaria*. More commonly the veil sticks to the cap and breaks into scales. As the cap expands the veil fragments remain more or less regularly spaced.

The tiny emerging cap at the bottom right in this picture is covered by a veil that is only just beginning to fracture, and at this stage none of the red cap surface is yet showing.

Although *Amanita* fungi are the best known of those whose universal veils leave prominently visible remains at the bases of the mushroom stems, there are several others, most notably members of the genus *Volvopluteus*. The large mushroom shown here is the Stubble Rosegill *Volvopluteus gloiocephalus* (until recently most often referred to as *Volvariella gloiocephala),* a grassland species. No remnants of the universal veil remain on the silky cap, however.

The partial veil

Many fungi protect their developing spore-bearing surfaces – gills or tubes, for example – by enclosing them in what is called a partial veil (covering just part of the fruitbody). As a veil it is short lived, since it has to fracture so that the fungal spores can escape, but remnants of the partial veil attached to either the stem or the cap (and sometimes to both) can be a helpful guide towards identification.

The partial veil of this Wood Mushroom *Agaricus sylvicola* is just beginning to fracture. Some fragments of partial veil material may be left attached to the rim of the cap, while others will adhere to the stem in the form of a ring that may either stretch upwards like a flared collar, or stand out, or hang downwards like a skirt.

The partial veil of this Horse Mushroom *Agaricus arvensis* has parted cleanly from the rim of the cap, leaving a distinctive cog-wheel pattern on a ring around the stem.

The remains of the partial veil are not always so distinctive. For example, the stem rings of the Honey Fungus *Armillaria mellea* vary tremendously from one sample to another. On the mushrooms shown here the stem rings are large and fluffy, but other examples of Honey Fungi may have much smaller rings.

The fluffy-capped Shaggy Inkcap *Coprinus comatus*, also commonly known as the Lawyer's Wig, is so distinctive that it is difficult to understand how anyone could have difficulty identifying it; however, another distinguishing feature is the neat little stem ring. As the fruitbody matures the ring 'lets go' of the stem and can easily be slid up and down. (Very few fungi have such 'free' rings.)

Often the stems of mature fruitbodies bear no trace whatsoever of the partial veil, and yet tattered shreds remain attached to the rim of the cap. This is generally so in the case of the Pale Brittlestem *Psathyrella candolleana*, a mushroom commonly found in mixed woodland or near to trees in fields.

Before drawing a veil (that was irresistible, sorry!) over this topic, there is another quite different form of temporary protective gill cover that you will certainly encounter if you take an interest in woodland fungi. It is characteristic of many of the species in a family known as the Cortinariaceae. Most fungi in this group have cobweb-like veils, and because of this some people refer to them collectively as the webcaps.

This kind of universal veil (known as a cortina) is very flimsy, so that when the cap expands the fine threads break, often leaving just a few barely-visible fragments of the web attached to the stem.

The presence of filaments from the cortina adhering to the stem becomes more obvious as the fruitbody matures and rusty brown spores begin falling from the gills. Some of the spores stick to the veil fibres on the stem and create a ring-like stained area around the mushroom stem.

Fungal Forms as Identifying Features

Field guides use a kind of shorthand to describe the shapes and textures of parts of a fungal fruitbody and the way in which the various parts adjoin one another. The most commonly encountered of these terms are illustrated in this brief section; these terms are used throughout the rest of the book when describing various fungi species.

Cap Forms:

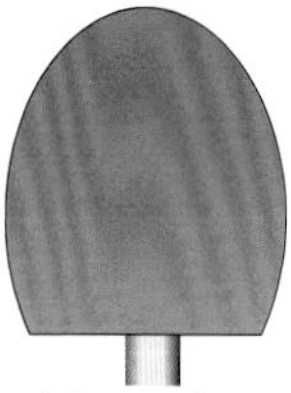

Oval (egg-shaped)

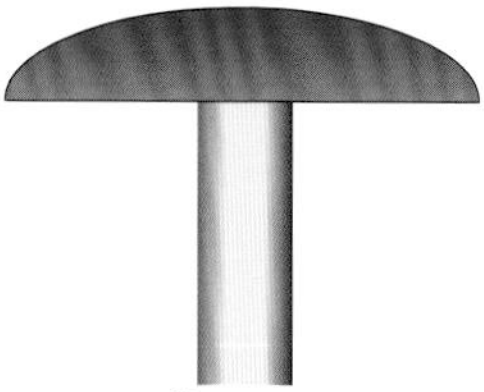

Convex

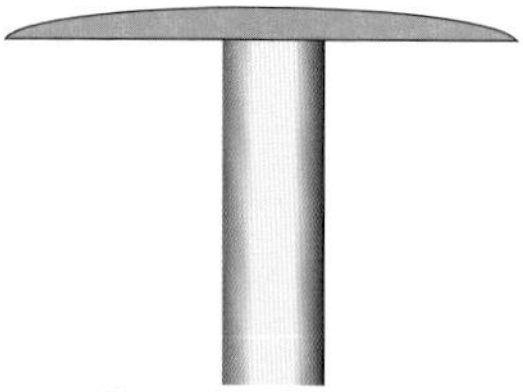

Broadly Convex

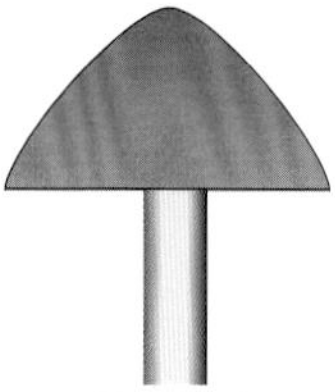

Conical

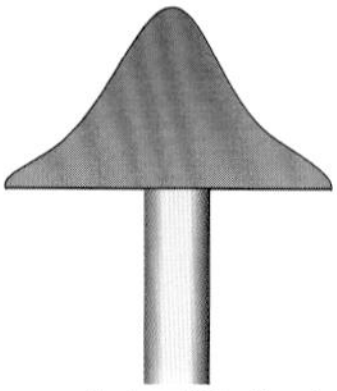

Campanulate (Bell-shaped)

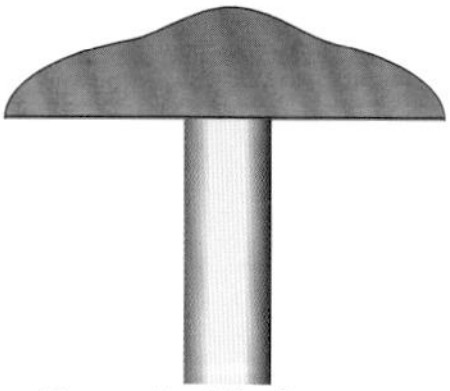

Broadly Umbonate

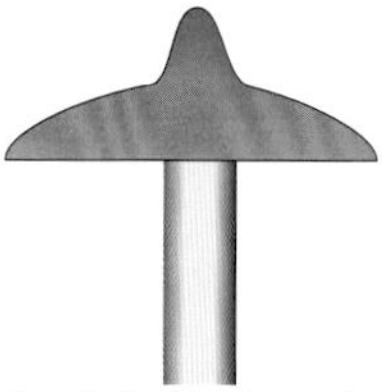

Acutely Umbonate

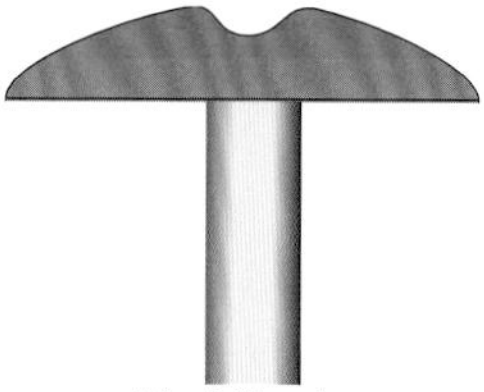

Umbilicate

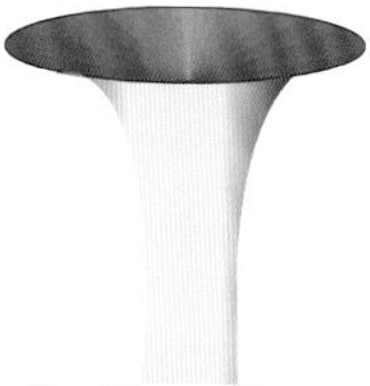

Infundibuliform (Funnelled)

Cap textures:

Smooth

Striate

Wrinkled

Scaly

Woolly

Fibrillose

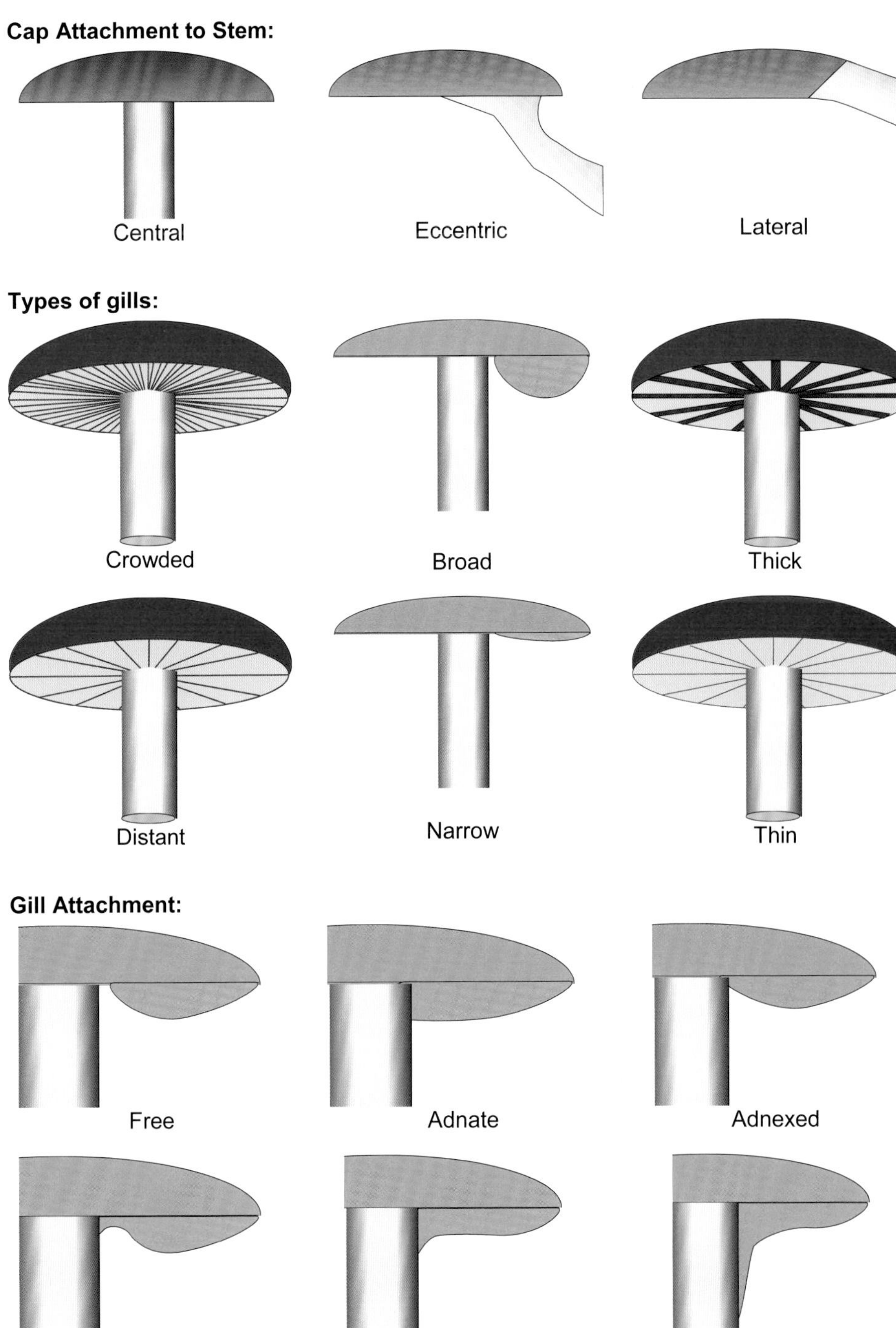
Cap Attachment to Stem:
Central
Eccentric
Lateral
Types of gills:
Crowded
Broad
Thick
Distant
Narrow
Thin
Gill Attachment:
Free
Adnate
Adnexed
Sinuate (Notched)
Decurrent
Deeply Decurrent

Stem Forms:

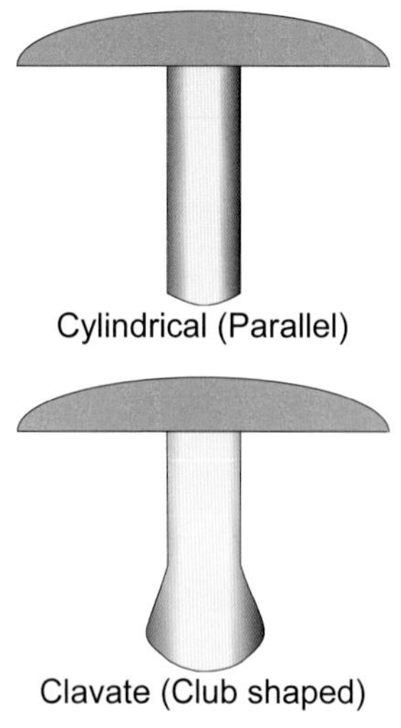
Cylindrical (Parallel)
Clavate (Club shaped)

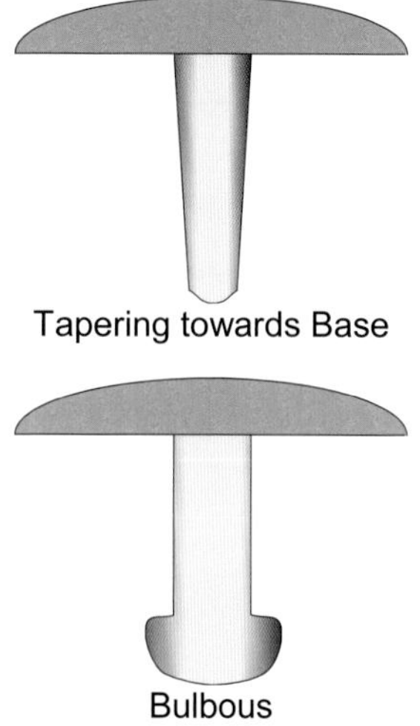
Tapering towards Base
Bulbous

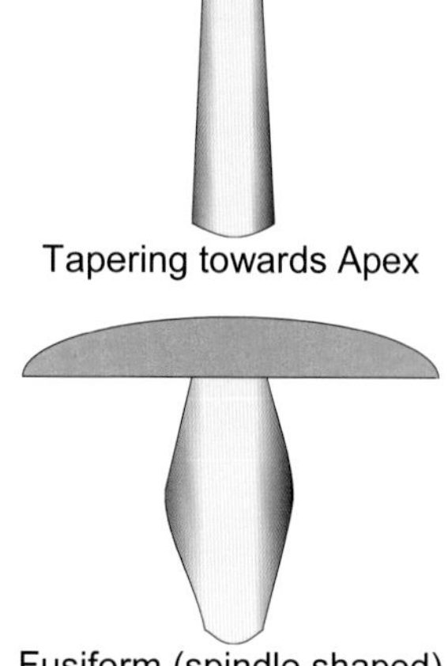
Tapering towards Apex
Fusiform (spindle shaped)

Ring Position and Form:

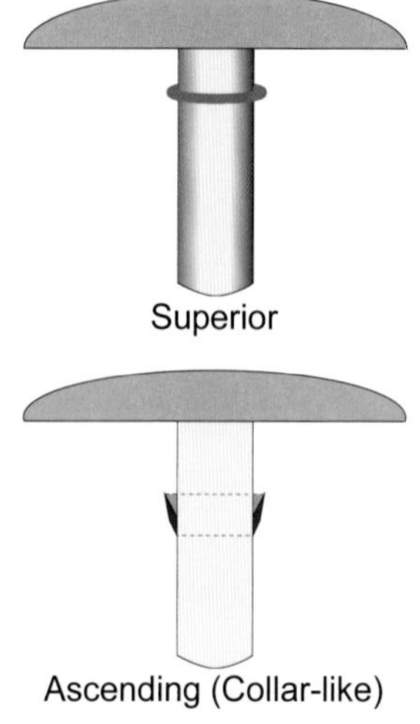
Superior
Ascending (Collar-like)

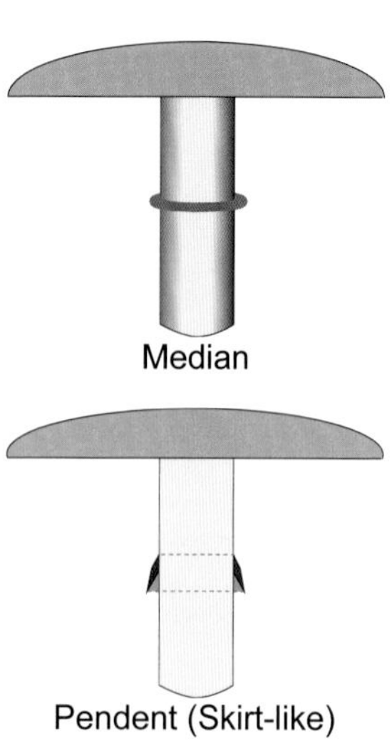
Median
Pendent (Skirt-like)

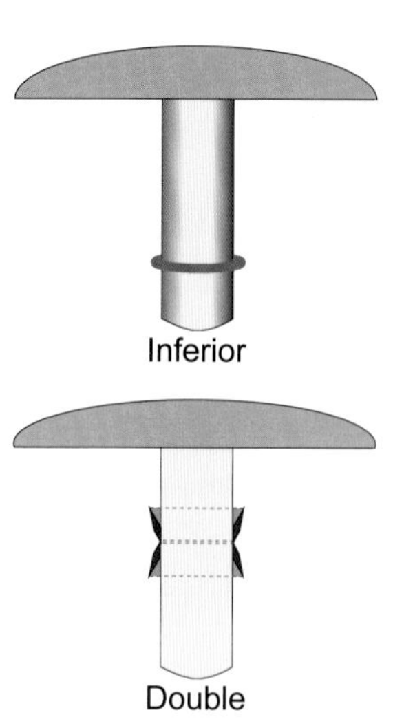
Inferior
Double

Stem surface texture:

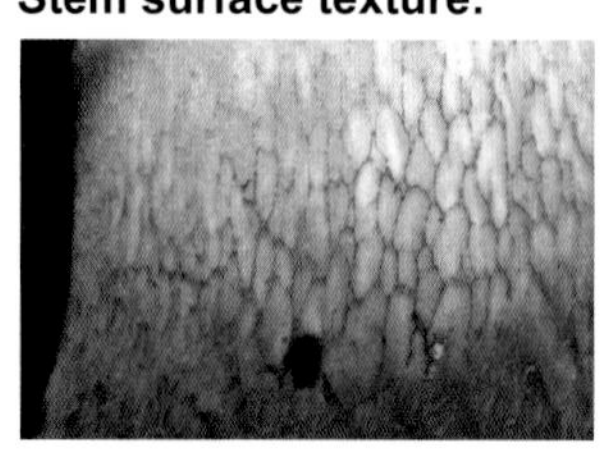
Reticulate (netted)

Fibrillose

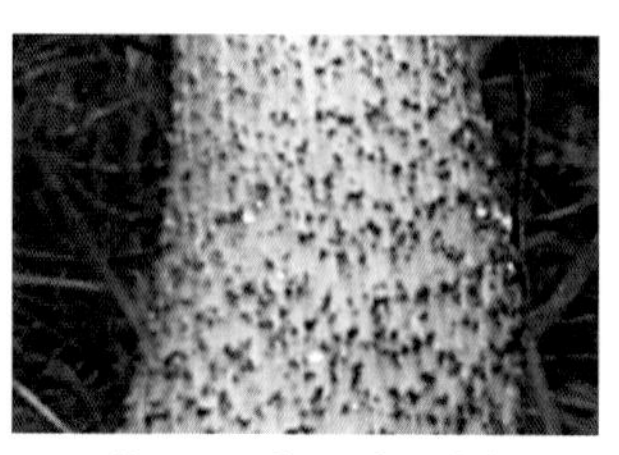
Squamulose (scaly)

Learning More

There is a lot to learn about fungi, and the more you learn the more aware you become of how much more there is still to learn. If your interest in fungi is for fun rather than a means of earning a living (for a fortunate few it can be both), make sure that the pursuit of knowledge is not at the expense of enjoying the beauty of this wonderful natural resource.

The beautiful Yellow Stagshorn *Calocera viscosa*

Chapter 2 - Breeding Habits and Feeding Habitats

Where fungi came from and how they grow, go forth and multiply

Any of the world's most beautiful sights (and sites) means so much more to those who have learned a little about its history - and in the natural world it is an understanding of the *natural history* that makes the big difference. Knowing where mushrooms come from, what purpose they serve, what they need, how they breed and how they feed is valuable not only for professional mycologists but also for amateurs with only a general interest in fungi.

For professional mycologists, greater understanding of the reproductive mechanisms of the kinds of fungi that are used in the production of food and medicines or fungi that improve forestry management brings obvious benefits; and creating conditions that accelerate the associated reproductive processes saves time and money and raises productivity.

How does all this help?

On the other hand, where pathogenic fungi cause diseases in plants or animals there are equally obvious advantages in knowing how to create conditions adverse to the viability of the fungi concerned

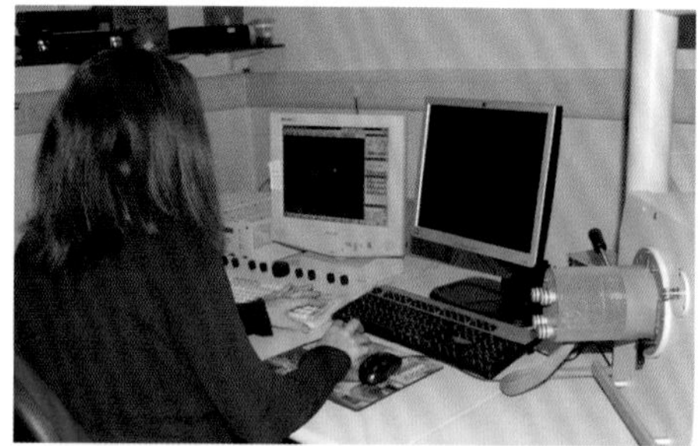

A scanning electron microscope (SEM), used in scientific research into fungi at Cranfield University. The enthusiastic amateur could buy a very nice second-hand SEM for about £200,000. If your budget is limited, it's possible to pick up a good optical microscope for 0.1% of this sum. (Microscopy is a topic in Chapter 10).

To appreciate the beauty and diversity of fungi, or even just to enjoy gathering wild mushrooms to eat, it's not necessary to understand how fungi feed and grow - and you certainly don't need to worry about the complexities of spore production and distribution. But learning just a little about these processes does help to explain the very varied forms that fungi take in their efforts to fit in to and exploit habitat niches. There is also another valuable benefit even for amateurs with only a general interest in mushrooms. As we learn more about the underworld of fungi and how these remarkable organisms reproduce, so more aspects of the mysterious behaviour of mushrooms become just that little bit more understandable and hence even predictable.

For example, as we begin to understand why certain weather patterns favour the production of fungus fruitbodies so we can plan forays with more confidence. Also, as we will see in later chapters, a basic understanding of the biology of fungi helps us not only to be in the right place at the right time but also to recognise tell-tale clues that can be so valuable in the search for some of the more elusive species.

We have to start somewhere, and perhaps a sensible starting place is the beginning. In the beginning there was no Life on Earth... and then suddenly there was. Equally mysteriously, some time later there were fungi. Being soft and squishy, fungi are not at all good at forming fossils, and so the physical evidence of fungal evolution is unfortunately rather sparse. Nevertheless, good progress is now being made towards unravelling that mystery, so let's start with what *is* known about where fungi originally came from and what they are (in all their glorious diversity) before investigating how fungi reproduce, feed and grow.

A fine display of Blushers *Amanita rubescens* beneath a row of silver birch trees – such scenes are the reward for being in the right place at the right time.

Fungi: neither animal nor vegetable nor mineral

Recent scientific research has shown that fungi have rather more in common with animals than with plants; and, although there is still so much that we do *not* understand, the more we learn about these amazing organisms the more evident it becomes that any clear dividing lines between kingdoms, while convenient for comparing, contrasting and communicating, are more a product of Man's desperate desire to divide and conquer than of any essential natural partitioning. After all, barring alien incursions from beyond our solar system, every living thing on Earth must be derived from the same evolutionary origin, and so periodically in the past things must have slithered, skipped or soared across the borders between our make-believe kingdoms. Had the fortifications of these kingdoms of convenience been impregnable, we would not exist – or at least not in animal form.

Out of the frying pan into the freezer? Once a red-hot dead place, Earth may have a cold bleak future ahead of it, or a total meltdown – but that's probably a long way ahead, provided we learn to treat our beautiful planet with the respect that it deserves. (Picture courtesy of NASA)

The Birth of Life on Earth

Current best estimates put the age of our planet at about four and a half billion years. Notwithstanding present-day concerns about global warming (which is to do with average global *surface* temperatures) and its contribution to climate change, since its birth Planet Earth has been cooling down fairly steadily, give or take a few relatively minor and short-lived perturbations. Initially our embryonic world was a white-hot dead place, but as it cooled so its chemical composition changed. It took at least 500 million years for Earth to cool to the point where its surface chemistry and atmosphere would allow primitive life forms to evolve and survive. When they could, they did, and among the descendants of those primitive organisms are what we now call bacteria. Some bacteria work overtime to cause trouble today, but they had to wait more than two billion years before there were any other life forms for them to annoy. Bacteria are very good at biding their time: from deep within a mine in New Mexico bacteria spores more than 250 million years old were excavated and found to be still viable. For longevity it's hard to beat being a bacterium!

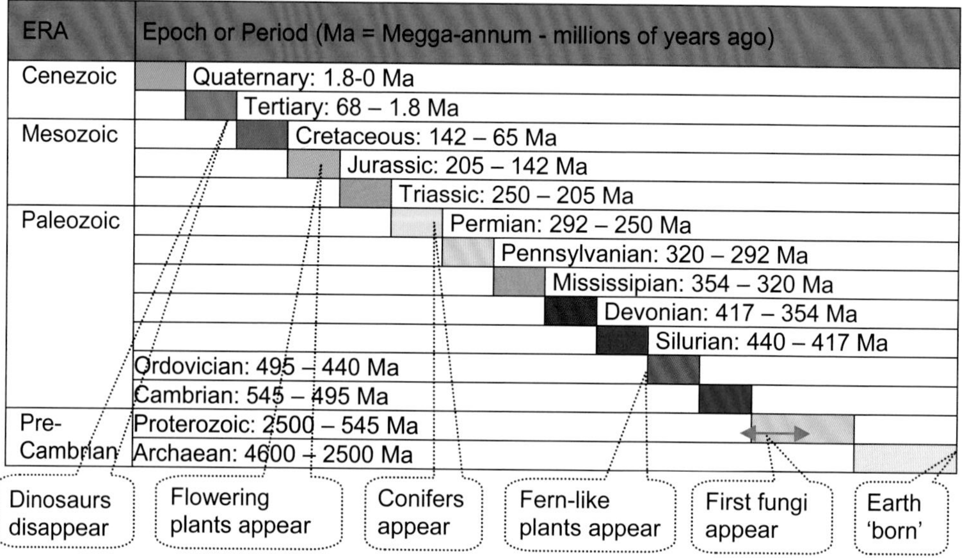

The first living organisms to evolve on our planet, some 3500 million years ago, were the Archaea. Capable of surviving in extreme environments, these single-celled organisms look rather like bacteria, although genetically they are as different from the e-coli 'bug' as we are. So the humbling truth is that our greatest grandparents were neither animals nor plants - nor, for that matter, were they fungi. We have all evolved from something much simpler, from basic single-celled organisms, mere microscopic blobs of DNA.

We know quite a lot about the kinds of microscopic organisms from which all larger life forms evolved, because many of them are still alive and well today - although most of the intermediate forms that link those archaic organisms to the diversity of animals, plants and fungi we now see around us have disappeared leaving few detectable fossil records. All is not lost, however: the science of genetics is beginning to throw light on our evolutionary past. It's a dim light for peering into the deep dark recesses of such a vast cave, but already this new field of research has thrown up more than enough evidence to convince biologists of the validity of a multi-kingdom model of Life on Earth.

Kingdoms of Life

What follows is a simplified view of the kingdoms of Life on Earth - although one thing we can be pretty sure of is that this view will have to be revised.

Archaea: the first life forms on Earth, and still by far the largest kingdom – so vast, in fact, that biologists do even attempt to describe such micro organisms in terms of species.
Bacteria: treated as a separate kingdom by some experts, while others combine the Archaea and Bacteria in a single kingdom with its own 'Empire' known as the Prokaryota (cells without nuclei).

The other five kingdoms, within an 'Empire' known as the Eukaryota (cells with nuclei), are:

Chromista: another huge kingdom only recently accepted as such, and containing various brown seaweeds, some of the algae that contain chlorophyll, and a huge array of other microscopic organisms that had previously been thought to be very primitive fungi.
Protista: including protozoa, single-celled organisms such as Flagellates, Sporozoans, Microsporidia and Ciliates - some of these are plant-like and others animal-like - as well as amoeba-like slime moulds, including the myxomycetes that were previously included with fungi.
Plantae: the plant kingdom of around 270,000 known species, which includes not only flowering plants and trees but also ferns, mosses and liverworts.
Fungi: mushrooms, some moulds and mildews, and many other related organisms that meet the entry qualifications for a diverse kingdom estimated to contain at least five times as many species as there are in the kingdom of plants.
Animalia: the animals, including birds, fish, insects and other invertebrates, amphibians and reptiles. And of course we ourselves, as mammals, are part of this kingdom which is thought to contain more than a million species.

Sorting out plants and animals seems pretty straightforward. Individual plants generally have to put up with the situation they are born into. They can't move about in search of water, warmth or food, but even so most plants have one big advantage over the animals: they can manufacture their own food.

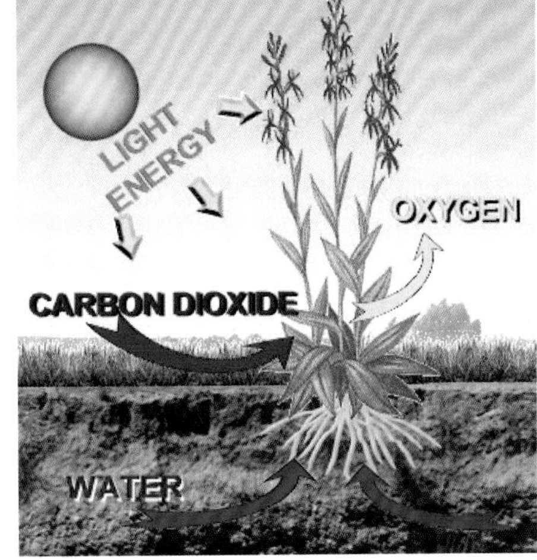

In this pictorial representation of the basic process of photosynthesis, a plant takes in water from the soil, carbon dioxide from the air, and energy via light from the sun; it uses these to produce sugars and starches upon which the plant feeds, releasing oxygen into the air.

All a plant needs is sunshine and moisture, and by a process called photosynthesis it can convert the sun's energy, water and carbon dioxide from the atmosphere into the sugars and starches that it needs to grow and reproduce. No animal can do that. Animals have to get their protein either by eating plants or by eating other animals that ultimately relied on plants for food. But, as if in compensation for that Achilles' heel, most animals have the ability to move from place to place in search of a comfortable local environment, or habitat (a Latin word originally meaning 'he dwells' but now implying a dwelling place), suitable for hiding from predators, capturing prey, or breeding to ensure continuity of the species. There may be more to life for members of the clan *Homo sapiens* – for example sport, art, paying taxes – but these are optional extras, and every other species on our planet seems to have opted out of them. There might just be a message for us here...

What about viruses?

Viruses are not generally given Kingdom status. This is because they are not made up of cells, the essential building blocks of all other life forms; and so, on their own, viruses are not able to replicate themselves. Viruses can and do reproduce, of course, and we know that to our cost new forms are continually evolving.

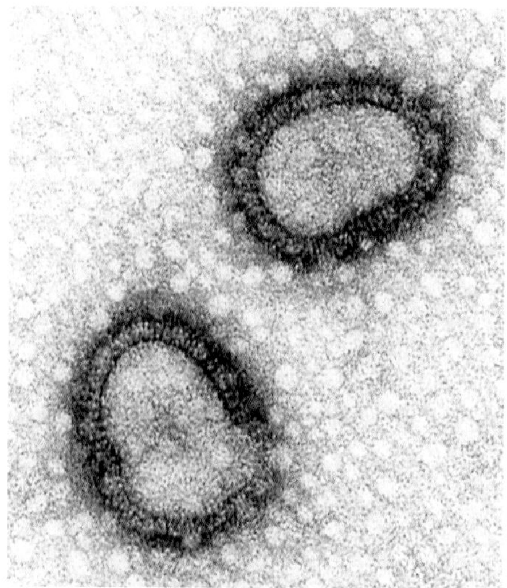

Influenza A virus particles visualised by electron microscopy.

Viruses mutate. Swine 'flu and other influenza viruses that make people ill nowadays are different from those that caused such devastation during the Spanish 'flu pandemic of 1918-19 and the Asian 'flu epidemic of 1957. In common with living cells, every virus contains genetic material in the form of DNA or RNA, and when a virus injects its genes (the blueprints for reproduction) into other organisms they are forced into producing copies of the virus.

Animals, plants and fungi too can become infected by viruses - often to the detriment of the health of the host, and sometimes the resulting disease is fatal. For example MVX (mushroom virus X), first recorded in 1996, seriously affected the UK's commercial production of Cultivated Mushrooms *Agaricus bisporus* in 2000-2001. The effects of this complex of viruses were subsequently reported from several other mushroom-growing countries across Europe. Cultivated forms of the Oyster Mushroom *Pleurotus ostreatus* have also been found to be susceptible to viral infections.

The Classification of Life Forms

Within each of the kingdoms there are many related life forms, which we call species. Life forms of the same species are capable of breeding with one another and producing fertile offspring, but they are not capable of producing fertile offspring by cross-breeding with different species. Those species most closely related are grouped together in the same genus (plural genera). Genera with sufficient characteristics in common are grouped into the same family, and in the same way related families are treated as one order. At the next level we have a number of classes, each of which usually contains several orders. Related classes are grouped at the highest classification level within a kingdom, which is the level known as phylum (plural phyla). So, from the top, the classification hierarchy is kingdom > phylum > order > class > family > genus > species.

In plant biology the term division is generally used in place of phylum to indicate a level below kingdom but above class. Large orders are sometimes split into two or more sub-orders. You may also come across the term sub-species, which is used to describe a subdivision of a species consisting of an interbreeding, usually geographically isolated population of the species in question.

Varieties - the spice of Life?

Where subdivision of a species consists of individuals differing from the remainder of the species only in certain minor characteristics, they may be described as a 'variety' of the species concerned. Garden flowers are cross bred to produce such varieties, which differ slightly in form or colour from the original species. In the fungus world there are also species that occur locally in varieties that look somewhat different one from another.

***Amanita muscaria*, the famous Fly Agaric, generally produces red-capped, white-stemmed mushrooms in Britain and Europe.**

Rare in Britain and Ireland but much more common in the USA, a Fly Agaric with an orange cap and an orange-flushed stem is recorded as *Amanita muscaria* var. *formosa*.

Types of Fungi

Within their own kingdom, fungi are classified in just the same way as other life forms, but because we rarely see much if anything of a fungus below the ground or within a tree until it produces a fruitbody, traditionally the physical features of the fruitbodies and the methods they use to produce and disperse spores have formed the basis of categorisation. Within the seven major divisions (phyla) recognised today the two main groups containing large fungi are known as the Ascomycota and Basidiomycota. Among the microfungi (including some kinds of fungi that do not produce spores or at least have not yet been seen to do so) are many that play important roles in all kinds of ecosystems. Large fungi are the main focus of this book; but because some microfungi can appear in large masses and often are very colourful, useful or damaging they are included in the table below:

Phylum	Features	Example	
Ascomycota (commonly referred to as the ascomycetes)	Mainly very small fruitbodies such as yeasts, but also cup and flask fungi	Orange Peel Fungus *Aleuria aurantia* is fairly common on compacted woodland paths.	
Basidiomycota (commonly referred to simply as the basiodiomycetes, the largest class within this phylum)	Producing large fruitbodies such as mushrooms, puffballs, and brackets; also rusts and smuts	Turkeytail *Trametes versicolor* is a bracket fungus that lives on dead wood.	
Chytrydiomycota	Mostly aquatic fungi but also some pathogens of animals	*Batrachochytrium dendrobatidis* may be the cause of the worldwide Chytridiomycosis skin disease of amphibians.	
Deuteromycetes (sometimes referred to as 'Fungi Imperfecti') - not a true phylum.	An entirely artificial grouping in which fungi with no known sexual state are listed	*Penicillium* species are fungi from which the antibiotic known as penicillin is derived.	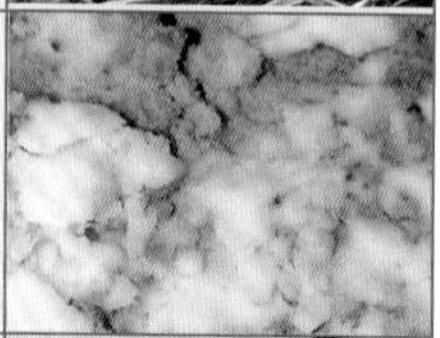
Glomeromycota (sometimes included within the Ascomycota)	Microfungi that form mutually beneficial relationships with most kinds of plants	All are of the genus *Glomus,* and nearly 100 species are currently known.	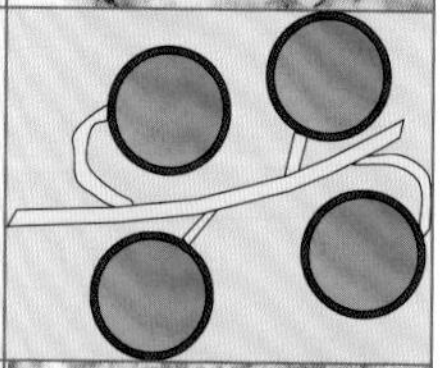
Zygomycota (commonly referred to as the zygomycetes)	Moulds and related microfungi with no obvious fruitbodies	*Rhizopus stolonifer*, a dark mould, is often seen on stale home-baked bread that has been made without preservatives.	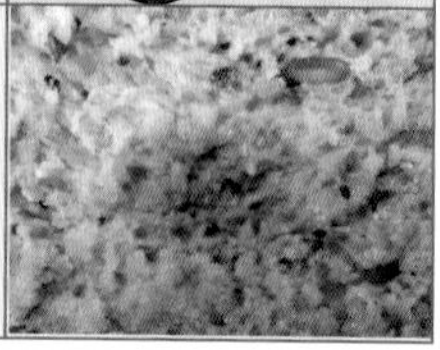

Below the level of phyla, the traditional classification of fungi in systematic groups (taxa is the technical term for all such groups) based on their physical characteristics has provided results sometimes at odds with the implications of findings from molecular systematic studies (including DNA sequencing) into the evolution of gilled and pored mushrooms and their relatives. For example, it seems likely that gilled mushrooms and puffball fungi may have evolved many times and that some cup-shaped fungi and crust fungi may even share a single common ancestor with some of the gilled fungi that we find today.

The Tufted Wood Mushroom *Agaricus impudicus* is an edible fungus that occurs mainly in coniferous and mixed woodland, although occasionally it is also reported from grassland habitats.

Recent genetic analysis suggests that many of the gasteromycetous fungi such as these Common Puffballs *Lycoperdon perlatum* probably evolved relatively recently from an ancestor that they share with mushrooms of the family Agaricaceae.

Equally surprisingly, it seems that fungi of the *Clavaria* genus, often referred to as fairy clubs, should also be included in the order Agaricales. The grassland fungi pictured on the left are Apricot Clubs *Clavulinopsis luteoalba.*

Even though some of the family-level relationships based on physical characteristics could well prove to be rather artificial, at present mycologists continue to use the traditional names of families, genera and species. Some genera have already been moved from one taxonomic family to another based on the results of molecular systematic studies using probabilistic computer modelling; nevertheless, as new species of fungi are discovered they are still being given names based on the existing genera (unless they are so different from anything found before that a new genus name is needed).

Conflict between Cladistics and Traditional Taxonomy

The conventional classification used by biologists down the ages can be represented in the form of a hierarchical 'tree' with species at the end of twigs on branches connected to a trunk. Such a model of Life on Earth would be ideal were it not for the process of evolution via mutations and extinctions, where new species arise by periodic modification of existing ones while others die out. An evolutionary model has to cope with such change processes, and for this a phylogenetic tree – a tree based on the order in which evolutionary events are believed to have occurred – has real advantages, particularly while our limited understanding of evolutionary changes is developing rapidly as computer power and mathematical modelling techniques improve.

Cladistic trees represent existing life forms and their ancestors in branched groups known as clades (from the ancient Greek word *klados* meaning branch). A clade is a monophyletic group - that is, a group comprising a single common ancestor and all of its descendants. A clade does not have to contain living representatives; the common ancestor and some or all of its descendants might now be extinct. A smaller clade that is located within a larger, more inclusive clade is said to be 'nested' within that clade. In phylogenetic systematics, only monophyletic clades need to be given taxonomic names. Names can be given to the nodes from which valid clades arise, so that when necessary moving a group within a cladistic tree is nowhere near as disruptive as reclassifying taxa in the Linnaean system.

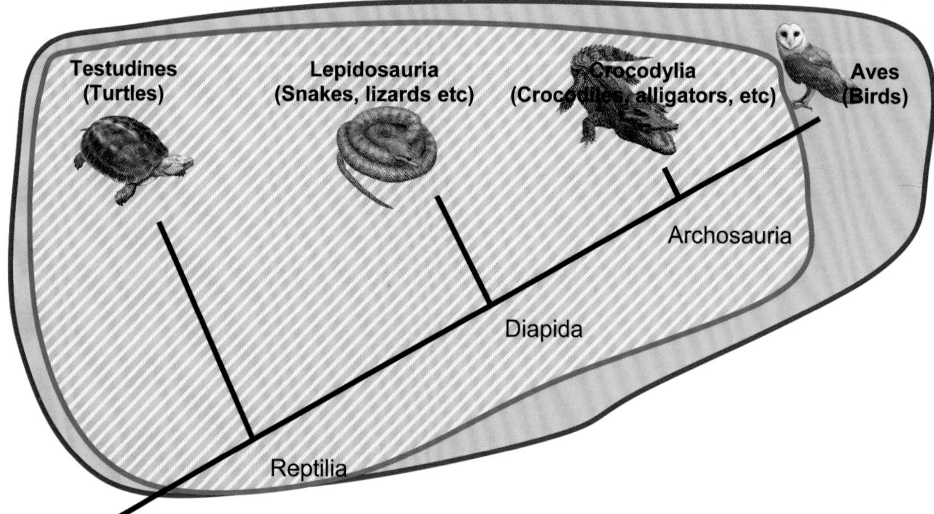

A cladistic tree within the kingdom Animalia. All birds and reptiles are believed to have descended from a common ancestor, and so the clade within the larger orange area above is termed monophyletic. If birds were to be excluded and only existing reptiles with their common ancestor included (the group within the green-bordered, cross-hatched area) then the clade would not contain all descendents of the common ancestor (such a grouping is termed 'paraphyletic'), and it could not be nested elsewhere in a larger cladogram should our understanding of the origin of Reptilia change.

Evidence of the distant ancestry of existing animals comes mainly from fossils, and the fossilised remains of bony creatures are easily recognised. Fungi are more difficult because they do not leave many fossil records, which is why DNA sequencing is so useful.

I Know My Place

We have our own niche in the kingdom Animalia, as indeed also do dogs and frogs and prickly hedgehogs. We all belong to the Chordata, a phylum comprising mainly vertebrates, creatures with spines (in the sense of vertebrae or backbones rather than prickles), although sea squirts and the like, which do not have bony vertebrae, also qualify for entry. It's not actually our vertebrae but our spinal columns - the hollow dorsal nerve cords, known as notochords - that count towards the award of Chordata status, and sea squirts also have notochords; however, these invertebrate sea creatures are separated from dogs and dog owners at the next level down:

Kingdom:	Animalia						
Phylum:	Chordata (just one of more than 30 recognised phyla within the kingdom Animalia)						
Class:	Mammalia (Mammals, including humans)	Reptilia (Snakes, lizards etc)	Aves (Birds)	Amphibia (Toads etc)	Chond-rycthyes (Sharks etc)	Osteich-thyes (Bony fish)	+ about ten other classes some of which are now extinct
Example:	Squirrel	Adder	Bullfinch	Toad	Ray	Roach	Sea Squirt

One thing that most of the classes within the Chordata have in common is that they include many of the animals that are at the top of the food chain.

Phylum:	Chordata (just one of about 34 recognised phyla within the kingdom Animalia)			
Class:	Mammalia			Amphibia
Order:	Primates	Carnivora	Insectivora	Anura
Family:	Hominidae	Canidae	Erinaceidae	Ranidae
Genus:	*Homo*	*Canis*	*Erinaceus*	*Rana*
Species:	*sapiens*	*lupus*	*europaeus*	*temporaria*
The author and some of his close relatives...	Man	Dog	Hedgehog	Frog

Our distant relatives the frogs belong to the class Amphibia, whereas we, together with our closer relatives the dogs and hedgehogs, belong to the class Mammalia. People are part of the family Hominidae; our genus is *Homo* and, as all other *Homo* species are extinct, we are now the only species in that genus. Our specific name is *sapiens*, meaning 'wise' – an accolade we should not take too seriously, perhaps, since it was we who awarded it to ourselves. You and I are *Homo sapiens*. (It is conventional to use italics when quoting species names.)

The naming convention applied to the animal kingdom is also used when naming fungi.

The Binomial System

Carl Linnaeus – a portrait by the German artist Alexander Roslin (1718 – 1793)

The twin-naming convention, known as the binomial system, was devised by the great Swedish naturalist Carl Linnaeus (1707 to 1778). King Adolf Frederick of Sweden granted Linnaeus nobility status, which he received in 1761; he then became Carl von Linné.

When a new species was discovered and described, its place in the classification structure was defined by a two-part (*Genus - species*) name. Rather than use the native language of the discoverer, it was common practice to use Latin or Greek words as the basis of names. (Recently other word forms have been deemed acceptable.)

Many plant, animal and fungi species have been renamed, some several times, as we have learned more about their physical characteristics, behaviour and chemistry and so revised our views of their positions within the hierarchy of classification, but the Linnaean binomial system remains unchallenged after more than a quarter of a millennium.

The binomial system that Linnaeus devised enables an author to refer to a species confident that it will mean the same thing to informed readers anywhere else in the world.

Type Species

Often referred to as a 'generitype', the type species of a biological genus is a species that best exemplifies the essential characteristics of the genus to which it belongs and to which the name of that genus is permanently linked. In botanical and mycological nomenclature, the type refers to a specimen or an illustration of a published species designated as typical of a genus. Currently, type species in zoological nomenclature are regulated by article 42.3 of the International Code of Zoological Nomenclature.

Usually scientific names refer to characteristics of the species. For example *Serratella ignita* (left) is an insect within the family Ephemerellidae. It has a very brief (ephemeral) adult lifetime and a translucent orange body that shines brightly (as if ignited and burning) when seen laying its eggs on rivers and streams during a summer sunset.

Occasionally the work of the biologist who discovers a species is recognised by allocating a Latinised form of his or her name to the species. For example the marsh plant commonly referred to in the British Isles as Parsley Water-dropwort - a term with as little meaning to people who speak no English as Smalstäkra, the Swedish common name for this plant, has for most of us - is universally known by the scientific name *Oenanthe lachenalii*. It is named after the late 18th Century botanist Werner de Lachenal, a professor at Basel University in Switzerland.

Right: Werner de Lachenal (1739-1800) - one of the few biologists whose names have been immortalised via the binomial system of naming plants, animals and fungi that was devised by Linnaeus.

In formal identification guides the scientific name of a species (in the form *Genus species*) is followed by terms that identify the person or persons responsible for that name. These authorities are cited according to the specifications of the International Botanical Congress. For example, the citation ***Grifola frondosa*** **(Dicks.: Fr.) S F Gray** recognizes the fact that Elias Magnus Fries (1794-1878) sanctioned the species name *frondosa* that was originally created by James Dickson (1738-1822) and that Samuel Frederick Gray (1766-1828) later transferred it to the new genus *Grifola*. The naming process for fungi is governed by an agreement known as the International Code of Botanical Nomenclature, the basic principles of which are explained in a little more detail in Appendix III.

Names cited most frequently are abbreviated – for example Carl Linnaeus is denoted by L., while Elias Fries is shortened to Fr., and Lucien Quélet is written as Quél. Appendix III includes a list of names appearing most often in fungi name citations. Within the text of this book I have followed the generally accepted practice for introductory texts and omitted the author citations; however, author citations are included in the Species Index.

The mushroom known as the Shaggy Parasol belongs to the genus *Chlorophyllum*, and its specific name is *rachodes*. Written in full, the scientific name is *Chlorophyllum rachodes* (Vittad.) Vellinga. (Note that the alternative spelling *rhacodes* is preferred by some authorities.)

The Shaggy Parasol has long been considered a good edible species; however, this woodland-edge mushroom is now known to be seriously toxic to some people.

A Filing System for Fungi
Taxonomists have set up a 'filing system' for recording descriptive information about fungi. As with any other large filing system you need to visit the appropriate building (**phylum**) and find the correct department (**class**). The next step is to locate the right filing cabinet (**order**), open the relevant **family** drawer and take out the **genus** file that you want. Inside that file there are the individual records containing **species** descriptions, within which there are several fields each describing one of the various **characters** (cap colour or spore dimensions, for example) that help to identify the particular fungus concerned.

Every species can be fitted in to the systematic classification hierarchy, but for some kinds of fungi it is very difficult to decide exactly where.

Let's continue with our example of the shaggy parasol - species *rachodes*, from the genus *Chlorophyllum*. Members of the family of close relatives of the shaggy parasol are known as the Agaricaceae (and note that italics are used only for names at species level, so *Chlorophyllum rachodes* is italicised but Agaricaceae is not). This is one of a number of families that make up the order known as the Agaricales. The Agaricales order itself is just one of many orders within the Class Agaricomycetes in the phylum Basidiomycota which, together with a group of fungi known as the ascomycetes and a motley crew of microscopic or non-fruiting fungi (or at least they are not seen to fruit and are outside the scope of this book) including many moulds and mildews, make up the kingdom of fungi.

Pursuing a little further the filing system analogy, there are two annoying problems at present, and they are unlikely to go away any time soon. First, some of the filing drawers have recently been moved from one filing cabinet to another. For example we now know that gilled fungi of the genera *Paxillus* and *Gomphidius*, which had for many years been included with other gilled mushrooms in the order Agaricales, are in fact more closely related to the pored boletes, and so they are now included in the order Boletales. The second cause of confusion is that some of the early records were wrongly filed, and moving them between genera has meant changing the names of some quite well-known fungi species.

Most of the large fruiting fungi that produce the cap-and-stem mushrooms we are likely to see during fungal forays belong to the basidiomycetes and fall within the orders Agaricales, Boletales, Cantharellales, Cortinariales, Gomphales and Russulales.

Other frequently-encountered basidiomycetes include the brackets (mostly in the orders Poriales, Ganodermales, Hymenochaetales and Fistulinales), crusts (Stereales), stinkhorns (Phallales), earthstars (Geastrales), earthballs (Sclerodermatales), puffballs (Agaricales), earthfans (Thelephorales), and the heterobasidiomycetes group commonly referred to as jelly fungi (notably the Dacrymycetales, Tremellales and Auriculariales).

There are also a few commonly-encountered large fungi within the Ascomycota, mainly in the orders Helotiales, Pezizales and Sphaeriales.

The Best Way to Identify Fungi

The key to successful identification of fungi is to use dichotomous keys. These comprise sequences of two-option decisions at the end of which you should either know with reasonable certainty the identity of the species concerned or, if you are *really* lucky, you might be in with a chance of having found a fungus species that was previously unknown to science (or at least unknown to whoever produced that dichotomous key).

The very worst way to try to identify fungi
What is most definitely *not* a good way to identify fungi is to thumb through a book or surf a website to see which photograph looks most like the sample you have found. Few books contain more than 1000 species – you are likely to come across a lot more than that if you take fungi foraying at all seriously – and 'forcing a fit' to a picture is always risky given the huge variations in size, shape and colour associated with varying growing conditions, habitat, time of year and stage in development.

A better approach
Fortunately, provided you check each of the macroscopic characteristics listed in an up-to-date field guide, many of the most beautiful fungi are easily identified to species level without microscopic examination and chemical testing. Unfortunately not all fungi can be separated by noting characteristics visible to the naked eye: microscopic examination and chemical tests are sometimes the only way that experts can be reasonably sure, and many field guides include advice on appropriate tests and the expected results. A few words of warning, though: like everything else in Nature, the more you learn about fungi the more you will want to know, so that a casual interest can soon become a passionate pursuit.

A photographic field guide can be a great help when identifying fungi. The pictures are an adjunct to the detailed scientific descriptions and should never be considered as a substitute.

Given the current great and growing interest in mushrooms and other fungi, it's hardly any wonder that every year amateur fanatics discover several species that are new to science. And in any case, getting out for long walks and plenty of fresh air has got to be good for you... as long as you avoid contracting chronic 'mycologist's stoop'.

How fungi reproduce

Flowering plants can reproduce by producing seeds. Many are also propagated by means of either root 'suckers' or vegetative 'runners'. Occasionally, cuttings get snapped off in strong winds or entangled in the fur of animals, eventually falling on suitable soil and taking root. Similar things happen with fungi: they too can reproduce by vegetative division (note how 'plant' language is still being applied to fungi) when part of a mycelium becomes disconnected from the rest.

Mycelium is made up of multi-branched networks of microscopically fine fibres called hyphae, and a typical hypha might be three microns in diameter (a micron being a thousandth of a millimetre). That makes a hyphal thread something like twenty times smaller in diameter than a human hair, so if you see fine fungal threads holding rotting leaves together what you are looking at are bundles of hyphae, not a single hypha. Only under a microscope are the individual hyphal threads discernable.

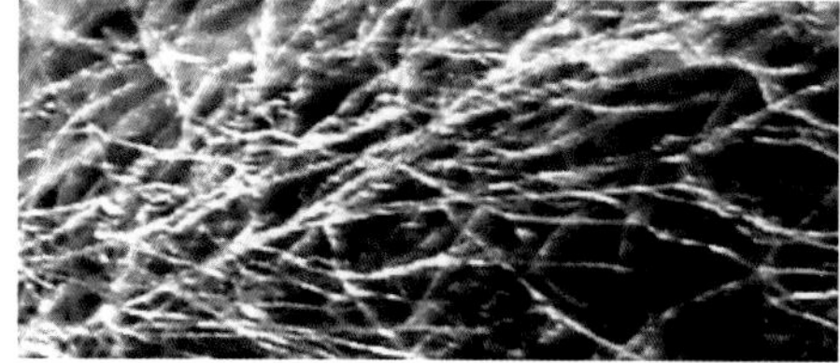

Hyphae are the basic building blocks of all parts of a fungus, but an individual fungal hypha is too fine to be seen by the naked eye. Even the tiniest of these mycelial threads, seen here magnified to ten times actual size, consist of bunches of several hyphal fibres.

Fungi may also reproduce by means of spores which, in the fungal kingdom, perform functions somewhat similar to seeds and pollen in the plant world (although no direct equivalent of the pollination process is involved).

With very few exceptions fungal spores are too small to be seen with the naked eye; most large fungi produce spores less than 20 microns long (a fiftieth of a millimetre) and they are therefore visible only with the aid of a fairly powerful microscope.

Vegetative reproduction

There are many ways in which a mycelium can become fractured. If a fungus-infected branch of a tree snaps off and falls onto a neighbouring tree, mycelial threads can cross from one tree to the other. Storms are often very bad news for trees, but they can be good news for fungi.

Porcelain Fungus *Mucidula mucida* (until recently generally known as *Oudemansiella mucida*) can sometimes be seen in the upper branches of ancient Beech trees whose crowns have spread so widely that the branches of neighbouring trees become intermeshed and rub against one another during windy weather.

Many fungi reproduce only by vegetative means or via asexual spores that develop on the mycelium itself. An example is *Trichophyton rubrum,* one of the fungi that can cause the disease *Tinea pedis*, commonly known as Athlete's Foot. Such species are referred to as *fungi imperfecti* – just as a flower with only male or female reproductive organs (stamens *or* pistil but not both) is known as an 'imperfect' flower. Fungi capable of producing fruitbodies within which sexual spores develop are sometimes referred to as the *fungi perfecti.*

Traditionally, fungi that do not have a sexual reproduction stage in their life cycles were placed into a rather artificial phylum known as the deuteromycetes; however, researchers are discovering that increasing numbers of these fungi do, albeit only very occasionally when the conditions are right, go through a sexual reproduction process, at which point the characteristics of their spore-producing parts can be studied. As a result many of the microscopic fungi previously listed as deuteromycetes species have had to be moved into the ascomycetes, and a few have even turned out to be basidiomycetes and hence relatives of species that produce the familiar cap-and-stem mushrooms.

Reproduction via sexual spores

Mycelia produce fruitbodies; fruitbodies produce spores; spores produce mycelia – a cyclic process providing us with something very like the *'Which came first, the chicken or the egg?'* conundrum. To describe the process in more detail, where is the best place to start? Employing the maxim of start small, let's begin with the spores and see how they are produced in the two main groups of fungi that we are likely to see.

The fungi that are the subject of this book produce large fruitbodies – from a few millimetres up to a metre or so across – and are sometimes referred to as 'macrofungi'. The macrofungi are greatly outnumbered by a vast range of microfungi, some producing fruitbodies so small that they nearly always go unnoticed; others rarely if ever fruiting but relying instead on vegetative reproduction.

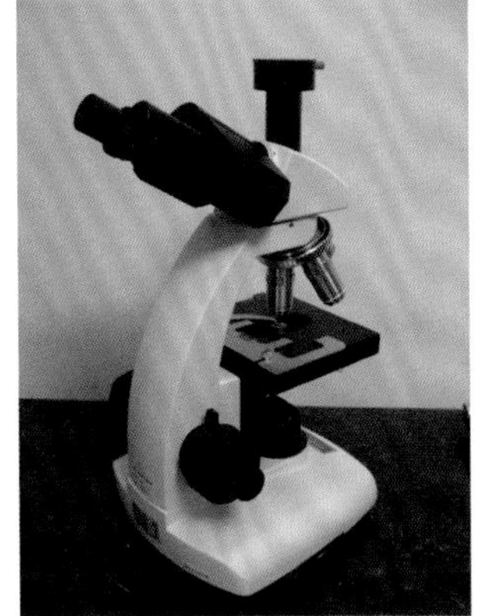

Most macrofungi produce sexual spores as a result of the combination of genetic material from two or sometimes more parents. The majority of the larger macrofungi are basidiomycetes, but a few conspicuous and interesting ones belong to the ascomycetes – the distinction being to do with how their sexual spores are formed. (Microfungi are outside the scope of this book.) Whenever you come across the word 'spores' from this point onwards please take it to mean 'sexual spores' unless stated otherwise.

Fungi spores are so small that the only way to study them in any detail is to use a microscope. Many amateur mycologists bring specimens home to study them using inexpensive microscopes capable of magnifying objects by up to 1000 times.

The diversity of spores

Not only do fungi produce spores of many different colours (when seen en masse, that is: individual spores are so small that they are almost transparent) – white, yellow, brown, olive, pink and black are common – but the size, shape and ornamentation of spores (surface structures such as warts and spines, for example) are also very varied. Often the best way to distinguish closely-related fungi species is to examine their spores under a microscope.

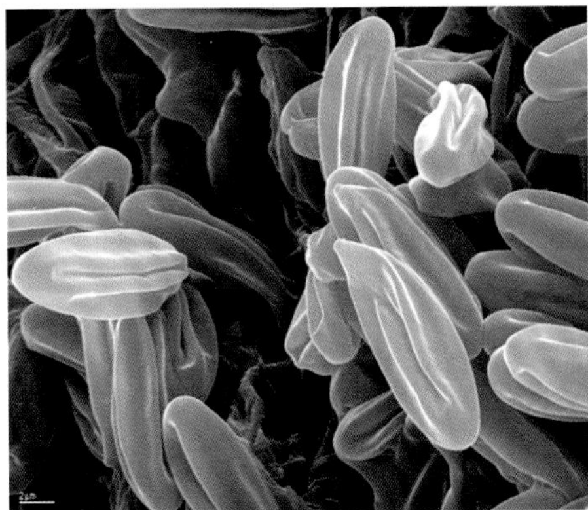

Scanning Electron Micrograph showing the longitudinally grooved ornamentation of dried spores of the Miller *Clitopilus prunulus*, a mushroom found in the grass of woodland edges. The common name is a reference to its mealy odour.

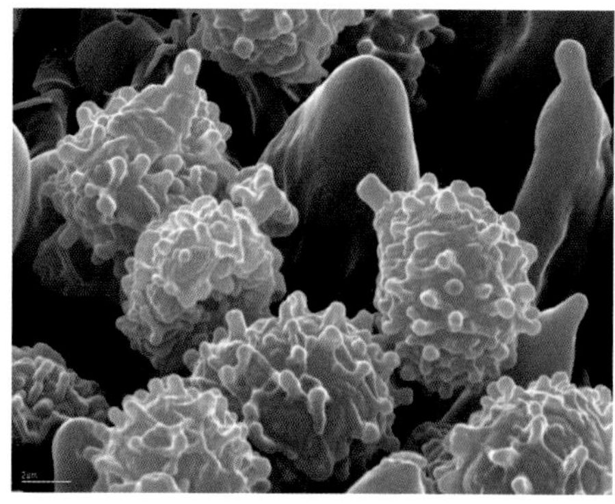

Scanning Electron Micrograph showing the warty spores of the Ochre Brittlegill *Russula ochroleuca*, one of the most widespread and abundant of woodland fungi.

Why bother with microscopic details?
It's a fair question. You will need at least a basic understanding of how fungi reproduce, grow and distribute their spores in order to understand all of the information in fungi identification guides and keys. On the other hand, if you aren't particularly interested in identifying with a high degree of confidence the fungi that you find, then learning about these fascinating (but, initially at least, rather confusing) matters is not strictly necessary.

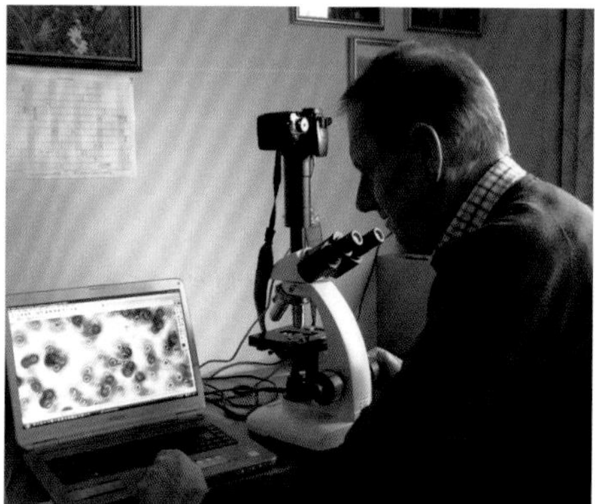

Images of fungi spores can be captured using a trinocular microscope with a digital camera connected to a personal computer.

Because this book is not intended as a formal field guide, the information in Chapters 3 onwards should still make sense even if you skip what follows in the rest of this chapter.

Staying with it? That's great, because now we come to some fascinating facts that will make you want to look a lot closer at many of the mushrooms and other fungi you find on your forays. In particular the features associated with spore production – microscopic cells known as asci and basidia – are of crucial importance in fungi classification.

Spore Production in the Basidiomycota
The spores of basidiomycetes develop on projections (pictured on the right) known as sterigmata (singular: sterigma) that emerge from microscopic club-shaped cells known as basidia (singular: basidium). Spores produced via basidia are sometimes referred to as basidiospores.

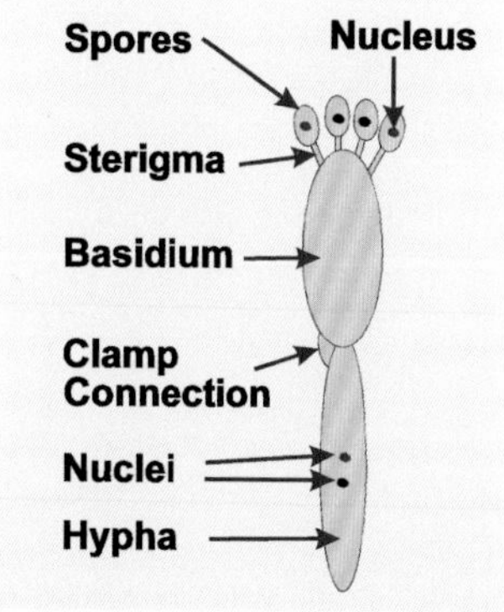

Structure of the spore-producing basidium of a typical mushroom. Each spore develops on a sterigma (they are usually in sets of four) that emerges as a protrusion from a basidium. As the spores mature the nuclei migrate from the basidium through the sterigmata and into the spores.

The connections between hyphal cells are defined by walls that form as 'clamps' when the cells divide; it is as clamp connections are forming following nuclear splitting (termed meiosis) that a pair of nuclei are transferred to the new cell.

When the spores are ripe they are released. Four-spored basidia are the most common, but some species produce only one or two spores on each basidium while others have up to eight spores per basidium. Just to confuse matters more, some fungi produce a variable number of spores on each basidium.

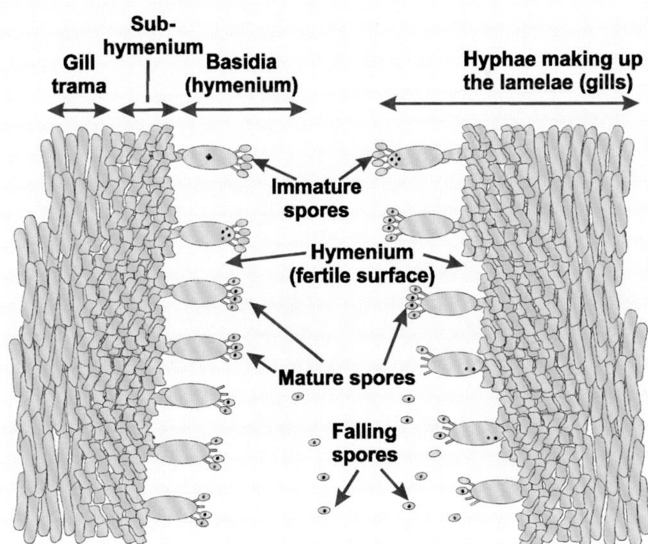

Arrangement of spore-producing basidia on the lamellae (gill walls) of a mushroom.

In a small number of genera the basidia are divided longitudinally, typically into either two or four chambers, by means of walls that are known as septae (singular: septum). You will therefore find in some identification guides phrases such as 'the basidia are septate'.

Like all of its other parts, a mushroom's gills are made up of hyphal threads, but the shapes of the cells within the hyphae are not the same everywhere. In the centre of the gill material, called the gill trama, the threads are formed from relatively long cells, whereas towards the fertile surface there is usually a thin layer of shorter cells called the subhymenium. The fertile surface itself, known as the hymenium, is made up of typically club-shaped spore-producing basidia often interspersed with sterile cells called cystidia (singular: cystidium). The distinctive shapes and sizes of cystidia are often unique to a particular genus or even to an individual species, and so microscopic examination of cystidia can be helpful in identifying fungi to species level. Apart from their diverse shapes and sizes, however, the role of cystidia is not well understood and, in particular, what their various adaptations contribute to fungi viability remains something of a mystery.

Cystidia on the gill faces of a mushroom are known as pleurocystidia, while those on the gill edges are called cheilocystidia. Cystidia may also be found on the surfaces of mushroom stems and caps, and these are referred to as caulocystidia (stem cystidia) and pileocystidia (cap cystidia). Cystidia are not confined to cap-and-stem fungi, however.

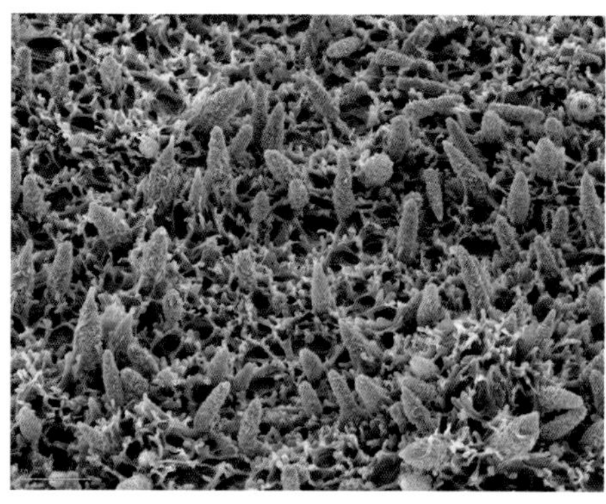

Cystidia of *Phlebiopsis gigantea*. This stump crust fungus is used in the biological control of root rot caused by *Heterobasidion annosum*, a parasitic bracket fungus that occurs at the base of pines and other conifers.

Why on Earth do Mushrooms have Gills?

We know that gills increase the spore-producing capacity of a mushroom, but how the spores escape from captivity is not immediately obvious. Using as an example the Pink Waxcap *Porpolomopsis calyptriformis* (until recently more generally referred to by its synonymous scientific name *Hygrocybe calyptriformis*), let's consider how spores are produced and dispersed so that sexual reproduction can occur.

The gorgeous Pink Waxcap *Porpolomopsis calyptriformis*. As the caps of this rare grassland mushroom expand they invariably split and the edges of their skirts flare upwards.

Because the majority of each gill surface faces another gill, you might expect that spores from one gill would simply be fired into the surface of the facing gill. Were there fungi growing on the moon that would indeed happen, but gills work very well here on Planet

Earth because we have an atmosphere. Air resistance brings the spores to a standstill before they have travelled more than a fraction of a millimetre, at which point they begin falling to earth under the pull of gravity. If they simply continued travelling in that direction, all of the spores from a mushroom would end up on the ground directly beneath the cap of their parent fruitbody – hardly an effective strategy for distribution. Fortunately yet another characteristic of the atmosphere on Planet Earth comes to the rescue: the wind.

When you take a spore print by placing a mushroom cap beneath a jar, the spores fall vertically without being deflected by wind currents. In the open there are always wind currents, and even in the lightest of breezes once they leave the protected region between two gills most of the tiny lightweight mushroom spores are carried well away from their place of origin.

How New Mushroom Colonies are Formed

For a new fungus to appear in territory well away from its parent, sexual reproduction is necessary. Unlike in the plant world, with fungi the sexual reproduction process is generally completed *after* spores fall on suitable soil or other organic matter, so the first requirement is for a spore to settle on to a suitable substrate where it can begin producing a mycelium.

As it grows outwards from its source, a primary mycelium needs to meet one or more compatible 'mates'. Only then can a secondary mycelium form that is capable of producing fruitbodies that are necessary to allow sexual reproduction to take place yet again.

Let's now look in a bit more detail at what happens when spores from two Pink Waxcaps fall upon suitable soil and germinate into primary mycelia close to one another.

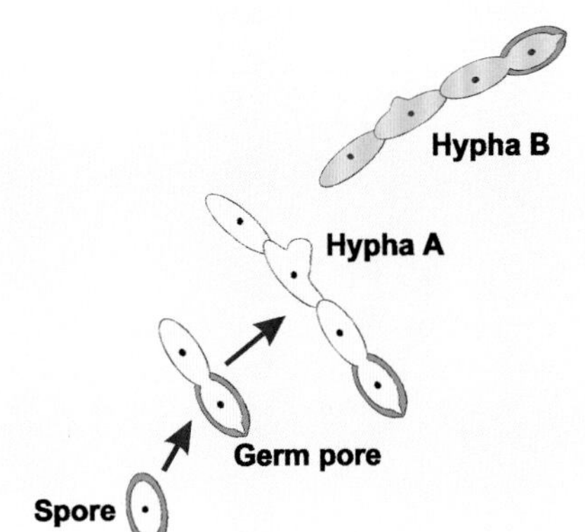

Hyphae comprise tubular sections separated by thin walls known as septae (singular septum); each cell has one nucleus per cell (called monokaryon cells). Hyphae can develop from spores that fall onto a suitable medium. These hyphae branch to form primary mycelia, which on their own are usually incapable of reproduction.

The two primary mycelia each have just one nucleus per cell (the nucleus being the structure, called an organelle, containing the cell's hereditary information and controlling its growth and reproduction). Primary mycelia can grow but usually they cannot reproduce sexually unless two of them meet and fuse to form a secondary mycelium.

In substrates rich in nutrients, the primary mycelial hyphae branch frequently and spread out slowly from the starting point, whereas in areas that are poor in nutrients the hyphae grow more rapidly and they tend to branch less often.

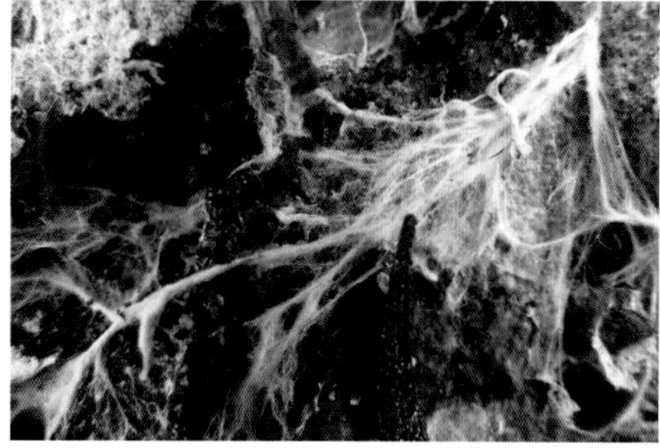

When hyphae bunch together and grow as bundles they are referred to as rhizomorphs (meaning 'root-like forms').

Often rhizomorphs are visible as white threads, although in the case of *Armillaria* species, commonly known as Honey Fungus, the rhizomorphs (example shown on the right) are black and remarkably tough.

Looking rather like bootlaces, Honey Fungus rhizomorphs grow through the soil until they locate new wood, at which point they fan out to invade and attack the tree. For this reason *Armillaria* infection of commercial timber plantations is much feared by foresters.

The meeting of two or more primary mycelia is in some respects analogous to the process of fertilisation in flowering plants, where pollen (the male part of a flower) from one plant is carried to another plant of the same species by the wind or on the head or legs of an insect, bird or other animal and enters the carpel (the female organ of the flower) so that pollination can occur. There is a significant difference, however, between what happens with flowers and with fungi: whereas flowers are pollinated while still attached to their parent plant, with fungi the spores are usually well away from their parent fruitbodies.

The two haploid spores (each spore cell being monokaryotic - having a single nucleus) from our two Pink Waxcap mushrooms each grow into a multi-branched tangle of hyphae - the underground mycelia. When they meet, the two mycelia join (in a process known as plasmogamy) and from their junction there emerges a secondary mycelium with dikaryotic hyphae (that is, with two nuclei per cell). It is from this secondary mycellium that new fruitbodies, carrying genes from both parents, will eventually emerge from the ground.

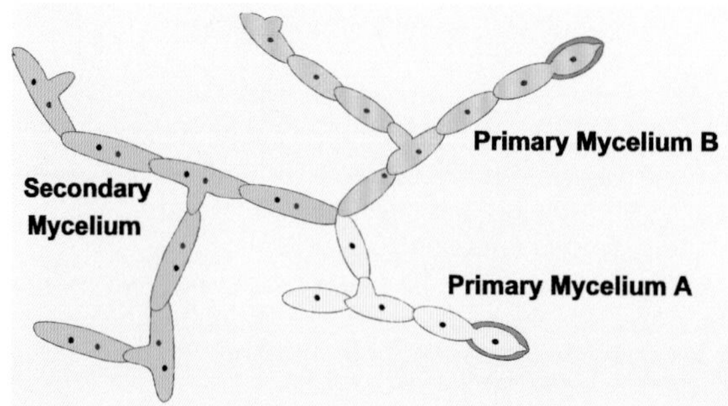

When compatible primary mycelia meet they can fuse to form a secondary (fertile) mycelium with two nuclei per cell (termed dikaryon) that is capable of producing fertile fruitbodies.

In the diagrams above, the growth of the mycelia is shown as an incremental process in which new haploid cells (each with a single nucleus) appear at the end of a primary hyphal cell or via a 'bud' branching from the side of a cell. The process by which new dikaryon cells are formed at the tips of secondary mycelia is also intriguing. The connecting structures involved in this process are clearly visible under a high-powered microscope, and examination of these structures, commonly referred to as clamp connections, provides information that can help with species identification.

Clamp Connections

The dikaryotic mycelial cells of a basidiomycete fungus cannot simply divide by normal mitosis, where one cell duplicates its genetic information (known as DNA replication) and splits in half to create two identical copies of itself; instead they must produce two daughter cells each with a copy of both parent nuclei. The creation of a new cell at the growing tip of the secondary (dikaryotic) mycelium is then achieved by the formation of what is known as a clamp connection. The key phases in this cell division process are illustrated below:

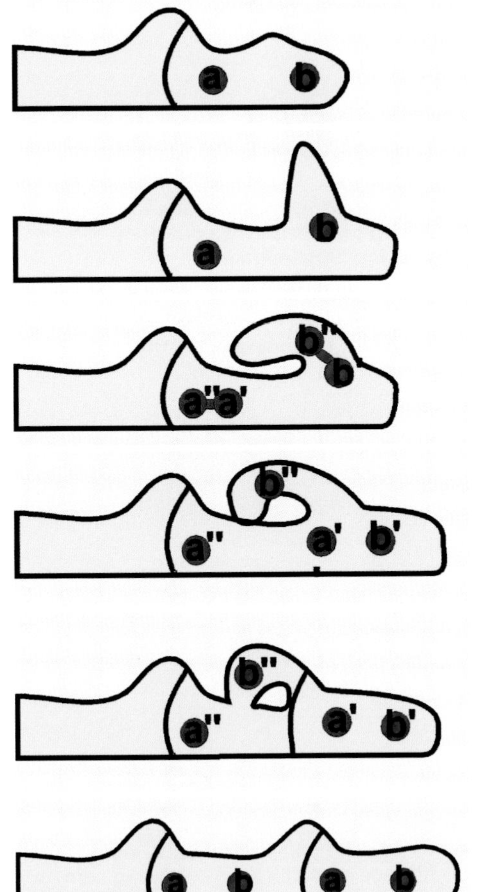

At the beginning of the process of creating a new hyphal cell, a bulge forms in wall of the terminal cell in between the two nuclei a and b.

The bulge extends and becomes a deep pocket that begins to turn back towards the rear of the cell.

The two nuclei, a and b, then divide by mitosis. These divisions are oriented such that the b'' nucleus is positioned in the clamp pocket.

The a' and b' nuclei move toward the front of the hypha, while the a" nucleus remains at the rear. The b'' nucleus moves towards the tip of what will become the clamp.

Next, a cell wall forms between the clamp, the posterior cell and the tip of the hypha. The tip is now a complete cell containing two nuclei. The rear cell contains only the a'' nucleus, but it becomes complete when the clamp, with its b'' nucleus, merges with the hypha of the rear cell.

In a few seconds from start to finish the new cell is complete and the extended hypha is ready to begin the division process all over again.

Development and Reproduction of Ascomycetes

Many of the ascomycetes do not produce large fruitbodies, and their complex sexual and asexual life cycles are of limited interest to those of us concerned mainly with macrofungi. Unicellular yeasts, for example, have both asexual and sexual reproductive cycles, although the most common mode of reproduction in yeast is asexual, by a process of budding. The nucleus of the parent yeast cell splits to create a daughter nucleus that then migrates into a daughter cell (looking very much like a bud) growing out from the parent. The bud then grows and separates from the parent cell, thus forming a new yeast cell. In other ascomycetes growth is via hyphae that extend at their tips rather as in the basidiomycetes. In many but not all of the ascomycetes the hyphae consist of tubular sections separated by dividing walls (septae) with central holes through which nuclei and other organelles can migrate. Reproduction is via spores formed within specialised hyphal cells known as asci (singular: ascus) that develop upon the fertile surface of a fruitbody.

Unscrambling the asci code – spore production in the Ascomycota

In shape most asci are cylindrical, although a few are more nearly spherical. Each ascus holds typically eight spores, although some ascomycetes species produce just a single spore per ascus while others can have as many as a hundred or more.

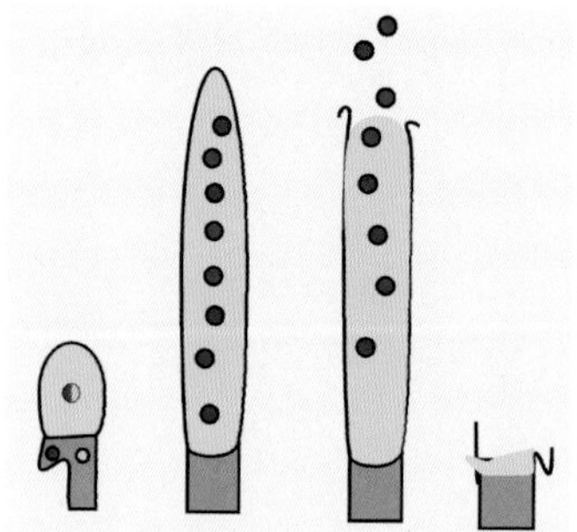

In many ascomycetes the fusion of two dikaryotic nuclei occurs at the end of a hypha, which then develops into an ascus wherein spores form and ripen.

Once the spores are fully mature, the top of the ascus bursts open and the spores are forcibly ejected.

The spent asci soon decay, even though the fruitbody may remain intact for several days.

The two main forms of large ascomycetes are cup or disc fungi, and flask fungi.

Some of the ascomycetes, such as Black Bulgar *Bulgaria inquinans* with individual discs typically 1cm across, produce fruitbodies that are very easily seen; however, many of the cup and disc species are smaller than 1mm in diameter and are easily missed.

Flask fungi such as *Xylaria polymorpha* (left), whose morbid appearance has earned it the unflattering common name of Dead Man's Fingers, are also examples of ascomycete species that produce large fruitbodies.

Cup fungi

The cup or disc fungi produce their asci on the upper surface of a fruitbody known as an apothecium. This fertile surface often appears smooth and shiny, while the underside of the (sometimes very shallow or almost flat) cup more often has a dull matt surface.

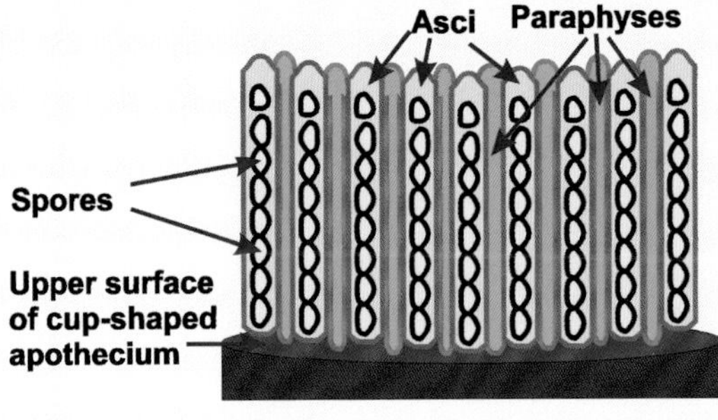

Structural details of the fertile surface of the apothecium vary from one species to another. All have asci within which the spores are produced, but features such as the shape and ornamentation of the asci and the spores, as well as other infertile cells such as paraphyses between the asci, are important in identifying particular species.

Not all so-called cup and disc fungi are recognisably either cup-shaped or disc-shaped, but all have fertile upper surfaces – or what would be the upper surface if you could unfold them and spread them out flat, since many have evolved to have extremely contorted surfaces and hence a very large fertile area crammed in to quite a small volume.

Peziza micropus **is a typical cup fungus, with its fertile surface on the inside of the cup. This wood-rotting species is most often seen on decaying stumps, trunks and branches of Beech, elms, willows and alders.**

Leotia lubrica**, commonly known as the Jellybaby fungus, has a cap with its margin turned down and often contorted; it looks very much like a cap-and-stem mushroom, and you might expect to find gills below the 'cap'; however, its fertile surface is actually on the top.**

Flask fungi

Quite different in their microscopic structure, although occasionally growing in communal groups shaped rather like some of the cup fungi mentioned above, the flask fungi produce their spores in spherical chambers known as perithecia (singular perithecium). Perithecia are no larger than 2mm across and in many cases much smaller than that. Among the most common are various *Nectria* species that appear as tiny hemispherical blobs on fallen twigs and branches. Each blob contains one or more perithecia. An example often seen on Beech wood is Coral Spot *Nectria cinnabarina*, with fruitbodies typically 1.5mm across.

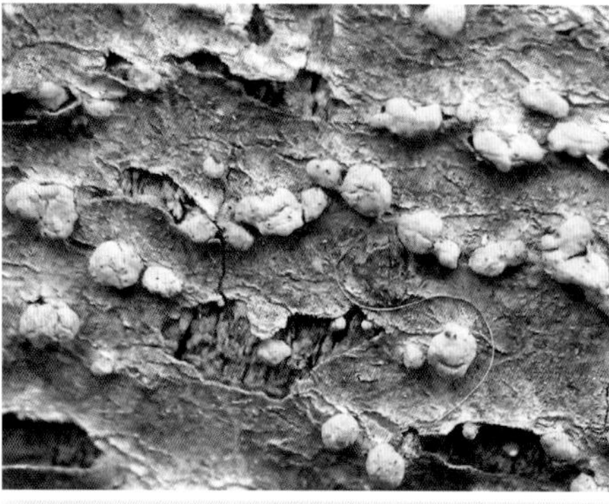

Coral Spot on a dead Beech branch. An individual blob encloses one or more flasks (perithecia) each containing many asci.

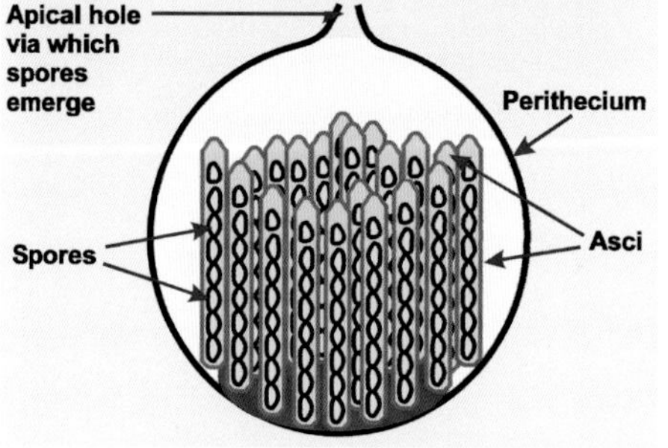

The way the asci are arranged inside the perithecium varies considerably, and this feature can be examined under a microscope. For example, in some species the asci are attached only to the base of the chamber, while in other species they line the walls as well as the base. As with the cup fungi, there may be paraphyses between the asci.

Finally, just as there are compound forms of cup fungi so also are there compound flask fungi. One such example is *Daldinia concentrica,* commonly known as King Alfred's Cakes.

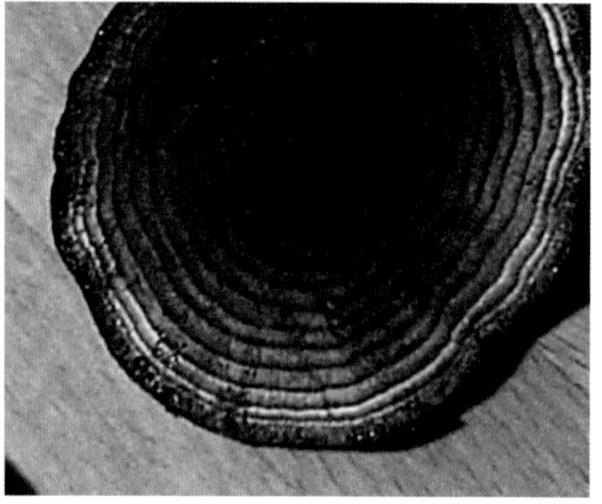

The outer layer of King Alfred's Cakes *Daldinia concentrica* is covered by perithecia embedded within a communal tissue known as a stroma (plural: stromata). Without a microscope all you can see are pimples on the black surface; these are the tips of the perithecia, each having a tiny opening through which the spores emerge.

In this sliced sample, concentric layers of infertile inner material are visible. It is for this feature that the specific epithet was chosen.

Fairy Rings

Both in grassland and in woodland, some kinds of mushrooms occur in rings rather than being randomly scattered about. Nowadays in Britain these phenomena are commonly referred to as fairy rings. (In Italy they are called witches' rings.) In the past these mysterious overnight appearances have been attributed to many causes, some natural, such as thunder and lightning, and others supernatural – the work of fairies, whose dancing feet cause the grass to wither and so allow fungi to break through the earth.

There is (perhaps rather disappointingly) a perfectly logical explanation.

1. Initially young fungal material known as a mycelium forms a small disc-shaped mat that grows below the ground by expanding outwards at its margin. During the fruiting season, which for many fungi is an annual event, mushrooms emerge from the soil in the location of the disc.
2. Having grown by consuming what goodness it can from the soil, the central part of the mycelium dies leaving an annulus of living mycelium. In the centre of this area no new mushrooms can spring up. Gradually, as the dead mycelium decays and water can penetrate more easily through the soil, grass and other plants return to the central area.
3. In successive years the fairy ring increases in diameter and mushrooms emerge from the growing rim of the mycelium. At their expanding (outer) edges the rings of mycelium of certain kinds of fungi release chemicals that promote more rapid growth of grass. As a result, even when they are not producing mushrooms the underground fungi betray their presence by creating rings of impoverished, yellowing grass surrounded by slightly larger rings of green grass that grows taller and more verdant than the rest of the lawn. Not all ring-forming fungi visibly affect the grass in this way; some leave no evidence of their underworld existence except during their fruiting periods.

Part of a huge fairy ring of Clouded Funnels *Clitocybe nebularis* in coniferous woodland. The age of the underground mycelium is roughly proportional to the diameter of the ring.

As a fairy ring grows ever larger in successive years, its annulus of mycelium will eventually reach a barrier, such as a wall or a deeply-rooted tree, so that the mycelium in that region is unable to extend. Then the growth continues in whatever directions it can. By this process a ring can get broken into a number of separate arcs.

A small fairy ring in the first year is replaced by a larger ring in year two, as mushrooms appear at the outer edge of an annulus of mycelium (coloured mauve in the diagram on the left). In the third year, unable to get past the broad trunks of two deep-rooted trees, the underground fungal ring has been cut into two separate arcs, with their mycelia no longer connected. The yellow arc of mycelium is now a clone of the original fungus.

Another common way that mycelia are broken into segments is during heavy rainstorms, when surface water gouges deep runnels on sloping ground. Similarly, when strong winds (or a garden broom) sweep rotting leaf litter from one place to another the fine threads of fungus mycelium growing on the surface of the leaves get broken into small pieces each of which is able to carry on growing if the conditions in the new location are favourable to the species of fungus concerned. By such means a living mycelium can split to become two or more separate clones. This form of asexual reproduction can occur with plants, of course, but it is even more common in the kingdom of fungi.

In our own kingdom of life, survival of both pieces of a dissected animal is far from the norm (the magician's trick with a box, a saw and a lovely lady being an illusory exception) although, for example, sea stars such as the Sunflower Starfish have the remarkable ability to grow new legs if they lose one or more; meanwhile, even more amazingly, the amputated legs can grow into new sea stars. This is possible because the sea star's vital organs are distributed throughout its body.

Some kinds of starfish have the remarkable capability to grow new 'legs' if one gets broken off. More amazingly, if the leg includes a small piece of the centre of the body then it can grow to become an entire new starfish. Chopping up starfish is therefore likely to be no more effective than chopping up roots of bindweed in the hope of eradicating that pernicious weed from a garden.

Unless its progress is prevented by an impenetrable barrier, the mycelium expands outwards from its starting point. When the conditions are right it throws up fruiting bodies whose sole purpose is to produce yet more spores which disperse so that new mycelia can get started somewhere else. (There is a suggestion that fungi may produce fruitbodies only when conditions are *unfavourable* for the mycelium, rather as desert cacti bloom when faced with terrible drought conditions: certainly, the stable atmosphere of a temperature and humidity controlled laboratory is not ideal for stimulating the fruiting of fungi.)

What constitutes ideal conditions for fruitbody production varies with different types of fungi, but changes in humidity and temperature certainly play a big part. For most fungi the conditions are right for fruiting in summer or autumn, although there are still plenty of fungal fruiting bodies to be seen throughout the year. A few fungi even fruit in sub-zero temperatures and when there is snow lying on the ground.

***Calocybe gambosa* is one of the few prized edible mushrooms that can be gathered in springtime. Because it generally puts in an appearance as early as the last week in April, this species has acquired the common name of St George's Mushroom. (St George's Day falls on 23rd April.)**

Spore production

The chances of any two microscopic spores falling on fertile ground close enough to one another for their primary mycelia to meet is very small indeed. That's why our Pink Waxcap, for example, has to produce a lot of spores and must also make sure that as many of them as possible are dispersed well away from the parent mycelium. Now we can understand why most gilled mushrooms have tall stems. The stem of a mushroom lifts the spore-producing underside of the cap up above the ground, where the wind can more easily sweep its spores away to distant sites. We can also see the reason for those gills: compared with a flat surface they increase by a factor of ten or even more the area of fertile material that is available for producing spores.

The densely packed (crowded) gills of the Dune Cavalier *Melanoleuca cinereifolia* provide a very large surface area upon which spores can be produced.

Hydnoid fungi have devised another strategy for maximising the area available for spore production: instead of a flat fertile area these hedgehog-like fungi have their undersides covered in a densely-packed array of spines.

A medium-sized mushroom can produce as many as10 billion spores. On windy days spores are carried thousands of metres up into the air, often drifting on high-altitude air currents from one country to another and even between continents. Earth's atmosphere is heavily laden with fungal spores for much of the year, and particularly so during hot, dry and windy autumn days when so many fungi are fruiting.

The Giant Puffball *Calvatia gigantea* is an occasional find but tends to be localised. In general appearance this edible mushroom is typical of the various puffballs and earthballs but very much bigger. A 22 kg monster with a girth of 2.64m was discovered in Canada in 1987. A more typical size is 1 to 2m in girth (35 to 70cm across the largest dimension). It has been estimated that the average giant puffball produces several trillions of spores.

In contrast with the norm for cap-and-stem fungi, the fertile surfaces of ascomycetes cup fungi are not on the underside of the cups but on the top or inner surface. When they are fully mature, the asci burst open under pressure from the expanding spores.

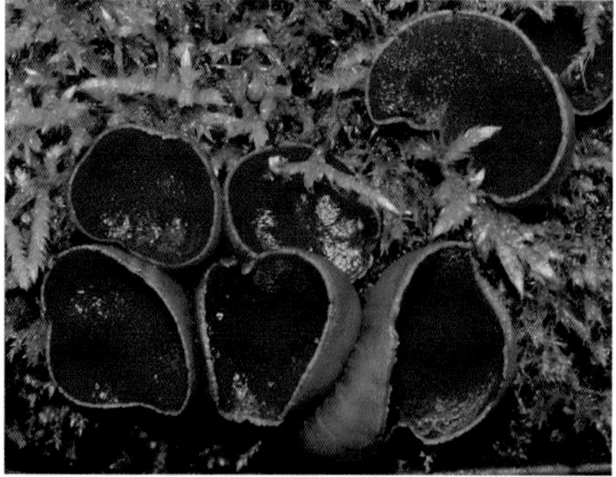

Scarlet Elfcup *Sarcoscypha austriaca* is a very common winter-fruiting cup fungus. The English name is a reference to the size, intriguing shape and startlingly bright colour – the ascomycetes answer to the brightly-coloured waxcaps.

Scarlet Elfcup belongs to the order Pezizales, a large group of cup fungi only a few of which produce conspicuous fruitbodies, mostly in shades of fawn and brown.

Some of the cup fungi react visibly and quite startlingly when their fertile surfaces are disturbed. Bay Cup *Peziza badia* (right) is one such example. If you drop specks of sand into a cup that is ready to release spores, several of the asci will burst open. Watch carefully and you will see a tiny cloud of spores emerge – a fascinating sight. Drop more specks of sand into the same cup and this time nothing happens: the ripe asci pods have already exploded and the others are not yet ready to release spores.

Some cup fungi - for example the Elfin Saddle *Helvella lacunosa* shown on the right – have stems upon which cups turned 'inside out' are perched. Sometimes the cups are so contorted that it is not immediately obvious which parts belong to the fertile surface.

Complex cap fungi such as morels have many fertile cup-like surfaces in a compound structure perched on a single stem. Their spores are launched into the air via asci.

Morels *Morchella esculenta* are spring fruiting fungi with deeply pitted (multi-cupped) cap surfaces delineated by a network of interconnected narrow ridges. These and several other kinds of morels are greatly prized edible fungi.

The Diversity of Spore-dispersal Mechanisms

Mushrooms with gills and those with tubes and pores rely on the wind to carry their spores to fresh fields (and woods) and pastures new, but other kinds of fungi have devised alternative strategies for distributing their spores. Puffballs and earthballs produce fruiting bodies where spores develop inside sealed sacs. At maturity an opening appears in the top of the sac – either a small hole or a ragged tear – thus allowing the wind or the rain to distribute the spores.

Rain washes the spores from earthballs, which may explain why they are particularly common on sloping grass-free footpaths.

When raindrops fall upon the flexible skin of a puffball, clouds of spores are released through a hole in the apex. Squeeze a mature puffball if you want to witness the release of spores - but be sure to keep your face out of the firing line!

Bird's-nest fungi have devised another cunning way of 'getting the children to leave home'. Within a sealed tub, what look rather like grains of rice grow into egg-shaped sacs of maturing spores. At maturity the lid breaks free exposing the eggs, known as peridioles, which get thrown out of the nest by raindrops rebounding from the sides. In this remarkable game of tiddlywinks some of the eggs can be projected half a metre and occasionally more.

Animal Couriers

It's wonderful how flowers get insects to distribute pollen, but it appears that fungi worked out this ruse first. Some spores can only start producing a primary mycelium once they have been through an animal's gut, a process that dissolves their tough outer skin; others rely on a scent like the smell of rotting flesh - a call to lunch for meat-loving flies.

Truffles, underground fungi that never see the light of day or feel the breath of wind, attract the attention of animals by emitting a powerful aroma. When dug up and eaten, the spores within a truffle pass through the animal's gut and are then deposited at a new location.

The strange fungi illustrated here are *Mutinus caninus,* commonly known as Dog Stinkhorns. They are not by any means the smelliest members (!) of the stinkhorn tribe.

As insects crawl over the sticky cap of the stinkhorn, some of the spore-laden 'gleba' sticks to their feet. Next stop, somewhere else... and every once in a while that becomes the birthplace of a new stinkhorn mycelium.

Fungi have exploited the opportunity for intercontinental travel, tagging along as excess baggage with people, food and manufactured goods. It's not possible to leave fungal diseases at home, and so the species that can infect people, pets or farm animals get spread to any country with suitable climatic conditions. Nowadays we can and do control our own surface temperature and humidity – our 'body climate' - by wearing suitable clothes and heating or cooling our homes. As a result, whereas in the past particular skin diseases were associated with different fungal species in cold, dry parts of the world compared with warm humid places, today a wider range of fungal species is able to contribute to human infections in many regions.

For fungi fans the intercontinental movement of mushrooms adds to the fascination (as well as the frustration) of trying to identify species not included in local or regional identification guides. Along with exotic pot plants, orchid substrates and imported greenhouse compost, many new species have arrived in Britain and Northern Europe. Climate change is likely to make their new homes increasing comfortable for them.

Tiny fungi that could not survive outdoors thrive in the warm moist atmosphere of the Tropical House at the National Botanic Garden of Wales, in Carmarthenshire.

Birds and winged insects provide another transport service that many of the microfungi rely on, and again in Europe climate change is causing a steady northwards movement of many of these creatures. Each year several new birds and bugs are sighted in Britain and Ireland, some only dropping in but others establishing breeding colonies and with them all that their associated fungi require to set up home.

Cattle Egrets *Bubulcus ibis* have been visiting Britain in increasing numbers in recent years. In 2008 a pair bred successfully in Cornwall, and in the same year Cattle Egrets were seen in Ireland for the first time.

Formerly rare in Britain and Ireland, much sought after morels are now fairly common in parks and gardens where bark chippings are used as mulch to smother weed seedlings. No longer dependent on the vagaries of the wind, spores of one morel species in particular, the so-called Black Morel *Morchella elata*, travel by truck. When tipped with loads from other sites and mixed in the spreading process, it's not unusual to find these morels littering a garden for just one season (late March and April) after which, in most cases, they are seen no more... until more loads of mulch are delivered.

Black Morels *Morchella elata* found in a hotel garden in southern Ireland in April 2004. For each of the next five years no morels were seen there.

The Redlead Roundhead *Leratiomyces ceres* is another attractive (but inedible) mushroom that is increasingly common thanks to the practice of spreading bark beneath shrubs in parks and gardens.

How Fungi Feed

Fungi cannot ingest food in the way that animals do, nor can they manufacture their own food as most plants do. Instead of the food going in to the fungus, the fungus must go in to its food source and absorb nutrients as it extends its habitat within the dead or living plants, animals or other fungi. (Grave robbing and even cannibalism are not restricted to the animal kingdom.)

When the food in one location is all used up, the mycelium extends hyphal strands into new territory where it secretes digestive enzymes that break down the substrate, allowing the fungus to absorb nutrients and water from its surroundings; this provides the energy needed for further growth and reproduction.

Wood-rotting fungus invading a log that has been lying in damp leaf mould. The branching network of rhizomorphs (bundles of white fungal hyphae) is clearly visible.

There are three main ways in which fungi feed. Their relationship with the organisms on which they feed may be:

- **Saprophytic** – taking nutrients from dead organisms or from organic waste
- **Parasitic** – feeding on living organisms, weakening or even killing them in the process
- **Symbiotic** – receiving food from other living organisms but providing benefits in return

Saprophytic Fungi

Most fungi feed by taking the nutrients they require from the remains of dead plants or animals, or from waste material (such as dung) produced by other living organisms. These fungi play a vital role, often together with insects and bacteria, in breaking down complex organic material into simpler chemicals that can be assimilated into the ground. The greatest diversity of saprophytic fungi occurs in woodlands, where the ground is littered with dead plant material such as fallen leaves, twigs and logs. The digestion of all this waste material is crucial, of course; otherwise, tree litter would pile up into an enormous rubbish heap through which no plants could grow.

The mycelium of these Stump Puffballs *Lycoperdon pyriforme* has penetrated a moss-covered oak log and is now throwing up an army of fruitbodies whose spores will be scattered far and wide by the wind; some may find other stumps in need of tidying up.

Most kinds of inkcap fungi are incurably addicted to dead wood and other waste vegetable material. These delicate little Hare'sfoot Inkcaps *Coprinopsis lagopus* have been feeding on the leaf litter and bark beneath eucalyptus trees. Without the help of such indomitable composters the forest floor would soon become a sterile desert piled high with the kinds of dead material that insects do not relish.

Saprophytes are not restricted to forested areas. Several of the inkcap mushrooms, for example, are commonly found on rubbish heaps, while in pastureland other kinds of fungi, in conjunction with flies, beetles, earth worms and other invertebrates, carry out the important job of breaking down animal droppings into manure that plants can make use of.

Dung Roundheads *Protostropharia semiglobata* (until recently generally known as *Stropharia semiglobata*) and other dung-rotting (coprophilous) fungi provide an invaluable service on grazing land. They break down animal droppings and turn them into nutrient-rich soil that grass and other meadow plants require.

Fungi-rotting fungi

Once a fruitbody has released its spores its work for the future of fungi is done, but it still has one more important service to perform. While slugs, bugs and a host of other animals (including people) eat certain types of fungi when they can find them, many mushrooms simply rot away, often assisted in the process by other fungi.

This decaying bolete is providing food for another kind of fungus, a mould.

When edible fungi become infected by moulds they are not usually safe to eat. (There are one or two exceptions where certain edible mould species are even considered to improve the flavour!)

The tiny gilled Silky Piggyback mushroom *Asterophora parasitica* grows on decaying *Russula* species - in this case *Russula nigricans*, which is commonly known as the Blackening Brittlegill.

Parasitic Fungi

It seems that some fungi are so impatient that they can't wait for their victims to die; they simply tuck in to the meal regardless, generally going for soft targets – the injured, the sick and the elderly. Although some of these parasites seem to have very little impact on their hosts, others cause serious and in many instances mortal damage.

Among the most damaging of all woodland parasites are some (but by no means all) kinds of honey fungus, *Armillaria* species. Here the fungus has already weakened an alder tree and will probably continue feeding on it for a year or two after the tree has died.

Honey fungus has the annoying capacity to colonise adjacent healthy trees, reaching them by means of black bootlace-like strings of hyphae known as rhizomorphs, which enable the fungus to transport water and nutrients across the open spaces between trees.

The Giant Polypore *Meripilus giganteus* is a common parasite of mature Beech trees. Although it may be several years after the first fruitbodies appear, in due course infection by this massive bracket fungus can prove fatal. As the root system decays, although still producing new leaves in springtime the tree becomes so seriously weakened that it has to be felled because of the risk of it being toppled by high winds.

Artist's Bracket *Ganoderma applanatum* is a common decomposer of fallen hardwood trees, but it can also colonise living trees, entering via wounds generally low down on the trunk. This long-lived bracket fungus rots both the sapwood and the heartwood until the weakened bole is no longer capable of supporting the weight of the tree.

Dutch Elm Disease

Parasitic attacks by the fungus *Ophiostoma ulmi* were responsible for the Dutch elm disease outbreaks that killed nearly 40% of Britain's mature elm trees from the 1920s through to the mid 1940s. In the late 1960s an even more devastating fungal disease, *Ophiostoma novo-ulmi*, was accidentally brought in to the UK in infected elm logs from North America. Since then 25 million elm trees in Britain and many more on mainland Europe have been killed by this ascomycetous fungal infection. But how did this disease suddenly infect so many trees?

A healthy mature elm tree is now a rare sight in southern Britain following the most recent Dutch elm disease outbreak, when more than 90% of the large elm trees were wiped out. This photograph of a healthy Wych Elm was taken in Perthshire, Scotland, in 2009.

The culprits responsible for spreading this more virulent form of Dutch elm disease were bark beetles (*Scolytus* species). As they lay their eggs within the elm bark, these beetles carry fungal spores with them, thus providing the fungus with a means of entering new trees. There is still no known cure for Dutch elm disease, although elm trees with a strong resistance to the infection have now been cultivated.

The first sign of Dutch elm disease – so called *not* because Holland was the origin of the problem but because the early research into this problem was carried out by scientists there - is a yellowing of the leaves on one or more branches. Soon the whole tree is invaded and all of its remaining leaves die. Within two years, and often more rapidly, the tree is finished and its branches rot and break off. Eventually the trunk is bare, the dead bark falling away to reveal a network of tunnels beneath the bark that were made by the beetle larvae. As for the fungal infection itself, its legacy is a brown stain within the dead timber and sticky spores attached to the tunnels beneath the bark. Once the larvae have pupated and emerged as adult beetles able to fly, they are already spattered in spores and hence able to spread the fungal infection to other trees.

Although the majority of Britain's mature elm trees have succumbed to this disease, no species have been lost. This is because elms produce lots of root suckers, and once the over-shading canopy of the parent tree is removed some of the saplings grow vigorously. Unfortunately, once these young elms develop a thick bark that is attractive to the beetles (generally after 15 to 20 years) they in turn become victims of Dutch elm disease.

Fungal afflictions of animals

Parasitic fungi that grow on and inside animals can cause health problems. In people, the diseases commonly called athlete's foot and ringworm are manifestations of infection by fungi mostly of the genera *Epidermophyton, Trichophyton* and *Microsporum.* Most people contract athlete's foot at some stage in their lives – often in swimming pool changing rooms because the fungi concerned thrive in these kinds of warm moist environments, where they feed on dead skin cells.

Ringworm is so called because worms were once thought to be somehow involved in causing the disease, and because the resulting lesions on human skin spread out circularly, with healthy skin growing back in the centre. (In effect, therefore, the red lesions are fairy rings.) Candida, the condition commonly known as thrush, is also a fungal infection; in this disease the fungus species most commonly involved is *Candida albicans.*

People are fortunate in having access to treatments that at least control and in many cases eradicate most fungal diseases of the skin. Other creatures are less fortunate. The Scarlet Caterpillarclub *Cordyceps militaris* (right) is one of several bug-killing fungi. Its chosen victims are insect pupae or larvae (usually of butterflies or moths), and the experience for the victims must be extremely unpleasant.

The *Cordyceps* mycelium colonises the insect and mummifies it, keeping it alive just long enough to generate the biomass necessary to produce another *Cordyceps militaris* fruitbody.

First catch your prey...

It is well known that some plants capture insects to supplement the meagre supply of nutrients available in areas of poor soil. To do this they employ a variety of tactics, from 'pitcher' wells into which bugs fall and drown to fly traps that are the design template for those macabre leg clamps once used to snare badgers, foxes and other wild animals. Yet another cunning ploy, a glue trap, is used by those remarkable plants of peat bog and wet heath, the sundews (right), which have a coating of red hairs on the upper surfaces of their leaves. Each hair is tipped with a drop of sticky liquid that has the ability to trap small insects, upon which the plant then feeds by absorbing enzymes into its leaves – a most un-plant-like method of feeding!

Certain kinds of fungi are also adapted to capture living prey. For example Oyster Mushrooms *Pleurotus ostreatus* (right) are able to trap nematodes, tiny eelworms that forage between the gills of the fungi. The mycelium of these carnivorous mushrooms forms drops (in the case of *Pleurotus*) or adhesive knobs (*Hohenbuehelia*) which contain toxins that paralyze the nematodes. The reaction of a nematode to these toxins when it comes in to contact with them is immediate: the worm stops wriggling and so becomes an easy victim for the hyphae of the fungus to penetrate. The hyphae home in on and enter the mouth of the nematode. At this point the poor defenceless creature is still alive, as the fungal hyphae extend inside it and consume the eel worm from within.

Fungi have developed many different forms of these nematode traps. Some use adhesive knobs; others construct two-dimensional or three-dimensional networks of adhesive cells; another form consists of a lasso-like structure made up of cells that inflate when a nematode pokes its nose in and touches one of the inner surfaces of the hoop (rather as an air bag in a vehicle inflates when a physical impact exceeds a pre-defined threshold).

Recently, both nematodes and hyphal rings (although of a non-constricting type) were found together in a piece of amber dating back some 100 million years, suggesting that this type of carnivorous behaviour is not a modern invention; however, when it evolved is unclear. Traps are not confined to the Basidiomycota; some ascomycetes have also been found to trap nematodes. Is this perhaps yet another example of parallel evolution?

Cannibal fungi

Fungi are quite capable of turning on other fungi, and here are just two of the many commonplace examples that illustrate the point. The Parasitic Bolete *Pseudoboletus parasiticus* feeds on Common Earthballs *Scleroderma citrinum.* Finding earth balls is no guarantee that you will see these rare boletes, but unless there are earthballs present Parasitic Boletes will certainly not appear.

Apparently being attacked by Parasitic Boletes *Pseudoboletus parasiticus,* this Common Earthball *Scleroderma citrinum* is shrunken and distorted. The ability of the host fungus to produce viable spores is not affected, although the quantity of spores produced may be below the capacity of a healthy earthball.

Even while this Rosy Bonnet *Mycena rosea* is busy distributing its white spores, a tiny fungal parasite known as Bonnet Mould *Spinellus fusiger* has colonised the cap and gills and is getting on with its recycling work.

Symbiotic Fungi

These are chummy fungi that live on (or sometimes inside) other living organisms without causing significant damage, while both the fungi and the organisms with which they live benefit from being together. For example where a tree is the symbiotic partner, the fungus is better adapted to scavenging the soil to absorb water and nutrients such as phosphorus, and via the roots it shares these with the tree; in return the tree provides the fungus with energy-rich sugars that it manufactures through the process of photosynthesis. Formed with the right kinds of fungi, such a relationship can stimulate root growth in trees and other plants, increasing their overall growth rate and making them more resistant to drought conditions and to disease.

Mycorrhizas

Lots of kinds of fungi, both ascomycetes and basidiomycetes, live in mutually beneficial relationships with trees. As a woodland fungus grows underground, its thread-like hyphae develop into a dense mycelial mat until it encounters the roots of living trees of a type with which it is compatible; then the mycelium and the root system link up to become 'mycorrhizal' partners in a cooperative food society. The literal meaning of the term mycorrhiza is 'fungus root' (from the Greek words *'mykes'*, meaning fungus, and *'rhiza'* meaning root) and in effect the two organisms become inseparable.

All milkcaps (*Lactarius* species) form mycorhizal relationships with trees, and some milkcaps are specific to just one tree genus. For example the False Saffron Milkcap *Lactarius deterrimus* is associated with trees of the *Picea* genus (spruce trees).

Ectomycorrhizas and endomycorrhizas

In some instances the fungus envelops the root, effectively increasing its diameter as well as connecting it to much more soil via the whole of the mycelial network. This type of interaction is termed an ectomycorrhizal (EM) relationship. The preface 'ecto' signifies that the fungus remains outside of the tree roots. Most trees benefit from mycorrhizal partners, and in forestry management it is increasingly common practice to 'inoculate' the soil in which young saplings are planted with the mycelium of appropriate species of fungi. Similar inoculation techniques can be used to reintroduce edible fungi to newly planted woodland or to replanted areas that had been previously clear felled.

Occasionally people ask how they can get rid of mushrooms from a garden, and more often than not specifically from the compost heap. Unless they are deadly poisonous species in a place where young children could pick them, it is not only unnecessary but also unwise to destroy these fungi, as in most cases they do far more good than harm. (It is also quite difficult to kill fungi, and it certainly cannot be done by smashing the fruitbodies!) Most plants, including garden flowers and vegetables, benefit from the presence of fungi in the soil, and in their natural environment the majority of plants are now known to depend on one or more mycorrhizal partners. Adding composted garden and kitchen waste to the soil in a flower bed or a vegetable plot does more than just increase the soil's nutrient content; the compost can also help by introducing more fungi into the soil together with nutrients that the fungi can share symbiotically with plant roots.

Mycorrhizas on conifer roots. Attached to the fine tips are tiny hair-like hyphal filaments, not easily visible in this x2 magnified image are the hyphae that extend outwards and scavenge the soil, delivering nutrients to the rootlets that are encased within the mycorrhizal sheaths.

In an endomycorrhizal relationship the fungal hyphae actually penetrate a plant's root system. 'Endo' means into, and in this kind of relationship the fungi, known as arbuscular mycorrhizal (AM) fungi, enter into the cells of the roots themselves.

Orchids and fungi

About ten per cent of the world's flowering plants (some 25,000 species) belong to the orchid family, Orchidaceae. At some stage in its life - and in many instances throughout its life - each of these plants is dependent upon one or more fungi that live within and around the root cells of the orchid. When the right kinds of fungi (many of which are *Rhizoctonia* species) get involved, it's a give-and-take relationship – initially, at least. The orchid provides the fungus with a protected growing environment, and it is even possible that the orchid provides some of the vitamins that the fungus needs. The other half of this symbiotic deal is that the fungus takes up water, phosphorus and other nutrients from the soil, breaking them down into a soluble form that the orchid can assimilate.

The Bee Orchid *Ophrys apifera* is a terrestrial species native to Britain, Ireland and most of mainland Europe. Bee Orchids take up to eight years to develop from seed to flower, during which time the plant depends on an association between its roots and fungi within the soil.

The seeds of an orchid are much smaller than those of other plants - so small that there is no room inside the seedcase for any significant reserves of food. An orchid seed cannot therefore complete the germination process and start growing until it has been infected by an appropriate kind of fungus. Once the fungus has entered the seed, coils of fungal hyphae then develop, infusing the roots (and sometimes also the stems) of the orchid. The association between orchid and fungus is essential at this stage because on its own the orchid cannot absorb nutrients from the soil. In some instances that dependency continues during the first few years of the plant's life; but, as the plant grows and produces leaves, its dependence upon the mycorrhizal partnership may decline or even cease, depending upon the species concerned. In the majority of instances only during the seedling stage is the orchid critically dependent upon its fungal partner, although some mature plants continue to benefit from the phosphorus and other nutrients that the fungi provide. Those orchids that lack chlorophyll (and of these there are just a few in Britain and Ireland but many more worldwide) would die but for the life support system provided by their fungal friends.

Far left: The Bird's-nest Orchid *Neottia nidus-avis*, an unprepossessing woodland wildflower, is devoid of chlorophyll and so cannot use sunlight to convert carbon dioxide into food as most plants do. Instead, throughout its life it is dependent upon fungal partners to feed it.

Near left: An epiphytic orchid growing on a tree in Fairchild Gardens, Miami. The seeds of this plant require fungal partners to germinate and begin growing, but in later life the orchid turns traitor and consumes the fungal hand that has fed it.

Lichenised fungi

Yet another kind of symbiotic relationship is found in lichen. Until recent times considered to be fungal species, lichens – or more formally lichenised fungi - are now known to be symbiotic communities of two or more organisms.

This stump is gradually being recycled with the help of a variety of fungi and lichens.

Most lichens consist of a fungus (termed the mycobiont) in a mutually beneficial association with one or more algae and/or cyanobacteria (acting as the photobiont – doing the photosynthesis work necessary to feed the community with organic nutrients). It is questionable what the alga gets in return, apart from shelter from harsh sunlight and a supply of water that the fungus collects and stores for later use by both partners. Indeed the algae and cyanobacteria (until recently the latter were called blue-green algae) within lichens are also found living alone, whereas most fungi that occur in lichens can only survive in lichenised forms. Some 1700 lichens have been recorded in Britain and ten times that number worldwide; most of the fungi involved are ascomycetes but a small number are deuteromycetes, and a few lichenised basidiomycetes are also known.

Lichens can live in some of the most extreme environments on the planet including arid deserts, high mountains, arctic wastelands, dripping rainforests and even salt-sprayed sea cliffs, often in locations where none of their component species could survive alone. Although they come in a rainbow array of colours and in many forms, it is usually possible to categorise lichens as either crustose (crust-like), foliose (leaf-like) or fruticose (no, it's nothing to do with fruits; fruticose means 'shrubby').

Lichen-encrusted rocks on the upper slopes of Cadair Idris, near Dolgellau in mid Wales

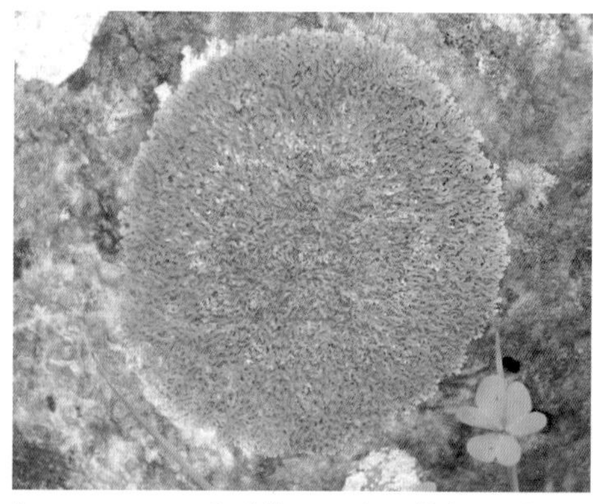

Among grey and white crustose lichens the bright orange foliose lichen *Xanthoria parietina* (above) is a common sight on rocks near the sea. Some crustose lichens in alpine-arctic regions are estimated to be several thousand years old.

Cladonia chlorophaea

Usually growing on soil, moss or rotten wood, the False Pixie Cup lichen *Cladonia chlorophaea* has a blue-green thallus (the lichen equivalent of a fruitbody) with upward-facing trumpet-shaped structures known as podetia.

Cladonia cristatella

Fruticose lichens usually stand up or hang down from the substrate to which they are attached. Shown on the right is Matchstick Moss *Cladonia cristatella.* In the USA this lichen is more often referred to as British Soldier because the red 'hats' are reminiscent of those worn by the British during the American War of Independence. (The red bits are the sexual fruiting parts of the lichen.)

Reproduction and distribution of lichenised fungi

Lichens can reproduce vegetatively when fertile parts of the lichen known as soredia, comprising fungal hyphae wrapped around algae or cyanobacteria, are released from the surface of the lichen and carried elsewhere by the wind or by an animal. They can also reproduce via spores produced by the fungal partner. The spores contain only fungal material, and so new lichens cannot form unless spores germinate on substrates where suitable algae or cyanobacteria are already present. Hence spores from one kind of lichen can meet up with a different algal partner to produce a new kind of lichen that looks quite different from its 'parent' albeit with no change in the fungal part of the organism.

Reasons for liking lichen

The chemical in litmus paper (which by turning either red or blue when dipped into a liquid substance indicates whether the liquid is acidic or alkaline) can be made from various kinds of lichens including, most commonly, *Roccella phycopsis.* This small fruticose lichen is most abundant along the Mediterranean Coast. Lichens have also been used to make dyes, cosmetics, perfumes and medicines (including some antibiotics); as a substitute for hops in beer making; and even in the manufacture of brandy from lichen-derived alcohol.

One of the most valuable services that lichens provide is as monitors of environmental quality. Lichens absorb minerals directly from the atmosphere and from rainwater, rather than via any soil filtration process, and so they are immediately affected by atmospheric pollution. Different kinds of lichens have different levels of pollution tolerance, and so the range of lichens found in a location can tell us a lot not just about the average quality of the environment but more particularly about the severity of any transient episodes of pollution. That's why there are so few lichens in and around centres of industrial activity unless the very highest standards of air pollution control are rigorously maintained. Gravestones, walls and trees in old country churchyards are usually much better places to look if you want to see a wide variety of lichens.

Stymied by Slime Moulds?

The group of organisms known as the slime moulds was considered to belong to the kingdom of fungi until recently. In common with fungi, they reproduce via spores; many are soft and slimy, at least during part of their lifecycle; and some have the appearance of fungal fruitbodies such as puffballs and stalkballs. Most non-scientific books about fungi simply referred to them as the Myxomycota or myxomycetes, and fungi field guides usually included a small selection of the many hundreds of species known to exist worldwide. Now better (but far from fully) understood, slime moulds are no longer considered to be fungi; they are now classed as part of the kingdom Protista. Despite this, people developing an interest in fungi come across slime moulds quite frequently and wonder what they have found. That's why I have included this brief section within *Fascinated by Fungi*.

Cellular slime moulds

This is a small group of slime moulds that live as separate amoeboid cells. When food becomes scarce they send signalling molecules to one another and come together in their tens of thousands to form a slimy mass, known as a pseudoplasmodium. The amoebae crawl en-masse to an open location and there grow into a fruitbody, some of the amoebae becoming spores, others forming a stalk to raise the spores up into the air.

Plasmodial slime moulds

Many more slime moulds are huge and often brightly coloured single cells with thousands of nuclei. In their motile (moving) stage these gooey masses, known as plasmodia, creep about slowly while feeding upon bacteria, microscopic fungi and decaying vegetation. Eventually the plasmodia metamorphose into fruitbodies, each comprising a thin stalk supporting a spore-producing capsule – not unlike some kinds of fungi.

A small selection of slime moulds

Fuligo septica

The sudden appearance of this slime mould on a tree stump or on bark mulch can be quite startling, and watching it crawl very slowly along is at least 'creepy' if not the stuff of nightmares. Common names include Flowers of Tan, Scrambled Egg Slime, and Dog Vomit.

At the spore-bearing stage the mass turns creamy ochre and hardens. At this stage, if the surface crust is broken clouds of powdery spores emerge.

Arcyria denudata

This is probably the most commonly encountered of the red slime moulds. The mature sporangia shown here are about 5mm tall and have a fluffy spore-bearing structure, but at the earlier plasmodial stage of development they are white and virtually impossible to distinguish from the many other similar species.

In the USA this slime mould is commonly referred to as Cotton Candy.

Lycogala terrestre

Pinkish red and up to 1.5cm across during the plasmodium stage, when they are mobile and wander in search of bacteria to eat, these slime moulds eventually turn brownish and becomes hemispherical before hardening and breaking up into a mass of powdery spores.

The common name Wolf's Milk has been applied to this colourful slime mould.

Reticularia lycoperdon

Looking rather like a blob of cavity-wall insulation foam, the sporangial stage of this slime mould is one of the largest commonly seen, ranging from 4 to 8cm across. Eventually the surface turns hard and silvery and then cracks, at which point wind, rain and insects can disperse the ripe spores.

One of the common names given to this slime mould is False Puffball.

Badhamia utricularis

So reminiscent of a bunch of miniature grapes with bloom-covered skins, this striking slime mould has ovoid sporangia 0.5 to 1.5mm across, usually suspended from a woody substrate but sometimes standing up vertically on thin brown stems.

Very often this slime mould occurs on dead wood that has already been colonised by corticioid wood-rotting fungi such as Hairy Curtain Crust *Stereum hirsutum.*

Tubulifera arachnoidea

Ranging from bright red to salmon pink when at its most noticeable, *Tubulifera arachnoidea* is more easily missed once fully mature, at which stage the spore-bearing sporangia turn brown and dull before breaking up and releasing their spores.

The name Red Raspberry Slime is commonly applied to this slime mould species.

Chapter 3 - Wood, Trees and Woodlands

Can't see the wood for the trees (or the fungi for the forest)?

Stourhead in Dorset, England. Autumn woodland colours help soften the blow of dying summer and the departure of wildflowers from the countryside - but a tree is much more than a pretty face on the landscape.

Timber for buildings, pulp for making paper, fuel for heating, fibre for clothing, fruits and nuts for food, shade and windbreaks for protection against the weather's worst extremes – to say that the value of trees to mankind is well understood by most people could be seen as stating the obvious. To suggest otherwise would be illogical. What more is there to say?

A lot more, for sure! The truth is that if these were the only goods and services that trees provided us with then we could get by pretty well without trees. There are alternative sources of food, fuel and so on. However, trees provide us with much more than all that. Via their leaves, trees capture carbon dioxide from the air, absorbing the carbon and using it to produce more timber, roots and leaves while releasing much of the oxygen back into the air. It has been estimated that one large tree continually recycles as much oxygen as ten people need in order to breathe. That's hardly a luxury; it's a vital element of our life-support system. And we now know that the viability of trees is inextricably linked to those mycorrhizal fungi that help them obtain the moisture and other soil-borne chemicals necessary for a long, vigorous and healthy life.

So what? Well, if something nasty happens to the fungi that help to feed the world's trees, our own life-support system would go on the blink and there would be very little that we could do about it. And if that makes you feel a bit hot under the collar, consider some of the other vital services that all those fungi-fed trees provide - climate control, for example.

The current concern about global warming, and its predicted consequence of climate chaos, highlights another of the hidden services provided by trees: a lot of carbon is locked up in the world's forests. We can either store it there in a benign form (just as fossilised trees in the form of buried coal are a benign form of carbon storage) or we can kill the trees and release their carbon into the atmosphere as carbon dioxide and other greenhouse gases that blanket the earth and prevent surface heat escaping into space.

Trees growing on a mountain slope cut down the rate of water run-off, not only minimising soil erosion but also reducing the peak river flow lower down the valley, preventing flooding or at least limiting the severity of what might otherwise be catastrophic floods. And then there is that other front-line service, pollution control.

Together with their mycorrhizal fungi, trees work tirelessly to clean up pollution on land, in the air and in the water. For example, leaves filter oxides of sulphur and nitrogen from the air, turning polluting chemicals into less harmful ones, while the roots and their mycorrhizas perform similar functions within the soil.

We need the world's forests. Without trees there would be no forests, and so we really must value and care for our trees. Therefore, it is crucial that we should do all that is necessary to ensure the survival of those mycorrhizal fungi that the trees rely upon. But if wood had not evolved from primitive plants there could be no trees, so perhaps a good starting point for understanding more about the lives of trees is to investigate the nature of wood itself, that wonderful material that enables trees to hoist their leaves high into the air, where they can turn sunlight into food for themselves as well as doing all those amazing things that help support animal life on our planet.

A brief history of trees

Trees, by which I mean large woody plants as opposed to merely tall fleshy ones (or merely giant ferns), evolved some 370 million years ago. That was about 180 million years after what is referred to as the Cambrian explosion, a brief period during which a great diversity and abundance of terrestrial life evolved rapidly on planet earth. At that time most of the continental land masses were crowded together in the southern hemisphere, and this enabled trees to spread quickly just about everywhere warm enough for trees to grow.

None of the earliest trees survive today, but fossils of an ancient species that we would immediately recognise today as a tree has been posthumously named Archaeopteris. This primeval tree had a trunk and branches consisting of timber very similar to the wood of trees living today; it had fern-like leaves, and it formed vast forests. With changes in climate and the emergence of new animal life forms, other trees evolved and Archaeopteris and many of its descendants became extinct.

In two small provinces in China a very ancient tree species survived until modern times, possibly with the helpful protection of monks. From a few relict trees more have been propagated, and samples can now be seen throughout the world. Known as the Ginkgo *Ginkgo biloba*, it is the only surviving species in its genus - indeed the sole surviving member of the family Ginkgoaceae, which occupies in lonely splendour the botanical order Ginkgoales. Fossils of trees from the *Ginkgo* genus date back to the Early Jurassic, and older Ginkgo-like fossils have been found dating from some 270 million years ago.

Leaves of *Ginkgo biloba*

The similarity (in shape, not structure) of Ginkgo leaves to the fronds of the maidenhair fern *Adiantum capillus-veneris* has resulted in the Ginkgo acquiring another common name: the maidenhair tree.

The Ginkgo is one of an estimated 100,000 or so species of trees presently in existence; however, just as we do not have an accurate figure for the numbers of species of animals, fungi or flowers that we have on our planet, so the figure for trees is also subject to a great deal of uncertainty.

Ginkgo biloba, the last of its kind, will probably be saved, although in the wild it is just one of thousands of trees threatened with extinction, many of which are critically endangered. With these trees we will also lose any tree-specific fungi, and whatever other ecological processes those fungi perform will also cease of course.

The structure of wood

The ingredients of wood are the organic polymers cellulose, hemicellulose and lignin, with a dash of pectin and trace amounts of other substances. (The terms cellulose, lignin etc refer in each case not to a single organic compound but to a large group of similar compounds that vary somewhat between tree species.) Cellulose and hemicellulose are made up of chains of various simple sugars such as glucose.

Cellulose is the main component of the cell walls of all kinds of plants, and this makes it the most abundant organic compound on our planet. About one third of all plant matter is cellulose, and it typically makes up over 40 per cent of the wood of trees. We are unable to digest the cellulose in our food (it used to be called roughage but nowadays it is more commonly referred to as dietary fibre) whereas certain animals - termites and many other insects, for example - are able to digest wood fully; this is because their guts contain microorganisms that can break down the cellulose.

Hemicelluloses are softer than celluloses. This is because whereas cellulose is crystalline, and therefore very strong and resistant to hydrolysis (not readily broken down in dilute acids or alkalis), hemicellulose has more of an amorphous structure that gives it little strength. Hemicelluloses are readily decomposed by dilute solutions of acids or bases and by certain enzymes. What is less clearly understood is the process by which hemicelluloses contribute to the strength of wood; however, research has demonstrated that when fungi attack timber it is often the hemicellulose that breaks down first, and with its decay the strength of the timber also declines.

Lignin is Mother Nature's adhesive. Being made up of organic compounds more complex than those in cellulose and hemicellulose, lignin is the least well understood of wood's main components. Lignin is tough stuff, and in wood it strengthens the cell walls and acts as a barrier helping to protect the cellulose and hemicelluloses against most kinds of fungal and microbial attack. It is lignin that gives tree trunks and branches the flexibility to bend with the wind and then return to their original shapes when the pressure is removed. Lignin also plays a crucial part in conducting water in a tree's vascular system, providing a waterproof coating to what would otherwise be water-permeable cell walls and so ensuring that the vascular tissue can conduct water effectively.

Typical composition of dry timber

Component	Softwood (conifers) %	Hardwood (broadleaves) %
Cellulose	45	40
Hemicellulose	25	40
Lignin	28	18
Pectin	2	2

Timber also contains trace amounts of starches and several other organic chemicals.

Handle anything made of wood and several things are immediately obvious. Wood is hard, not just on the surface (like an egg) but right through. Some parts are harder than others and often a different colour, and there is a visible grain to all wood – fibres aligned parallel with one another and for the most part packed in fairly straight bundles, although, where a tree has branched or a surface bulge or burr has formed, the grain twists and turns.

Splitting a log along the grain is relatively easy, but breaking wood across the grain is another matter altogether - it has to be so or trees would snap and fall in the lightest of breezes. When fungi attack a tree they exploit these structural characteristics: like most other living things they tend to seek out the line of least resistance. (Perhaps in this respect fungi are like us in that doing more work than is absolutely necessary goes against the grain.) Divide and conquer seems to be their strategy... so where are the natural divisions in wood?

Look at a cross-section of a tree trunk or a large branch and you will see that the wood is not the same all the way through. Even what most people would consider the 'wood itself', technically referred to as the xylem, is a two-layer sandwich. There is often a dark reddish-brown region in the centre, known as the heartwood; this is the tree's backbone, although unlike a human spine it plays no active part in the life of the tree. It is, in effect, dead wood (not to be confused with rotten wood). Beyond this inner core is a region of usually lighter-coloured sapwood, which pipes moisture up from the roots, through the trunk and along the branches and twigs to the leaves.

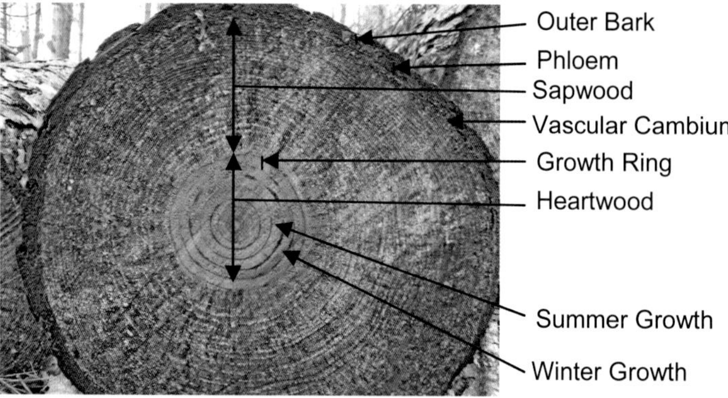

Cross-section of a conifer trunk showing the red-brown heartwood surrounded by sapwood and then an outer layer of what is commonly referred to as bark but which also includes the cambium, the phloem and the outer bark

The xylem (which comprises the heartwood and the sapwood) is surrounded by a relatively narrow annulus known as the vascular cambium, whose role is to distribute 'food and drink' to the growing parts of the tree. Beyond the vascular cambium is the phloem, which works tirelessly during the growing season; by day it takes the products of photosynthesis down to the branches, trunk and roots, and during darkness it transports soil nutrients up from the roots to the trunk, branches, twigs and leaves.

Finally we come to the outer bark, the tree's overcoat. This is yet another multi-layer sandwich, and one of its key roles is to protect the working parts of the wood from physical damage, extremes of temperature and drying winds. Although fungal fruitbodies are often to be seen emerging from cracks in the bark of a tree, in most instances the fungal mycelium will be feeding on material deeper within the woody core of the timber.

In essence, what happens as a tree grows is this: tubes within the sapwood part of the xylem carry water and mineral salts drawn – almost invariably with assistance from mycorrhizal fungi – from the soil via the roots and up through the trunk, branch and twig network to the leaves where, by photosynthesis, sugars are produced. These energy-rich sugars are transported, via cells in the inner layer of the phloem, down through the twig, branch, trunk and root network, and on the way most of the sugars are siphoned off via the cambium and directed inwards to feed the outer rim of the sapwood. The rest of the nutrients are sent, again via the cambium, to the phloem to renew its inner cell structure, as the tired old phloem cells are continually being pushed into the bark and hence towards the outside world.

As the tree grows, therefore, not only do new young shoots extend the growing twigs (primary growth) but all existing parts of the tree increase in diameter (secondary growth) so that the circumference of a tree trunk provides a rough and ready basis for estimating its age. Fastest growth occurs during the spring and summer months followed by slower or zero growth during autumn and winter. Deciduous trees shed their leaves in autumn and are then unable to photosynthesise food, and so their growth ceases altogether. Evergreen trees can continue growing in winter but they do so much more slowly in the short cold days. In good years, when the trees have plenty of moisture, warmth and sunlight, the growth rate is highest and so the dark rings of winter are spaced further apart. Poor growing years are evidenced by closely-spaced rings. Different tree species grow at different rates and vary greatly in life expectancy. One of the oldest trees in Europe is a yew in the village churchyard at Fortingall, near central Scotland's Loch Tay. Experts have estimated this yew to be at least 3000 and possibly closer to 5000 years old. Unfortunately, because the trunk of the tree has been hollow for as long as records relate, accurate dating by counting growth rings in a core sample is not possible. Today only a couple of living fragments of the original trunk remain, but back in 1769 the trunk of the Fortingall Yew (even in those days split into two sections) was reported as having a girth of 65.5 feet (getting on for 17m).

The oldest age-verified living trees are Bristlecone Pines *Pinus longaeva* growing in mountainous regions of western USA. Still producing a few bits of new growth, although like the Fortingall Yew much of their trunks have died long ago, these ancient trees spend many months of the year in snow-clad dormancy. The harsh high-altitude climate has helped preserve the dead timber so that the age rings can be counted right through core samples. Nicknamed Methuselah, what is thought to be the oldest surviving Bristlecone Pine lives in a secret location in the White-Inyo mountain range of California; it is known to be nearly 4800 years old, and the odds are that it will easily survive every person living on our planet today.

An ancient Bristlecone Pine. Being a conifer this slow-growing tree produces timber that is categorised as 'softwood', even though it is a very close-grained and tough timber indeed.

A Bristlecone Pine high up on the edge of the tree-line of Wheeler Peak, eastern Nevada, was cut down in 1964 by research workers. This old pine was posthumously named Prometheus after forestry staff realised that it was nearly 5000 years since that tree had been a seedling: a ring count on the trunk told them that they had just killed the oldest known living plant on the planet! The sawn-off stump and some parts of Prometheus can still be seen today, but as with all pines (and other coniferous trees) there was no chance of it producing any regrowth from the stump.

What is the secret of this remarkable longevity? Apart from the low moisture content of these mountain pines and the strong concentration of fungicidal compounds in their heartwood, perhaps the harshness of the climate and the hardness of the slow-growing timber of Bristlecone Pines are major survival factors. Certainly, neither fungi nor insects seem keen to take on the challenge. On the other hand there are fungi that could claim the contest a draw, as they can rival the oldest of these old timers for longevity.

How trees cope with growth

Because the outer diameter of the sapwood of a trunk or a branch increases during each growing season as new water-transport tubes are added to its outer rim, the cambium must also increase in diameter. The phloem has to grow to accommodate this expansion too, and it does this by producing new material on its inner rim. All this expansion puts the outer region of the bark under tension, and something has to give. The result is that we see old trees with either a deeply indented corky bark, as for example on oaks, or a paper-like bark whose outer layers split and peel, which is what happens to the trunks of eucalypts.

Where does the heartwood come from? It is simply old sapwood whose arteries have become furred up (with tannins and other acidic compounds that are toxic to most fungi), and so that part of the wood is now very hard indeed and plays no part in the life of the tree. Heartwood is, in effect, as dead as a piece of human toenail, but it can go on for many years serving a useful purpose in helping to hold the rest of the tree together. In some kinds of trees the division between the tough heartwood, capable of withstanding great pressure, and the springy sapwood that is strong under tension is quite abrupt, with an easily discernible colour change. The most powerful longbows were made from lengths of yew wood straddling this junction, the dark brown heartwood, particularly strong in compression, facing towards the archer and the lighter-coloured sapwood, with its greater tensile strength, facing the foe.

Heartwood-rotting fungi

Fungi discovered the difference between heartwood and sapwood long before people did. When trees die different fungi attack different parts of the timber. But like Burke and Hare towards the end of their notorious careers, some fungi just can't wait for the grim tree-reaper to declare the banquet open. It's not uncommon to find old trees still growing and producing flowers and seeds while their inner heartwood is being consumed by fungi. (Various beetles and bacteria rely on fungi to soften up the quarry, after which they too munch at the heartwood of such old trees.) This selective preference of certain fungi for heartwood is one of the reasons that some trees continue living for many years with what appear to be severe parasitic fungal attacks. For example Beefsteak Fungus *Fistulina hepatica* attacks the heartwood of oaks and occasionally other kinds of broadleaf trees.

Beefsteak Fungus *Fistulina hepatica*. This red bracket is seen mainly on older trees, most often near the base. Rarely does such an infestation kill the tree right away, because the heartwood that it feeds upon is not essential to the tree's vascular system.

Fungi that consume mainly the heartwood are generally much less damaging to a tree (in the short-term at least) than those that are partial to the sapwood, which is a vital part of the tree's digestive and respiratory system. Damage to the bark exposes the cambium to fungal infection (which is one more reason why the inventor of the power strimmer has so much to answer for), letting spores bypass the protective phloem and enabling mycelium to grow and penetrate the heart of the tree. Fortunately, in the tree world at least, heart attacks are not necessarily precursors of sudden death.

For more than twenty years this hollow riverside tree has sheltered walkers from sudden rainstorms – not merely beneath its canopy but inside the trunk. The fungi that consume heartwood are specially adapted to tolerate the strongly fungitoxic compounds that are concentrated in this part of the timber.

Another heartwood rotter is the Dryad's Saddle *Polyporus squamosus*. Although Beech trees are particularly susceptible to attack by this common parasitic bracket fungus, it also attacks Sycamore, Ash and Horse Chestnut - in fact its annual fruitbodies can be found on most kinds of broadleaf trees except oaks. Typically, the spores enter the timber of the tree via wounds where branches have been broken off. (Vehicle collisions with roadside trees frequently lead to fungal attack, with Dryad's Saddle fruitbodies appearing within a year or two.)

Dryad's Saddle *Polyporus squamosus* fruiting on the trunk of a living Ash tree. The crown of the tree appears healthy, betraying no evidence of the inner malaise.

Sapwood rotters

Anything that disconnects the sapwood of a tree from its vascular cambium and phloem is a real killer. Bark-boring beetles can achieve this very effectively when, in their larval stage, they create networks of tunnels between the bark and the sapwood before pupating.

Bark-boring beetle infestation is not easy to spot in the early stages, when curative treatment might just be possible. The tunnels made by the larvae are difficult to miss once the bark begins falling away from the trunk of a dead tree.

Some of the most feared forestry fungi have a very similar effect, and top of this list are some kinds of honey fungus, *Armillaria* species. When a parasitic *Armillaria* rhizomorph reaches a new host and enters via a wound in the roots or in the bark of the lower trunk, it grows through and kills the phloem and the cambium; then a white sheet of mycelium spreads up the trunk beneath the bark, separating the bark from the rest of the wood. Honey Fungus can kill a tree just as quickly as a Grey Squirrel or a power strimmer does by stripping a ring of bark from around the trunk. For a while the canopy of the tree may appear to be healthy, because the sapwood can still pass water upwards to the leaves to replace moisture lost by respiration, but the downward movement of sugar-bearing sap ceases and the infected cells cannot be replaced. The Honey Fungus soon invades and begins consuming the lignin in the sapwood, so that by the time fruitbodies are visible the tree is unable to hide other symptoms of its sickness – early leaf fall followed soon afterwards by slabs of bark parting from the trunk.

Few trees can survive wholesale removal of their bark. A remarkable exception is the Cork Oak *Quercus suber*, from which the outer bark is stripped once trees are about 25 years old. (A major market for cork is as stoppers for wine bottles, of course.) A new outer bark is formed and it grows progressively thicker in succeeding years, so that every ninth year the trees can be stripped again – up to a dozen times or more during their long lifetimes. However, while Cork Oaks seem able to struggle on for several years carrying heartwood-rotting brackets such as Beefsteak fungus, an attack by sapwood rotters such as Honey Fungus sounds their death knell just as it does for any other kind of oak.

Honey Fungus at the base of a Cork Oak

Cork Oak trees just one year after the bark has been removed from their trunks

Bark, harvested manually from cork oak trees near Monchique, Portugal

Honey Fungus *Armillaria mellea* and Dark Honey Fungus *Armillaria ostoyae* are bad for many kinds of trees, including orchard species such as oranges and almonds - they can even attack coffee plants. Unless you are a forester or it's your orchard that is under attack, you might accept the fungiphile's argument that this is not *all* bad news, because it certainly results in some spectacularly beautiful displays of mushrooms (and some people enjoy eating them). But there is another side to these controversial mushrooms...

Just as one man's food is another man's poison so also what are normally parasitic fungi can serve as supportive symbionts to certain woodland orchids and other rare plants. It seems these kinds of mutually beneficial relationships can exist even though the *Armillaria* rhizomorphs are also connected to and feeding upon the roots of nearby trees. In effect the fungus is serving as an intermediary, enabling the orchid or other woodland plant indirectly to parasitise the trees.

The rare woodland wildflower *Monotropa uniflora* (a native of North America, parts of eastern Asia and Japan) is commonly referred to as either the Ghost Plant or Indian Pipe. This non-photosynthetic flowering plant is now known to be able to draw nutrients indirectly from nearby trees via the mycelia of the Honey Fungus *Armillaria mellea*.

Split Gill *Schizophyllum commune* colonises trees that are already stressed by excessive heat and drought. This parasite consumes mainly the lignin in the sapwood and produces annual bracket-like fruitbodies that are white and hairy on their upper surfaces and have brown gills beneath. Unusually for a gilled mushroom, the fruitbodies of this parasite can tolerate extreme environmental conditions. The gills are split along their length, these splits closing up and the whole fruitbody shrivelling to half its normal size during dry weather, opening and expanding again when rain moistens them. The tough, leathery caps usually occur in multi-tiered clusters.

Split Gill *Schizophyllum commune* fruiting on the trunk of a drought-stressed poplar.

The Split Gill shows little or no preference for any particular kind of tree, and so you are just as likely to find it on pines or even such fungus-resistant trees as juniper, laurel and eucalyptus as on Ash, birches, elms, oaks and willows. As with Honey Fungus and other parasitic fungi, the Split Gill continues to consume its host after the tree has died.

Fungus-infected timber is commonly referred to as 'rotten' wood, but the appearance of fungal infection can vary greatly depending on the kind of fungus involved. The hyphae of wood-rotting fungi secrete enzymes that break down the cellulose, hemicellulose, lignin and pectin into chemicals that the fungus is capable of absorbing. Most rot-producing fungi consume cellulose and hemicellulose, but there are some that consume mainly lignin and others that are capable of consuming all three major components of wood. Compounds toxic to fungi, in particular tannins in the case of broadleaved trees and phenolic compounds such as turpentine in coniferous trees, become concentrated in the non-living heartwood. This is why, when a branch breaks and falls to the ground, the heartwood cells are usually much slower in decaying than are the sapwood cells.

Brown rot is caused by fungi that digest mainly the cellulose and hemicelluloses; the decaying wood turns brown and cracks into blocks of mainly lignin. All brown-rot fungi are members of the Basidiomycota; examples are Hoof Fungus *Fomes fomentarius*, which attacks living birches and Beech, and Split Gill *Schizophyllum commune*, as well as the infamous Dry Rot fungus *Serpula lacrymans* that can do so much damage to timbers in damp cellars and leaky roofs. (The term 'dry rot' is an oxymoron, of course, since moisture is essential for fungi to attack timber.)

Fungi that consume mainly the cellulose and hemicellulose in timber leave behind the tough, characteristically reddish-brown lignin. Wood stripped of its cellulose components by fungal decay tends to break up into small red-brown blocks. This conifer stump will eventually be finished off by other kinds of fungi that are able to consume lignin.

There are far more white-rot fungi than there are brown-rot fungi. Whereas all brown-rot fungi belong to the Basidiomycota, the white-rot fungi group includes some members of the Basidiomycota (for example Honey Fungus) and many more belonging to the Ascomycota (such as Candle-snuff Fungus *Xylaria hypoxylon*) which consume dead wood rather than living trees.

White-rot fungi attack mainly the wood of broadleaf trees, initially consuming the lignin, reducing it to carbon dioxide and water and leaving the off-white spongy cellulose and hemicellulose - hence the term white-rot. Brown-rot fungi show a marked preference for conifers, destroying the cellulose first but doing little damage to the lignin. However, just as most people are not entirely carnivorous or vegetarian, so also there are many fungi that consume bark, sapwood and heartwood and are capable of consuming not only the cellulose and hemicellulose components of the wood but also the lignin.

Giant Polypore *Meripilus giganteus* fruiting at the base of an old Beech. This bracket fungus is often seen on hardwood trees, notably Beech but very occasionally also on oaks. A weak parasite that usually takes many years to kill a tree, it is one of several bracket-like fungi able to consume not only cellulose and hemicellulose but also the lignin components of timber.

Fungi-induced lines and colour stains in timber

The ability of some fungi to stain wood has been known about and exploited for centuries. 'Spalted' timber, as it is called, can be used to make attractive furniture, picture frames and other ornaments.

A common cause of spalting is when two or more different kinds of fungi infect wood; they sometimes fight over territory, erecting barriers, known as zone lines, to protect their patches. Dark meandering black or reddish-brown zone lines of mycelium define these boundaries. When thoroughly dried so that the mycelia die, the resulting spalted wood can be used to make attractive turned fruit bowls and carved statues.

Zone lines rather than the wood grain itself are the main attraction of this piece of spalted Beech. When it has been dried, planed and sanded the surface patterning can be very attractive.

Zone lines themselves are made of tough mycelia and they do not significantly weaken the wood; however, if left untreated the fungi that cause zone-line spalting will go on to consume the timber. For this reason spalted timber has to be dried out thoroughly before it can be worked to produce long-lasting artefacts.

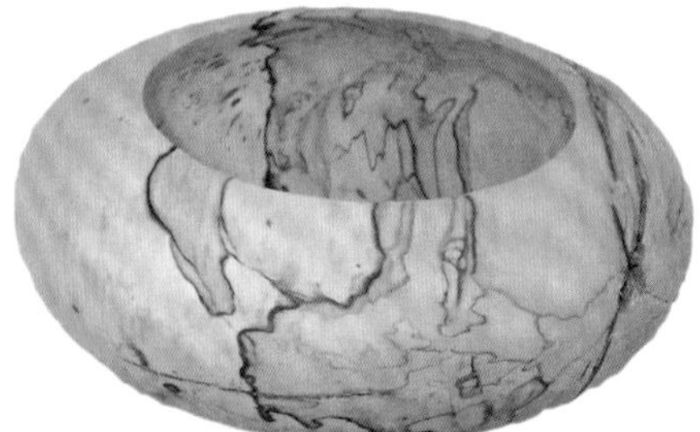

Spalted wood has been used to produce this turned wooden bowl with its attractive patterning. The timber is maple.

The colour resulting from spalting depends on the fungus species involved, and it is not always black or brownish. A remarkable colour effect is caused by Green Elfcup *Chlorociboria aeruginascens,* an ascomycetous fungus whose blue-green fruitbodies are rarely seen because they most often occur beneath the bark of fallen branches and felled trunks. Much more common on the forest floor are pieces of blue-green wood – mainly from broadleaf trees and in particular beside streams and ponds where the ground is very moist. The staining is evidence of Green Elfcup mycelium in the timber.

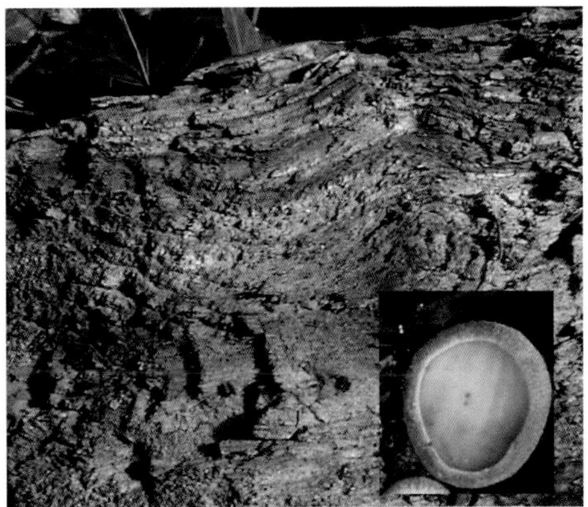

This partly rotted wood has been stained by the mycelium of Green Elfcup *Chlorociboria aeruginascens*, whose fruitbodies (inset) are rarely seen. Once dried out thoroughly, the fungus dies and the blue-green stained wood is still quite durable. This kind of colourful 'spalting' has always been much sought after by wood turners and cabinet makers.

Rather than rely on finding green-stained timber, some woodworkers break an infected log into tiny pieces and sprinkle it among other hardwood which they store in continually damp conditions in a spalting bin. It can take up to a year for the fungus to colonise the new wood, but pre-treating the logs with a white-rot fungus such as Dead Man's Fingers *Xylaria polymorpha* speeds the process by pitting the surface and making it easier for the *Chlorociboria* fungus to penetrate the interior of the wood.

Telling the trees from the wood

To understand woodland fungi it is obviously helpful to know a bit about the structure of wood and the ways in which fungi feed upon it. What also becomes clear as soon as you begin looking for particular kinds of fungi is that all trees are not equal. Some mycorrhizal mushrooms are particular when picking partners, and some parasites and saprophytes are choosy consumers, attacking only one type of living tree or feeding fussily on certain kinds of dead wood but ignoring others. When your field guide tells you that a fungus species is associated solely or mainly with certain types of trees, that information is helpful only if you know how to recognise those trees. We need to know about the wood *and* the trees.

Conifers and Broadleaves (Gymnosperms and Angiosperms)

Gymnosperms are a class of plants whose seeds are bare (not enclosed in an overcoat). The Ginkgo is a gymnosperm, as also are the trees that bear their seeds in cones – the conifers. Most gymnosperms have green needle-like leaves that remain on the tree all through the year. Not all gymnosperms are evergreen, however. For example, the Ginkgo drops its leaves in autumn as do some kinds of conifers – larches, for instance. Conifers carry their male and female reproductive organs in separate cones, the male cones producing pollen grains that are borne on the wind to the female cones within which seeds then develop. This group is more commonly referred to as softwoods, because many conifers are fast-growing trees whose dried timber is lighter and softer than wood obtained from broadleaf trees... but there are plenty of exceptions to this generalisation.

Angiosperms (flowering plants) produce seeds within the carpel (the female reproductive organ) of the flower, and the encased seeds develop in what we know as the fruits of the tree (in the case of apple trees), nuts (as in Hazel), or winged seeds (as in Sycamores). Angiosperm trees have broad leaves rather than needles, and most of them are deciduous – their leaves die and fall to the ground in autumn. Some broadleaf trees – laurel, holly and rhododendron for example – retain their green leaves throughout the year, so that the terms evergreen and deciduous cannot be used as synonyms for conifer and broadleaf.

The angiosperm trees are often referred to as hardwoods, even though some broadleaf trees produce very soft timber. For example wood of the Balsa trees from the rain forests of Central and South America has large, thin-walled cells containing very little lignin. When kiln dried, balsa wood is 60% air and therefore much lighter than most other hardwoods, which are much denser and harder. Slow-growing yew trees, on the other hand, provide timber that is denser and much harder than the wood from many broadleaf trees. If you had to have a plank fall on your head, would you choose the Balsa, nominally a hardwood, or the Yew, classed as a softwood? The terms hardwood and softwood cannot, therefore, be sensibly interpreted as describing the hardness of wood but rather as defining the class of tree from which it was obtained. All other factors being equal, however, soft timber is likely to succumb more rapidly to fungal decay than timber that is very hard. But, as we know, all other things rarely *are* equal. In particular, timber from different trees contains varying amounts of fungi-toxic resins. Untreated larch (which is classed as a softwood) resists decay for many years whereas when a branch from an alder (a broadleaf tree and therefore classed as a hardwood) falls on damp ground it can rot away within a year.

Trees in Europe

At the end of the Tertiary Period, 1.8 million years ago, Europe's climate was warm and the composition of its forests was very similar to the (few) natural forest areas remaining in Europe today. Then, at the beginning of the (current) Quaternary Period, came the Ice Age – not one long freeze-up but a series of climatic changes in which an ice sheet would form in Scandinavia and move southwards to be joined by another Alpine ice sheet moving across to meet it. Ice sheet progression and recession occurred several times, and in between (during the inter-glacial periods) the climate became warmer for a while.

At times when Europe was covered by ice, no plants or fungi could live there (save for in a few small sheltered oases of warmth where some particularly hardy species, known as glacial relicts, survived); however, during each interglacial period plants (including trees) and fungi were able to move in progressively and colonise the lands of Northern Europe.

Some scientists are convinced that we are currently in an interglacial period and that, despite all the current concerns about climate chaos and its links to global warming, it is only a matter of time before the glaciers return to wipe out Northern Europe's plants, trees and fungi yet again.

The most recent glaciation (the Devensian) began some 73,000 years ago and ended about 10,000 years ago, when trees again invaded Europe's tundra landscape and forests evolved here in what was the early Stone Age (Paleolithic). Hardy pines, birches, Aspen and various willows were the pioneers, with Hazel and oaks finding niches in warmer areas. Later, as the climate warmed further, other trees moved in from the south and some of these were able to oust the pioneer trees and dominate the forests. Inevitably, as time went by the cutting and ploughing tools of Man played an increasingly significant part in determining the species structure and coverage of forests in all but those areas with the most difficult terrain.

Tree-historic Invaders of Britain and Ireland

For as long as Britain and Ireland were connected to what is now mainland Europe, tree colonisation there followed much the same pattern as in other western European countries of similar latitude. Trees spread northwards throughout Britain some 8000 years ago, the Midlands and south-east England having escaped the worst extremes of glaciation throughout the previous million years of periodic cold and warmer climatic conditions in what was known as the Pleistocene.

Pollen records suggest that the succession of trees has not been entirely consistent between glaciations, but because there are difficulties in translating pollen fossil records into tree-species distribution maps any conclusions based on this limited evidence should be treated with caution. Nevertheless, it is pretty clear that at the beginning of the current (Holocene) inter-glacial period trees did not recolonise the whole of Britain and Ireland all at once, and neither did they all arrive together. Some species have been here thousands of years longer than others, and so perhaps it is understandable also that they are not all equally involved in relationships with mushrooms and other fungi. each tree species (and in particular each of the tree genera) interacts differently with the fungal kingdom. Some really get stuck in; others remain more aloof.

Biologists consider it most likely that in sheltered parts of Britain some of our native junipers survived the last glaciation and that these relict junipers expanded their range as the climate warmed up. Birch, willow and pines may also have survived in a few coastal niches of western Ireland and south-west England; but, from studies of pollen and seed deposits in peat, and using radiocarbon dating, scientists have deduced the likely sequence of recolonisation of Britain by trees from southern Europe. Genetic sequencing is now revealing more about where these trees originated. (The start date of colonisation by a particular species would have been dependent not merely on the increased range of temperatures in southern Britain but also on how far the trees had to travel across mainland Europe and their rate of movement by natural seed dispersal processes.)

The land masses of Britain and Ireland became disconnected (whether there was a land bridge or merely an ice sheet connection) about 12,000 years ago, whereas the land bridge between England and mainland Europe remained intact for a further 6000 years. Thereafter, colonisation by trees from mainland Europe would have become more difficult – at least until people took to moving plants from one place to another, as for example the Romans seem to have done extensively whether by accident or intent.

As Britain's permanent ice cap disappeared an advance party of birches and willows crept northwards, followed by Scots Pine and Hazel. Later the heavyweights moved in – oaks and alders, followed by Ash, elms and Holly; then Beech and limes began their slow march northwards and westwards as the seasonal temperatures rose towards their present values. The more vigorous of these latecomers gradually shaded out the smaller pioneer trees, reducing their coverage substantially except for in the cold north of Scotland and a few other marginal habitats. Beech and limes were particularly slow movers and not well suited to the acidic northern and western soils; their natural range in the UK is still mainly restricted to southern England and eastern parts of South Wales.

Eventually most of our landscape, save for the highest mountains and the most windswept coastal cliffs, was populated by what has come to be known as the wildwood. Whether this was dense woodland or more of a patchwork of woods and scrub is still under debate. The countryside would be much the same today but for the arrival of the only animal species that alters rather than adapts to its habitat. That's us, of course. Not content with hunting and gathering, we became farmers some five thousand years ago, and from then until the eighteenth century AD we lived in a managed but essentially rural landscape, an artificial but nonetheless beautiful countryside shared with the diversity of wildlife, plants and fungi that Nature had brought in as the ice receded.

Tree Colonisation of Northern Europe

Period	Dominant presence	Minor presence	Niche species
Preboreal (11,560 years ago to 10,640 years ago)	Pine species and Birches encroach on tundra	Willow species and Aspen	Hazel and oaks colonise sheltered warmer areas
Boreal (10,640 years ago to 9220 years ago)	Pine species and Hazel	Oaks and then elm species and Ash	Spruce species colonise mountainous areas
Atlantic (9220 years ago to 5660 years ago)	Oak, fir and spruce species	Hazel and Beech	Pine species remain dominant on coastal sand dune areas
Subboreal (5660 years ago to 2400 years ago)	Fir and spruce species and Beech	Oak, elms and lime species plus Ash and Hornbeam	
Subatlantic (2400 years ago to the present day)	Increasing plantations of spruces and pines	Fir species and Beech, plus oaks, birches and Hazel	Alders colonise areas of wet land

The first thing that farming needs is arable and grazing land, and because the wildwood was quite unsuitable it had to go. In the fertile valley floors and on lowland hills most of the tangle of trees, bushes, brambles and bracken had been cleared by 2000 BC, leaving to Nature only steep precipice land and the less productive mountainous areas.

Although nearly 90 per cent arable and pasture farmland, the British landscape still contains a valuable and diverse patchwork of fragments of ancient woodland unchanged from 'wildwood' times, formerly coppiced and managed woodland now for the most part left to grow wild, and commercial forestry plantations comprising mainly imported fast-growing coniferous trees.

With the industrial revolution came significant changes to the ecology and biodiversity of metal-rich and mineral-rich areas; however, perhaps the biggest and most long-lasting impact of the industrial revolution was on woodlands. We needed straight, fast-growing timber for fencing, roofing and pit props. Oaks and Beech grow slowly and are inclined to twist and branch. Scots Pine and Yew, our only large native conifers (Juniper, Britain's other native conifer, is of little commercial value for its timber) were no match economically for fast-maturing imported tree species, and so monoculture plantations of spruces, larches, various firs and Corsican Pine quickly replaced many of our native forests.

Without the right mycorrhizal fungi it would have been difficult if not impossible for trees to colonise the barren wasteland left by the receding ice; fortunately, fungal spores are far more mobile than tree seeds, and so as trees extended their northern limits the fungi they needed (and some they would be better without) were ready to pounce on the opportunity.

Beech woodland supports its own characteristic community of fungi species.

All of our native trees form mycorrhizal relationships with fungi, and so around trees that have lots of EM fungal partners you are likely to find many kinds of mushrooms and other large fruitbodies. Some kinds of trees are more prone than others to parasitic fungal attacks, and the range of parasites concerned in these attacks varies from one tree genus to another. Certain fungi occur on only one tree genus or on a restricted number of tree genera. But, in the end, every tree dies and becomes food for grave-robbing saprophytic fungi most of which, like people, have their own food fads and fancies.

So when people gather leaf mould from beneath woodland trees can we expect fewer litter-rotting fungi to grow there? Certainly! But the impact goes wider than that. EM fungi also draw nutrients from well-rotted lower layers of leaf litter, and so these fungi may decline too, and since one of their main functions in the woodland ecology is to nourish tree roots, inevitably the trees also fare less well. In the extreme, trees whose leaf litter is continually raided may die of thirst or starvation. It certainly can happen.

Bluebell woods, so splendid in springtime, are usually also great places for seeing a wonderfully diverse range of fungi later on in the year.

With the imported trees came some of the fungi that are mycorrhizal associates of particular tree genera. So, while we may lament the loss of much of our ancient woodland, in terms of fungal diversity we are probably better off with the varied mixture of natural woodland and managed plantations that we have today. Perhaps we should just be thankful that a few fragments of ancient woodland have survived. It is still possible to see veteran oaks and Beeches many hundreds of years old, and they are of tremendous interest from a mycological point of view not only for the many fungi that are associated with them but also for the diversity of lichens that they support.

Native and Naturalised Trees in Britain and Ireland

When a mushroom identification guide says '*Leccinum carpini* occurs mainly under hornbeams' there is an implicit assumption that readers will know what a hornbeam tree looks like. In summer, perhaps... but given that many of our fungus forays occur in late autumn and early winter when most deciduous trees have already shed their leaves, how many of us can recognise even the more common of our native trees from their leafless silhouettes and the texture and colour of their bark? Not everyone by any means, which is why this brief profile of some of our most common tree species is included in this book. (If your answer to the above question is yes, just skip the next section.)

Our native trees live in association with ectomycorrhizal (EM) fungi, arbuscular mycorrhizal (AM) fungi – the latter formerly known as vesicular-arbuscular mycorrhizal, or VAM - or sometimes with both kinds. Mycelia of EM fungi live in the top 10cm or so of soil, extracting nutrients from leaf litter and other decaying vegetation beneath and near to the trees – although 'near to' needs qualifying. Hyphal threads can spread tens of metres from the fine tree rootlets that they sheathe. Even so, when looking for the fruitbodies of EM fungi areas with plenty of leaf litter are usually best. Shallow dips in the woodland floor and sheltered places against boundary walls often form collection points for wind-blown leaves. We are unlikely to see AM fungi during forays, because they do not produce large fruitbodies and they inhabit mainly the soil layers below the EM fungi, sometimes as deep as six metres below ground level.

Parasitic fungi have also become specialised. Some of them are found only on trees of one family (such as the Fagaceae, which includes oaks, Beech and Sweet Chestnut trees) or even just one genus (for example *Betula* – the birches). Identify the right kinds of trees and you stand a chance of finding the parasitic fungus you are looking for.

When trees die their remains are recycled by saprobes (insects, fungi and bacteria that consume dead matter). Again, the kinds of fungi that grow on say the fallen pine needles are different from those found among dead leaves under a Sweet Chestnut tree.

Which trees are best for macro fungi? Well, it's certainly not a simple matter of deciduous trees versus evergreens, or even broadleaf trees versus conifers. Some broadleaf trees have lots of EM fungal partners; others have none – and similarly with conifers. What follows, therefore, is a basic tree-recognition summary with notes on the diversity of fungi commonly found beneath and/or growing on each. Where a particular type of tree has one or two notable fungi specifically or mainly associated with it, a picture and very brief details are included here. More information on those fungi can be found in Chapter 4 for EM fungi, Chapter 5 for parasites and other bracket fungi, and Chapter 6 for saprophytic fungi that occur among leaf litter and on fallen trunks, branches and twigs.

Comments on the range of fungi likely to be found with each tree species can only ever be a general guide: soil type, tree age (and in particular age diversity within a plantation), altitude and exposure to salt spray, sun and drying winds are all factors that can make a difference. For this reason, with fungi forays as with other voyages of exploration, it's a great help if you can tap in to local knowledge.

Tree 'Family Trees' and Genera 'General Knowledge'

Evolution has resulted in character divergence much more often than convergence, and so in the 370 million years or so since the first woody trees appeared on earth something in the order of 100,000 species have evolved and survived (and many times that number have evolved only to meet with extinction). That estimate of the number of extant tree species is subject to enormous uncertainty, however: the majority of trees live in tropical rain forests which, from a botanical viewpoint and in many other respects, are more unexplored than explored.

Then there is the problem of deciding whether a tree is a new species or merely a variety of a known species... a topic of limited importance to most fungus forayers, certainly in Europe where the tree species of major significance may well amount to no more than 0.1% of the world's present tally of tree species. Get to know Europe's twenty most common woodland tree genera and you are pretty well set up to make real progress in the pursuit of forest fungi.

Trees within the same genus are usually associated with the same kinds of fungi, but unfortunately the features that place trees in the same genus are not always immediately evident to an untrained eye. Anyone other than a qualified botanist could be forgiven for assuming that willows and alders are closely related. After all, willows and alders are great pioneer trees having no crucial dependence on specific EM fungi; both are associated with riverbanks, marshes and other wet places; and both produce catkins in springtime. In fact they belong to different taxonomic orders, the catkin method of wind-blown pollen distribution being just one of many examples of convergent evolution - a good idea devised independently by more than one innovator.

Alder catkins

Willow catkins

The good, the bad and the fungi

There are more than 100 native and naturalised trees in Britain, most of which also occur in Ireland. In addition quite a lot of recent introductions have been planted over large areas, creating new types of woodlands whose fungal communities may be very different from those of ancient woodlands. Some of these plantations may throw up big surprises for inquisitive fungiphiles.

The much-simplified tables below show the systematic relationships between some of our most common native and introduced trees - although the information presented here comes with the caveat that scientific research into the origins of trees is still ongoing and further revisions are inevitable and probably imminent. (For example only recently have lime trees, formerly the Tiliaceae, been combined with the mallow family Malvaceae.)

The fungi ratings for the various tree genera are based on my own observations and are merely a rough guide to the relative diversity of large fruitbodies commonly found growing on or under the trees. (Be aware that location, tree age and soil type can also make a big difference!)

Flowering Trees

This is a far from complete list; however, the fungi associated with one particular hardwood tree are usually also found with other trees of the same genus. (Sometimes the affinity stretches more widely to include trees from other genera within the same family.)

Order	Family	Genus	Common names	Fungi rating
Fagales	Fagaceae	*Quercus*	Oaks	🍄🍄🍄🍄🍄
		Fagus	Beech	🍄🍄🍄🍄🍄
		Castanea	Sweet Chestnut	🍄🍄
	Betulaceae	*Betula*	Birches	🍄🍄🍄
		Alnus	Alders	🍄🍄🍄
		Carpinus	Hornbeam	🍄🍄🍄🍄🍄
		Corylus	Hazel	🍄🍄🍄
Malvales	Malvaceae	*Tilia*	Limes	🍄🍄
Malpighiales	Salicaceae	*Salix*	Willows	🍄🍄
		Populus	Poplars; Aspen	🍄🍄
Rosales	Rosaceae	*Prunus*	Blackthorn; Cherry	🍄
		Crataegus	Hawthorn	🍄
		Sorbus	Rowan; Whitebeams	🍄
	Ulmaceae	*Ulmus*	Elms	🍄🍄🍄
Sapindales	Sapindaceae	*Acer*	Field Maple; Sycamore	🍄
		Aesculus	Horse Chestnut	🍄🍄
Lamiales	Oleaceae	*Fraxinus*	Ash	🍄
		Ligustrum	Privet	🍄
Dipsacales	Adoxaceae	*Sambucus*	Elder	🍄🍄
Aquifoliales	Aquifoliaceae	*Ilex*	Holly	🍄

Coniferous Trees

While Britain and Ireland have fewer native and naturalised conifers than they have broadleaf trees, in many areas conifer forests dominate the landscape and so provide most opportunity to see woodland fungi. You just need to be choosy about the types of trees.

Order	Family	Genus	Common names	Fungi rating
Pinales	Cupressaceae	*Juniperus*	Juniper	🍄
	Pinaceae	*Pinus*	Pines	🍄🍄🍄🍄🍄
		Abies	Firs	🍄🍄🍄
		Larix	Larches	🍄🍄🍄
		Picea	Spruces	🍄🍄🍄🍄
	Taxaceae	*Taxus*	Yew	🍄

Quercus robur – English Oak; and _Quercus petraea_ – Sessile Oak

In Britain we have just two native oaks plus a few naturalised imports, but there are more than 500 oak species worldwide. English Oaks, also known as Pedunculate Oaks because their acorns have long stalks, are magnificent sights when fully grown. Reaching a spread of 45m and often a little taller than their spread, these slow-growing trees have wide root systems. Sessile Oaks, more common on upland acid soils, have stalked leaves while their acorns are sessile, having no stalks. The problem is remembering which way round it is!

The trunks of Sessile Oaks are generally less branched and the crowns are narrow in comparison with the spreading crowns of English Oaks. (There are other distinguishing features – for example, the lobes of the leaves of Sessile Oaks are more forward pointing, and the acorns are shorter and more conical than those of English Oaks.) Incidentally, oak apples are galls caused by the tiny larvae of the wasp *Andricus kollari*. These insects live as larvae within the oak apples, boring their way to the outside world when fully mature.

An ancient English (pedunculate) Oak

Leaves & flowers

Acorn (*Q. petraea*)

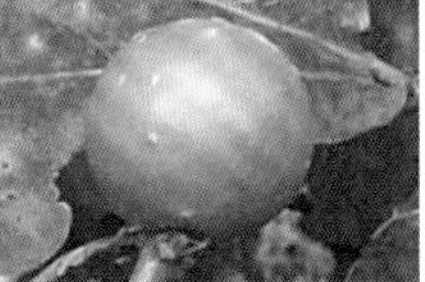

Oak apple

Bark

Quercus ilex - Holm Oak

This evergreen, also known as Holly Oak, was brought from the Mediterranean region to Britain some 400 years ago. Some of the leaves are spiny, which is why its specific epithet refers to Holly.

Often found near the coast in Britain and Ireland, the Holm Oak is sensitive to frost. These trees rarely exceed 20m in height and often have very dense crowns (unlike the young specimen shown below, which has an unusually sparse crown).

Holm Oak

Leaves

Acorns

Fungi associated specifically or mainly with oaks

Oak trees are host, home and harvest for many kinds of fungi, and because fallen oak leaves take two or three years to rot they provide habitats for many more litter-recycling species than can be found beneath trees with fast-decaying leaves (for example Ash trees). Here are three conspicuous fungi that are either specific to oak trees or at least are rarely seen anywhere else.

The Oakbug Milkcap *Lactarius quietus* is an EM fungus whose mushrooms often appear in huge numbers among the leaf litter beneath oak trees.

***Grifola frondosa*, commonly called Hen of the Woods, is a polypore that appears in the autumn at the bases of old oak trees. This weak parasite grows on the roots. It is not an instant killer, and so once you find an infected tree it is usually possible to return and see fresh fruitbodies there for several successive years.**

The Oak Mazegill *Daedalea quercina* is a saprophytic fungus found on dead oaks. In Britain and Ireland this bracket hardly ever occurs on any other kind of wood.

Oak trees are also the specific host for the rare bracket fungus *Piptoporus quercinus*, known as the Oak Polypore, which is on the UK Red Data List and is protected by law under Schedule 8 of the Wildlife and Countryside Act. Picking or damaging this species is therefore strictly prohibited.

Fagus sylvatica - Beech

Beech trees are attractive throughout the year. In early spring their red, pointed buds open to reveal bright green leaves that darken through May, June and July. These majestic trees, which can attain a spread of 30m and a height somewhat greater than that, often retain their leaves long after they have turned from green to brown. (Copper Beeches, *Fagus sylvatica 'purpurea'*, are cultivars that self-seed; they can be seen in hedgerows and on woodland edges as well as in formal parks and gardens.) Slow rotting leaves and mast (the 'nuts') from Beach trees prevent undergrowth from taking over the forest floor.

An ancient Beech (above, right) in springtime, and a Copper Beech (above, left) showing off its summer finery.

Flowers(♀)

Flowers(♂)

Beech mast (seeds)

Bark

Beeches support a variety of mycorrhizal, parasitic and saprophytic fungi, and so Beech woods, which are concentrated in the south east of England and South Wales, are particularly productive venues for fungus forays. Here are two conspicuous fungi that are either specific to Beech or at least only very rarely seen anywhere else.

The Beechwood Sickener _Russula nobilis_ is an EM fungus whose red caps push up through leaf litter beneath Beeches.

Porcelain Fungus _Mucidula mucida_ (in the past generally referred to as _Oudemansiella mucida_) is a saprophytic mushroom found mainly on dead or dying Beech trunks and branches.

Castana sativa - Sweet Chestnut

The Romans probably brought Sweet Chestnut (also known as Spanish Chestnut) trees to Britain, and in the south of England and Wales the climate is warm enough for self-sown seeds to germinate. Further north most of the Sweet Chestnuts you see would have been planted. The timber is still sometimes used for fencing, particularly on smallholdings, while shoots of coppiced Sweet Chestnut are a traditional source of poles for hop growing.

Long (male) catkins appear in early summer, and later the fruits develop from the female flowers. The nuts, which are protected inside spiny bracts, ripen in late autumn and are at their best in December. (Roast chestnuts are traditionally associated with log fires at Christmastime, of course.)

An ancient Sweet Chestnut

Flowers

Seeds

Leaves

Bark

Although the Sweet Chestnut is reported to be an ectomycorrhizal tree, few of the associated fungi from its native lands seem to have opted to join it in Britain and Ireland. There are, however, plenty of leaf-litter mushrooms to be seen under Sweet Chestnuts as well as a few bracket fungi that seem to be particularly partial to its bark and timber. Here is one of the bracket fungi commonly seen on Sweet Chestnuts, mainly on standing trees but also occasionally on fallen trunks:

Beefsteak Fungus *Fistulina hepatica* is often seen on the trunks of Sweet Chestnut trees; it feeds on the dead heartwood, and so perhaps strictly it should be classed as saprophytic rather than parasitic. This striking bracket fungus occurs also on other tree species.

Betula pendula – Silver Birch; and _Betula pubescens_ – Downy Birch

Within the birch family, Betulaceae, Silver Birch is the most common species in Britain. Unless damaged early in life, a Silver Birch has a single trunk up to 30m tall with attractive pendulous branches. The bark of immature trees is silvery-white, but in time it develops diamond-shaped black protrusions on the lower trunk. In April male and female catkins occur on the same tree, and the leaves turn yellow from late summer into autumn.

Silver Birch (left) and Downy Birch (right) are pioneer trees, colonising clear-felled forest areas. Where they occur together, these very similar species often produce hybrids.

Silver Birch leaves and catkins

Downy Birch leaves

Bark of an old Silver Birch tree

Downy Birch *Betula pubescens* copes well with waterlogged soil. It is very similar in appearance to silver birch, and hybrids between the two are common and can cause confusion. The branches of Downy Birch do not droop at the ends as do those of Silver Birch, and its leaves have shorter stalks and are duller green than those of Silver Birch. Downy Birch can quickly colonise wet heath and moorland.

Birches are ectomycorrhizal and provide homes for many large and colourful fungi, including several from the genera *Amanita, Cortinarius, Lactarius, Leccinum* and *Russula*. The Fly Agaric *Amanita muscaria* is found more often with birch than with any other tree species, as also is *Leccinum scabrum*, which has the common name of Brown Birch Bolete. But here is one spectacular bracket fungus that is rarely seen anywhere other than on birch trees:

The Birch Polypore or Razor-strop Fungus *Piptoporus betulinus* is a large wood-rotting bracket specific to birch trees. It may even be weakly parasitic on ailing birches, but certainly as soon as a birch tree dies this bracket is likely to appear, causing rapid decay of the trunk and any branches that remain attached.

Alnus glutinosa – Black Alder; and _Alnus incana_ - Grey Alder
Black Alders are a familiar sight beside rivers and lakes and in marshes and boggy moorland. Their roots help to limit erosion of riverbanks during heavy spates (high, fast-flowing water). In the past alders were coppiced and the wood used to make charcoal for drawing and as a filtration medium. Until the mid 1940s alder charcoal was also used in making gunpowder. Grey Alder was introduced from mainland Europe in the late 1700s.

In the 1990s, the fungus *Phytophthora alni*, a relative of the fungal blight that attacks potato crops, infested many of the riverside alders of southern England and Wales. Thousands of mature trees have been lost as a result.

The alder catkins (male and female on the same tree) form in the autumn, and pollination occurs in the following spring. The leaves are initially sticky with hairs on the underside, unlike similarly-shaped Hazel leaves which have hairs on both sides. Alder leaves are generally smaller and darker than those of Hazel, with which they are sometimes confused.

Riverside Black Alders in winter

Leaves & flowers (♀)

Flowers (♂)

Bark

In alder carr woodland (overgrown fen, swamp and bog), many trees have their feet in water throughout the year; this is not good habitat for large fungi. In drier places, however, there is a range of EM fungi specifically or commonly found with alders.

The Alder Scalycap _Pholiota alnicola_ is rarely found anywhere other than on fallen alders. (Only very occasionally does this greasy-capped mushroom grow on willows and birches.)

Corylus avellana – Hazel

Hazel woodlands are often coppiced so that each plant produces many near-vertical branches rising from ground level. If they are not coppiced, however, Hazel trees can grow to a height of 10m and produce strong trunks. In early spring, male catkins open to release their pollen. Tiny female flowers, which appear on the same plant as the male catkins, are bright red; they capture wind-blown pollen. The leaves appear after the catkins; they have a few soft hairs on the upper surface and are more hairy beneath, and they alternate along the stems. In autumn the nuts make these trees easy to recognise... until the squirrels strip them of their bounty. Hazel coppices are ideal habitats for dormice.

Hazel growing in limestone pavement **Flowers ♀ and ♂** **Bark** **Nuts** **Leaves**

Hazel woodland provides some very productive territory for fungus forays. Although few wood-rotting brackets appear on their hard trunks and branches, these little nut trees are ectomycorrhizal and have several fungal associates including *Neoboletus luridiformis, Boletus edulis, Amanita rubescens, Lactarius pyrogalus, Hydnum repandum, Russula foetens* and many more. All of these fungi can be found not only with Hazel but also with several other kinds of trees, but it is the great diversity of mycorrhizal fungi found growing with Hazel them makes an autumn visit to Hazel-rich coppice woodland so worthwhile.

Hazel Gloves _Hypocreopsis rhododendri_ grows on old hardwood trees. In Britain this rare ascomycete fungus is found only on ancient coppiced Hazel, where it is thought not to feed directly on the timber itself but to be parasitic on Glue Crust fungus _Hymenochaete corrugata_. (It is not always possible to see the host fungus, which may be covered by Hazel Gloves and by mosses.)

***Carpinus betulus* – Hornbeam**

Hornbeams, native to south-east England and introduced elsewhere, provide very hard timber - so hard that it has acquired the common name ironwood. This was the traditional raw material for making wooden-axled cartwheels and gears in early machinery.

Leaves

An ancient Hornbeam **Seeds** **Bark**

At a glance very similar to Beech trees, Hornbeams are easily overlooked. Their leaves are of similar shape and colour but rather smaller and more deeply furrowed between the veins than Beech leaves. Mature Hornbeams have fluted trunks, whereas Beeches are much smoother; however, the most obvious distinction becomes apparent when the seeds appear. Hornbeam seeds have wings, whereas those of Beech trees do not.

Hornbeams have many EM fungal partners, including *Cortinarius, Russula* and *Lactarius* fungi. The rare bolete *Strobilomyces strobilaceus* is another of the EM partners occasionally found beneath the spreading branches of old hornbeams.

***Strobilomyces strobilaceus*, commonly known as Old Man of the Woods, is a very occasional find under Hornbeams.**

Tilia platyphyllos – Large-leaved Lime; _Tilia cordata_ – Small-leaved Lime
A tardy straggler in the procession of trees entering Britain after the ice receded, the Small-leaved Lime is mainly found in southern England and in Wales. At up to 45m in height, this elegant tree - its old-fashioned name is Linden Tree - is one of our tallest broadleaf species. The boles of Small-leaved Limes sprout a mass of twiggy shoots.

Large-leaved Limes, rare in Britain, are mainly found in southern Europe and do not have twiggy boles. Experts are divided as to whether they are native to Britain. To add confusion, these two lime species interbreed to form a fertile hybrid known as Common Lime – the ones we see most often in parks and along avenues, where they attract aphids that deposit sticky honeydew droppings on cars (and people!). Limes flower in summer and are pollinated by insects rather than the wind. In autumn their little grey nuts, attached to light bracts that act as parachutes, are carried away on the wind. Lime wood was used in the manufacture of piano keys.

Small-leaved Lime **Flowers** **Seeds** **Leaves** **Bark**

Limes have numerous EM fungi associates including a few boletes and several species from each of the genera *Entoloma, Cortinarius* and *Inocybe*. Litter-rotting fungi are also prolific under limes; look out particularly for Spindleshank *Gymnopus fusipes*.

The Lurid Bolete *Suillellus luridus* (until 2014 generally known as *Boletus luridus*) is one of at least eight boletes that are known to form mycorrhizal relationships with limes.

***Salix alba* - White Willow; *Salix fragilis* – Crack Willow; *Salix caprea* - Goat Willow**
Common in England and eastern Wales but less so in the west of Wales, White Willows thrive in wet ground, and so they often flank rivers and streams. Left to grow naturally on exposed riverbanks, White Willow and most notably its close relative the Crack Willow tend to split in stormy weather. To avoid this problem the trees are often either coppiced or pollarded. White Willow is a traditional basket-making material, and it used to be woven to make sheep hurdles. Cricket bats are made from a cultivated derivative of the White Willow, while weeping willow cultivars are often grown as ornamental trees in parks and large gardens. Goat Willow or Pussy Willow is a smaller tree, rarely exceeding 15m in height, with short, oval leaves.

White Willows

Pussy Willow catkins

Goat Willow bark

Goat Willow leaves

White Willow leaves

Other than two fairly rare milkcap fungi (*Lactarius* species) with which willows are known to be ectomycorrhizal, the only large fruitbodies commonly associated with these waterside and wetland trees are a few parasites and rather more wood-rotting fungi. One of these rotters is particularly partial to dead willow wood...

Blushing Bracket *Daedaleopsis confragosa* is most often seen on dying and dead willow branches, although it sometimes has other hosts including birch. This very common saprophyte has slot-like pores that usually turn reddish when bruised.

***Populus niger* – Black Poplar; *Populus alba* - White poplar; *Populus tremulans* - Aspen**

The Black Poplar is now quite rare, and the few wild trees that remain in Britain and Ireland tend to inter-breed with derived cultivars including the tall, slim Lombardy Poplars that are planted as windbreaks and occasionally along avenues.

Leaf

Black Poplar **Seeds**  **Bark**

The Aspen, with its long-stemmed round leaves that flutter in the slightest breeze, and the introduced White Poplar *Populus alba* are facultatively mycorrhizal, as indeed also are Black Poplars. All poplars are parasitised by several kinds of bracket fungus as well as by various black leaf fungi.

Hoof Fungus *Fomes fomentarius* is often found on birch trees in northern Britain but also grows on poplars. This tough bracket fungus is also known as the Tinder Bracket, because in the distant past it was used to transport 'fire' from place to place. Poplars infested by this polypore soon die, whereupon the fungus continues to feed saprophytically on the decaying trunk for typically a year or two.

Prunus spinosa - Blackthorn

The popularity of Blackthorn comes partly from its brilliant white flowers. Opening long before any leaf buds have burst, they brighten up hedgerows at what can otherwise be a very dull time of year. Sloes, the fruits of the blackthorn, are the other big attraction: they are a vital ingredient of Sloe Gin. (The other ingredients are lots of gin and a little patience.) Blackthorn is mainly used as hedging, but individual trees can grow to more than five metres in favourable situations.

Blackthorn **Flowers** **Sloes** **Leaves** **Bark**

In common with that other popular hedging tree, Hawthorn, Blackthorns do not provide much opportunity for those out on fungi forays. They are mycorrhizal with some *Entoloma* fungi, but only rarely are fruitbodies seen beneath Blackthorns. Other members of the *Prunus* genus (part of the rose family Rosaceae) include plums, damsons and almonds. Wild Cherry *Prunus avium* is planted in forests, where it provides equally infertile territory as far as macrofungi are concerned; however, occasionally a large wood-rotting bracket fungus appears at the base of a dying Cherry tree, recurring annually until the tree has been reduced to a rotten stump. Its common name is the Giant Polypore.

The Giant Polypore *Meripilus giganteus* produces caps up to half a metre across and whole fruitbodies extending to a metre or sometimes more. Often seen on Beech, this short-lived bracket fungus is one of very few fungi capable of decaying the roots, trunks and stumps of dying and dead *Prunus* species. Another bracket typically found on blackthorn and other *Prunus* tree species is *Phellinus pomaceus*, commonly known as Cushion Bracket.

Crataegus monogyna **- Hawthorn**

Most lowland hedgerows, especially those around permanent pasture, contain plenty of Hawthorn. Farmers like this thorny bush because cattle do not. The pale hard wood is sometimes used for carved walking sticks.

In 100 years a Hawthorn can also grow into a moderately big tree, and plenty of gnarled old specimens are to be seen in remote valleys. Its blossom is usually white or white with a hint of pink, but some specimens have striking pink blossom. Hawthorns berries, called haws, provide a valuable source of winter food for birds.

Hawthorn with berries in autumn **Flowers** **Leaves** **Seeds (haws)** **Bark**

Morels *Morchella esculenta* are sometimes found in spring beneath Hawthorns, and in summer and autumn Chanterelles *Cantharellus cibarius* are quite a common sight beneath old Hawthorn hedges, often nestling close to exposed roots.

Perhaps the most common spring mushroom associated with these trees – again an EM fungus - is the Shield Pinkgill *Entoloma clypeatum.* Blackthorn, Wild Cherry and several other members of the rose family, Rosaceae, (to which Hawthorn and the many *Prunus* species belong) are also able to form EM relationships with Shield Pinkgills and possibly also with a few other *Entoloma* species.

The Shield Pinkgill *Entoloma clypeatum*, a spring-fruiting mushroom, occurs fairly often beneath old Hawthorn trees.

Sorbus aucuparia – Rowan, or Mountain Ash

This lovely tree is a very common sight beside upland streams and reservoirs, and it is a popular ornamental tree for gardens, parks and avenues. Despite having acquired the common name Mountain Ash (because of its leaf form rather than that of its flowers) this is not a close relative of other Ash trees, which belong to the olive family. The Rowan belongs to the rose family. Bright orange Rowan berries provide a splash of colour from mid summer through to late autumn and occasionally into the New Year.

Rowans in early autumn **Flowers** **Leaf** **Berries** **Bark**

Despite having smooth bark, the Rowan is a good host for lichens; it is known to form AM fungal associations but is not generally noted as a partner for EM fungi. Rowans are therefore of most interest to fungi forayers when live trunks are being attacked by parasitic fungi or when dead Rowans are decaying with the help of saprophytic species.

Shaggy Scalycap _Pholiota squarrosa_ sometimes attacks damaged Rowan trunks, eventually killing the trees and continuing to feed as a saprobe on the dead timber as it decays.

Ulmus procera – English Elm; Ulmus glabra – Wych Elm

Before the devastation of Dutch elm disease, a fungal infection that wiped out most of the mature elm trees during the 1970s, the English Elm was a very common sight in lowland Britain. It is instantly recognisable by the leaves, which have bristly hairs on the upper surface. An English Elm can grow to more than 30m, but few of those we see today reach much more than 10m in height before the bark crinkles and the tree dies.

The seeds of (possibly native) English Elms are set near the apex of the fruit, whereas those of the native Wych Elm are more central. Both were common in Britain prior to 1970. The leaves of Wych Elm are generally larger (typically 10cm long compared with about 7cm for those of English Elm). The term 'wych' means pliant.

An old Wych Elm in springtime

Wych Elm seeds

Wych Elm leaf

Wych Elm bark

Elms have few EM fungal partners, but because so many large elms have died there has been plenty of opportunity to watch the gradual decay of fallen trunks and branches. Dead elms are host to a great variety of fungi, including such mushrooms as *Cycloocybe cylindracea* more commonly associated with poplars, *Grifola frondosa* most often seen on oak trunks, and various other polypores.

Wrinkled Peach *Rhodotus palmatus* is found on dead and rotting elm trunks. The only species in its genus, this beautiful mushroom is instantly recognisable by the reticulate wrinkles on its cap surface. At the peak of Dutch elm disease this species became a common sight in northern Europe, but it is now quite a rare find in most parts of Britain and Ireland.

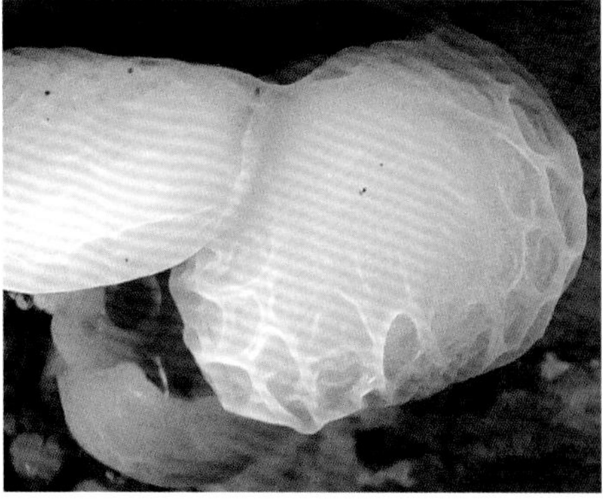

Acer pseudoplatanus - Sycamore

The Sycamore is a member of the maple family, Aceraceae. (The Latin *Acer* means sharp, and wood from maple trees was used for making spears.) In spring the young Sycamore leaves are rich red or orange, but in autumn they cannot match the vibrant colours of other maples. Sycamores grow to a spread of 30m and up to 40m tall. The distinctive flowers - pollinated by insects, which is not the norm for trees - produce winged seeds that spin like helicopter blades as they are carried away from the parent tree on autumn winds.

Flowers (♀) **Flowers (♂)**

Sycamore **Leaves and seeds** **Bark**

Sycamores may have reached Britain (from southern Europe) as early as Roman times, although they seem to have been scarce here until the late eighteenth century. These tough trees cope well with wind exposure, salt-laden air, and even industrial pollution. Creamy white and hard, Sycamore timber can be planed to a smooth finish, making it a useful furniture and flooring material. Wavy-grained Sycamore, known as fiddle-back wood, is still used today in the crafting of top-quality violins.

The invasive behaviour and exotic origin of Sycamore does little to endear it to nature conservationists, who make vigorous efforts to control and eradicate it. Sycamore woodland in autumn can certainly look like a mycological desert: these ubiquitous deciduous trees have very few EM fungal partners. So, although they have AM fungal associates and they do provide food for insects, for some parasitic fungi and for many litter-recycling species, from a fungi foray point of views Sycamores are boring.

Tar Spot *Rhytisma acerinum* appears on the leaves of Sycamores and other maples from late spring onwards. Although it must reduce the effective surface area available for photosynthesis, this parasitic fungus seems to have little or no effect on the health of the trees themselves.

Aesculus hippocastaneum **- Horse Chestnut**

This magnificent tree was introduced into Britain from the Balkans in the late 16th century. The soft, lightweight timber is not much used nowadays, although at one time artificial limbs were carved from it. Shiny mahogany-brown nuts of the Horse Chestnut are eagerly gathered by children for playing 'conkers' – a tradition at least 200 years old. These nuts, which develop in spiny cases, are ripe in September and October (the 'conker' season). A related North American species has red flowers; its glossy nuts peering from split spiny cases have earned it the nickname of Buck-eyes. Pink- and red-flowered Horse Chestnut trees seen in Britain and Ireland are hybrids between 'our' Horse Chestnut and Buck-eyes.

In winter and early spring Horse Chestnut buds develop and swell. They are very sticky - a feature that helps to prevent damage by small insects. The distinctive palmate leaves usually have five or seven leaflets

Flowers

Leaves and seeds

Horse Chestnut in full bloom

Sticky buds

Bark

Horse Chestnut trees can reach a height of 35m, but in recent years disease has caused 'die-back' of many of our finest old Horse Chestnut trees. Horse Chestnuts form mainly AM associations with fungi, and in Britain and Ireland they have no known EM partners.

Horse Chestnut trees are not immune to parasitic attack. Often seen also on Beech, Sycamore and other hardwoods, one of the most common fungi to attack Horse Chestnut is the Dryad's Saddle *Polyporus squamosus*.

Fraxinus excelsior - Ash

Ash trees can live for more than 400 years, reaching a height of 45m in ideal situations. They seem to do best in sheltered, sunlit locations.

Coppiced Ash has long been the timber of choice for tool handles, because its lightness, strength and pliability make it very good at absorbing shocks. Many fine Ash trees are cut down for more basic reasons, however: Ash makes great firewood which, should the need arise, will burn well even when freshly felled.

Ash tree in springtime

Flowers ♂ and ♀

Ash keys

Leaves

Bark

Few plants and even fewer fungi grow under Ash (although Ash trees are known to form EM relationships with some boletes and at least one *Amanita* species); this is despite their buds being among the last to burst in spring and their leaves falling early in autumn if there is even the slightest frost. Dead standing Ash trees and fallen trunks and branches are home to many conspicuous wood-rotting fungi, however, including several of the larger ascomycetes such as Dead Man's Fingers *Xylaria polymorpha* and King Alfred's Cakes *Daldinia concentrica.*

Ash trees belong to the olive family, Oleaceae. Despite the similarity of leaf shape, the Rowan or Mountain Ash *Sorbus aucuparia* and the true Ash *Fraxinus excelsior* are not closely related; in fact Rowans belong to the rose family, Rosaceae.

King Alfred's Cakes *Daldinia concentrica* produces hard, inedible fruitbodies that appear most often on Ash trees but also occasionally on Beech. Inside the fruitbody there are concentric silver-grey and black layers – hence the specific epithet.

Sambucus nigra – Elder

Often growing as multi-stemmed bushes rather than trees, Elders have fragile hollow stems that tend to fracture unless growing in sheltered sites. Elder flowers are used to make cordial and white wine, while the ripe berries, popular with birds, can be used to make preserves and as the basis of a red wine. Elder leaves, however, are poisonous.

Frequently seen in old churchyards, Elders flourish in soil with high nitrogen content. In woods, they colonise dung-rich spoil heaps outside disused badger setts and the disturbed soil among rabbit warrens, where their fast-growing shoots quickly get above the browsing height of small herbivores. When birds eat the berries, the seeds are dispersed in their droppings.

Elder bark, leaves and flowers were all used to make dyes; but perhaps the most common use of Elder was always, and perhaps somewhere it still is, by generations of children teaching one another to hollow out the pithy stems in order to make pea-shooters and penny whistles.

Flowers **Berries**

Elder in winter **Leaves** **Bark**

Despite having very soft wood, Elder is resistant to attack by Honey Fungus *Armillaria mellea*, which causes so much damage when it infests forests and gardens. Elder forms AM fungal associations but has no known EM associates; however, on and under Elder trees and bushes you can usually find a few saprophytic fungi.

The wood rotting jelly fungus *Auricularia auricula-judae*, commonly known as Jelly Ear, is found most often on dead or dying Elder trunks and branches, although it can occasionally be found on other deciduous hardwood trees and shrubs.

Ilex aquifolium – Holly; and other broadleaf evergreens

Usually less than ten metres tall but occasionally reaching 20m, Holly is a native of Britain and Ireland. It grows in hedgerows, on woodland edges and less frequently in open deciduous and coniferous forests.

Flowers (♂) **Berries**

Few plants or fungi live beneath Holly **Leaves** **Bark**

Tough prickly leaves on the lower branches of Holly deter many creatures that might otherwise steal birds' eggs from nests among its branches. The upper leaves are less well armoured, sometimes having no spines at all. Few plants or fungi can live among fallen Holly leaves which, like other evergreens, contain toxins and are very slow to rot and are a poor growing medium for large litter-recycling fungi. (The ascomycete *Trochila ilicina* and the basidiomycete *Marasmius hudsonii* are exceptions that are partial to Holly leaves.)

Holly Parachute *Marasmius hudsonii*. Found on damp dead leaves of Holly, this tiny gilled mushroom has a cap rarely more than 5mm in diameter; it is immediately recognisable because of the red-brown pointed hairs (inset picture, right) that cover the cap pellicle.

Other generally fungus-free evergreens

Many other evergreens can create mycological deserts. (Of course, any associated AM fungi will still be active in the underworld.) Like Holly, Box *Buxus sempervirens* and Privet *Ligustrum ovalifolium* can suffer from leaf fungal attacks such as Tar Spot, but waste no time searching for mycorrhizal fungi beneath their shelter. Unlike Holly, however, these popular hedging evergreens can and sometimes do fall victim to attack by Honey Fungus.

Native Conifers of Britain

There are just three conifers native to Britain although a great many exotic pines and firs have been brought in, mostly during the past two or three hundred years.

Pinus sylvestris - Scots Pine

An evergreen with a fairly straight trunk and initially the conical form typical of so many conifers, the Scots Pine develops more of a spreading top as it ages, particularly when it is planted well separated from its neighbours. This frost-hardy tree is grown commercially for fence posts, telegraph poles and building timber; it is also planted along with deciduous trees to provide frost protection for young Beech trees and oaks.

The needles of pine trees are bound together by a basal sheath that holds them either in pairs, in groups of three or in groups of five. Scots Pine needles are bound together in pairs – a useful diagnostic feature.

Cones (♂) **Leaves**

Scots Pine **Cone (♀)** **Bark**

The most common two-needle non-native pine in Britain is the Corsican Pine *Pinus nigra* var. *maritima*, which was introduced to Britain in 1759. Corsican Pine needles, which are more than twice as long as those of Scots Pine, grow in twisted pairs. Grown for the high value of its timber, there are large plantations of this conifer at Thetford Forest in East Anglia, at Newborough Forest in North Wales, and in places as far north as the east coast of Scotland. Stands of Corsican Pine were also planted in Ireland following its entry into the European Union.

Pines are ectomycorrhizal with a wide range of basidiomycetes, but most notably with boletes. Only rarely are there bracket fungi on the trunks, but several root-rotting fungi attack the bases of pines. Pine needles can take a decade to decay on well drained sloping land; they act as a blanket, preventing bracken and other rank vegetation from moving in and hiding whatever fungal fruitbodies are under the pines.

Fungi associated specifically or mainly with pines

Pine forests are great places for fungi. Once the trees are mature enough to provide a dense canopy there are usually not many forest-floor plants away from clearings and tracks. (Broad-leaved Helleborines are exceptions but hardly a disappointment when they show up!) Pines are mycorrhizal with a whole host of fungi, and although dense needle litter is difficult for most mushrooms to munch on there are plenty that thrive on the springy forest floor beneath old pine trees. A few interesting parasites are partial to pines, too.

The Bovine Bolete *Suillus bovinus* is an EM fungus, its mushrooms often appearing under Scots Pines especially on and beside forests footpaths. Pines of all sorts are very popular with fungi: in Scotland, for example, some 200 species of fungi are reported to form EM relationships with Scots Pines.

Buttercap *Rhodocollybia butyracea* is one of a group of closely-related pine-litter rotters that produce fruitbodies in summer and autumn. Their appearance is very variable, but the greasy feel of their cap surfaces, even in dry weather, makes them quite distinctive. (A much-used common name for this mushroom is Greasy Toughshank.) Buttercaps are also common and often abundant under birches.

Wood Cauliflower *Sparassis crispa* is a parasite found at the bases of pines and very occasionally other conifers. The creamy-white fruitbodies are edible if collected when they are young.

Abies grandis - Grand Fir; _Abies procera_ - Noble Fir; and _Abies alba_ - Silver Fir
In plantations these fast growing conifers grow straight and tall – up to 65m in the case of the Grand Fir (also known as the Giant Fir). The needles, dark-green and shiny on the top and whitish beneath, grow in two rows at almost 180 degrees to one other. The first seeds of *Abies grandis* were brought to the UK from America in 1831 by the young (he died aged 35) Scottish botanist and plant hunter David Douglas. *Abies alba* is native to mountainous areas of central Europe. After a slow start this fir can add a metre per year to its height; however, its timber is very soft and the trees are prone to frost damage if planted in exposed locations. The European Silver Fir can be distinguished by its needles, which have notched tips. *Abies procera* (syn. *Abies nobilis*), the Noble Fir, is another of David Douglas's introductions to Britain. Brought from the mountains north of Canada's Columbia River Gorge in 1830, this elegant conifer can grow to a height of 60m, but it needs acid soil. Douglas-fir plantations are also common in Scotland and west Wales, where the high rainfall suits these drought-intolerant trees very well.

European Silver Firs

Cones (♀) **Cones (♂)**

Leaves **Bark**

True firs have just a few EM fungal associates, including the Rufous Milkcap *Lactarius rufus*. Needing plenty of water, these tall trees do well in sheltered parts of western Britain. Douglas-firs *Pseudotsuga menziesii* (which are not actually true firs) are host to several EM fungi including species from the genera Tylopilus, *Inocybe* and *Russula*.

The Dusky Bolete _Tylopilus porphyrosporus_ is one of the many EM fungal associates of Douglas-firs. (The common name Douglas-fir honours David Douglas, who introduced this conifer to Britain in 1826.)

Larix decidua – European Larch; and *Larix kaempferi* – Japanese Larch

The European Larch *Larix decidua* was brought from the Alps to Britain around 1620 and grown for timber. Larch is still popular today, mainly as a long-lasting fencing material; and, since the introduction by John Veitch in 1861 of the canker-resistant Japanese Larch *Larix kaempferi*, a species capable of hybridising with the European Larch, we now have many intermediate forms of larch throughout Britain and Ireland.

The cones of Japanese Larch have turned-back tips – a useful aid to identification, because the cones of European Larches have straight tips. From a mushroom-hunter's point of view there seems to be no significant difference between these two trees.

European Larches (*Larix decidua*)

Cone (♀) *L. decidua*

Cone (♀) *L. kaempferi*

Cone (♂) + leaves *L. kaempferi*

Bark *L. decidua*

Because they are deciduous conifers, larches let plenty of light through to the forest floor in autumn, winter and springtime, and so there is often dense vegetation beneath these trees. This makes sombre-coloured mushrooms even more difficult than usual to spot. As if to compensate for this, some of the fungi associated with larch trees have brightly coloured caps. Larch trees form EM relationships with many fungi including several bolete species.

The Larch Bolete *Suillus grevillei* is specifically associated with larches. These attractive mushrooms with their bright shiny orange caps are easy to spot even in long grass. The caps usually change colour from orange to yellow as they expand and mature.

Picea abies – Norway Spruce; and _Picea sitchensis_ - Sitka Spruce

Mature spruce trees allow very little light to reach the ground beneath their dense canopy. Spruce forests are therefore dark, forbidding places with little or no floral vegetation. Fungi don't mind that one little bit, of course, as they have no need of light.

Norway Spruce

Young cones (♀)

Mature cones (♀)

Leaves

Bark

Spruce leaves (needles) are dark green, four-sided and pointed – sharp enough to draw an 'ouch' if you kneel on one that is pointing upwards. The cones of Norway Spruce, up to 15cm long, have no stalks; they are shed intact to release their seeds. Sitka Spruce, was introduced into Britain from North America in 1831 and is now widely planted here; it is a taller tree but with much shorter cones.

With its woolly cap margin, the Yellow Bearded Milkcap _Lactarius repraesentaneus_ is surely one of the most beautiful of all the conifer forest fungi. Rarely found in Britain, where it is restricted to Scotland, this northern European species is quite common in Scandinavia and is ectomycorrhizal with spruce trees.

The False Saffron Milkcap _Lactarius deterrimus_ is so often associated with spruce trees that many people refer to it as the Spruce Milkcap. With varying proportions of orange and green, the caps are far from uniform in appearance; therefore, as with so many milkcaps, the growing habitat is an important diagnostic feature.

Taxus baccata - Yew

Yew trees are particularly common in the chalk and limestone areas of southern England. Throughout Britain and Ireland they have also been planted in many churchyards. These evergreen trees grow slowly and live for hundreds of years. Some old Yews are thought to be over 2000 years old and, because many Yews have trunks formed by the coalescence of several stems, they tend to become hollow when they grow old. Longbows were made from Yew, a durable wood that has also been used to turn bowls and as a veneer by furniture makers down the ages.

In early spring, Yews can be seen in flower, and in late summer the fruits appear with their bright arils (the fleshy red covering over the seeds) looking rather like small acorns before they eventually ripen into bright red 'berries'. The seeds inside the fruits are poisonous.

Leaves **Cones (♂)**

Yew **Cones (♀)** **Bark**

Yew trees do not form ectomycorrhizal associations, and very few large fungi are ever found in their grass-free shadows; however, they are not entirely immune from parasites, and one or two bracket and crust fungi can occasionally be seen on the trunks and larger branches of old Yews.

The polypore *Laetiporus sulphureus* sometimes attacks Yew trees. Having infected one Yew in a forest, the fungus can quickly spread to its neighbours. This large and colourful bracket, commonly referred to as Chicken of the Woods, is an unselective parasite most often seen on broadleaf trees such as oaks and beeches.

Yew trees contain deadly toxins, and although Chicken of the Woods is generally considered edible some authorities counsel against eating these fungi when taken from Yew trees.

Juniperus communis **– Juniper**

A small evergreen conifer growing either with a narrow pointed crown or as a ground-hugging shrub, Juniper has separate male and female trees. This, the smallest of Britain's native conifers, generally favours the chalk-rich soils of south-east England but also occurs on limestone heaths and moors. There are colonies of wind-cowed branching Junipers throughout Scotland, in Ireland's Burren, and on the Great Orme in north Wales.

Juniper **Cones (♂)** **Cones (♀)** **Bark**

Junipers are great if your interest is in ascomycetes, rusts and sooty moulds; however, they are not productive places for large mushrooms and brackets.

Problems with aliens

Alien species that have evolved outside the ecosystem into which they are brought can compete with (and in the case of animals and of parasitic plants and fungi either prey or parasitise upon) native species. An example of this is the Grey Squirrel, which has competed so successfully with our native Red Squirrel that reds are now restricted to Scotland and just a few locations further south. Grey Squirrels damage trees by stripping the bark. Once the bark has been removed all the way round a trunk, the tree almost invariably dies.

Imports rarely come alone. The newcomers may have immunity to various disease organisms that are transported with them, but native species have not developed such immunity. Signal Crayfish were brought in to increase the productivity of aquaculture in the UK, but inevitably some escaped into the wild. With them came crayfish plague, a virulent disease caused by the fungus *Aphanomyces astaci*, and it has since decimated many populations of the native White-clawed Crayfish.

Alien trees can be equally problematic. For example great damage is caused to native flora and fauna by *Rhododendron ponticum*, a Victorian introduction that has spread into the wild in Britain and Ireland. In suitable habitats it crowds out most other wild plants. The leaves are toxic to most animals; 'mad honey disease' is caused by grayanotoxin, which is found in the nectar of the flowers of Rhododendrons.

Forests, Woods and Coppices

Wherever there are woodlands there will be woodland fungi, but some places are much more productive than others (from the point of view of those interested in mushrooms and other large fruitbodies, that is). Many factors determine how 'good' a particular area is as a fungi foray site. Apart from the obvious matters of accessibility and safety (some forests are on precipice land little of which can be searched by *anyone* regardless of their agility and boldness), the mycological interest is partly determined by the trees themselves:

Tree types. As we have already seen, not all trees are treated as equals by fungi that produce large fruitbodies, so Beech woodland and Scots Pine forests are richer in macro fungi than say Cherry orchards or Eucalyptus plantations.

Age range. Many kinds of trees form relationships with certain kinds of fungi early in life and switch their allegiance to other mycorrhizal partners when they become mature trees. Woodland where saplings have been planted annually over many decades usually has more kinds of fruiting fungi than one where the trees were planted all at the same time.

Tree mix. Some fungi are polygamous in their mycorrhizal relationships and may produce fruitbodies annually in mixed woodland but far less frequently in forest monocultures.

Locality. Two plantations containing the same mix of tree species of similar age ranges can have different fungal features; terrain and climate also have big influences.

Soil acidity or alkalinity. Some EM fungi are solely or mainly associated with trees on acid soils – for example the Oakbug Milkcap *Lactarius quietus* - while others show a marked preference for woods on chalky or limestone-rich (alkaline) soils – the Beechwood Sickener *Russula nobilis* is one such example. Magpie Inkcaps *Coprinopsis picacea* are most often found in nutrient-rich alkaline woodland, and in Britain and Ireland they are rarely seen other than in mature Beech and Ash woods on chalky soil. Where the apparent preference is marked, good field guides make reference to the relevant soil characteristics.

Soil depth. Wherever trees are well spaced out so that sunlight and wind can dry the surface layers quickly, shallow soils are graves for most macro fungus mycelia, which cannot survive desiccation.

Soil management: The well trodden soil of footpaths, although often populated by various kinds of earthballs and saddle fungi, is generally less productive for other woodland fungi than areas of moss-covered springy (but undisturbed) ground. On the other hand, when the soil between trees is regularly cultivated to control weeds, the mycelia of fungi in the soil immediately below the leaf litter are continually damaged also, and so they do not usually produce as many fruitbodies as they would if the soil were left undisturbed.

Terrain: Steep slopes are generally poor places for terrestrial litter-rotting fungi, because leaf litter does not stay there for very long, and heavy rains can sometimes cut deep scours into the surface soil. Within most woods and forests there are areas of little or no slope, and provided they do not hold standing water for long periods these are often the most productive for those fungi that feed on fallen leaves and twigs. The same cannot be said of mycorrhizal fungi, however: when you fancy a feast of Ceps, slopes beside woodland tracks or the sides of drainage ditches often provide the majority of finds. In pine forests on sandy soil near the coast, north-facing slopes tend to dry out more slowly than those exposed to the full impact of the midday sun and so are often the best places for summer boletes. The mushrooms on south-facing slopes are usually smaller and, in dry weather, wrinkled and discoloured even before the caps have expanded fully.

Dead wood management. For thousands of years people have collected firewood from forests, reducing the amount of dead wood left to decay naturally. As a result, less carbon is locked up in forests, and the habitat for birds and animals and the amount of food for saprobes, including wood-rotting fungi, is reduced. Rotting wood also stores water that plants, fungi and animals can draw upon during drought. When forests are opened up for recreational activities such as cycling, standing dead trees and fallen branches are sometimes cleared up and burnt. Tidy woodlands usually support fewer fungi.

Understory. Woodland floors with plenty of mossy mounds, especially those containing cavities where dead stumps and buried branches lie rotting away, should put a spring in the step of any mushroom hunter. Fungi in this kind of woodland soil are able to cope well with extremes of temperature, making the success of forays there less weather dependent.

Rainfall. Mushrooms need moisture; however, the fact that the west of Britain has much higher average annual rainfall than the east of the country is not reflected in a markedly higher concentration of fungal fruitbodies in the west. What does make a big difference is prolonged heat, drought or strong drying winds during what should be the fruiting season; in those kinds of conditions the mushrooms tend to be fewer, smaller and short lived.

Longitude: Some forest fungi can cope with cold weather while others are better equipped to survive heat and drought. For example, if you want to see *Amanita virosa*, the infamous Destroying Angel, then northern Europe is the place to go. Although from the same genus, *Amanita caesarea*, a highly-prized edible mushroom known in southern Europe as Caesar's Mushroom, is rarely if ever reported further north than France but is plentiful in Italy, Spain and Portugal.

Altitude: Although some fungi that are common in alpine sites are rarely seen in the lowlands, by and large the higher you climb the fewer fungi species you can expect to find. It's not simply a matter of temperature, because the lowland forests of Norway and Sweden are far more prolific sources of fungi than the high mountain tops in Snowdonia. One crucial rule for finding upland forest fungi is not to look for them above the tree line!

Coppice Woodland

Coppicing is the practice of cutting certain kinds of trees and shrubs to ground level to encourage vigorous regrowth. Managed properly, coppice woodland can provide a continuous and sustainable supply of timber, and because small areas are harvested in rotation there are always places where shade-loving animals, plants and fungi can thrive. Compare that with clear felling, where all of the trees mature at the same time and are then removed, with great disturbance, and it's easy to understand why so many conservation organisations are reviving the practice of coppice management.

A mature coppice in springtime

Trees and shrubs that are coppiced produce shoots that grow rapidly, nurtured by a large rootstock and its attendent networks of mycorrizal fungi. For example some willows can put on a metre of growth in a month. Wind throw is not a threat to coppice woodland, as it is to taller trees, and so some coppiced stools (the term given to the stumps from which regrowth occurs) can live for many hundreds of years – far longer, in most instances, than would have been possible if they had not been cut at all.

Alders, willows, Hazel, Ash and Sweet Chestnut are ideal subjects for coppicing. They are simply cut down to just above ground level and the timber harvested. After a few years another crop is ready for gathering in, and the process is repeated over and over again. Most conifers (Yew is an exception) cannot be coppiced successfully, however, because they die once the main trunk is cut down.

Conifer Forests

Comprising mainly such trees as spruces, pines, firs and hemlocks, the world's conifer forests are for the most part concentrated in the colder parts of the northern hemisphere in areas where the soil is acidic. These so-called boreal or taiga forests cover vast tracts of North America, northern Europe (including most of Scandinavia), Russia and Northern China. The majority of Britain's confer forests are plantations of spruce, fir and pine, covering large parts of Wales, north-west England and Scotland. Less than 10 per cent of Ireland is forested, but in recent decades efforts have been made to recreate forests - not only of Sitka Spruce but also of broadleaf trees - and the coverage is gradually increasing.

Eventually all evergreen trees shed their leaves and produce new ones, and as the conifer needles fall to the forest floor they form a thick springy mat that is only slowly broken down by fungi. Forest ecosystems depend on the support of these fungi, which convert the decomposed needles into nutrients and supply them to the trees via their roots.

In evergreen conifer forests, very little light penetrates the thick canopy to reach the forest floor. These are gloomy places where few flowering plants can survive. The understory comprises mainly mosses, liverworts and of course fungi and lichens on fallen trunks and branches with, perhaps, a few ferns that can just about cope in low-light conditions.

Broadleaf Woodland

Broadleaf woodland is composed of trees with leaves that are generally broad and flat rather than needle-like. Whereas most conifers are evergreen, the majority of broadleaf trees are deciduous – Holly is one of the exceptions most often found in broadleaf woodlands. By and large, therefore, during the cold months of winter broadleaf woodland stands leafless, sap no longer circulating through trunks and branches. This is probably no bad thing, for if the spreading crowns of broadleaf trees such as oak and beech held snow on their leaves rather than letting most of it fall through bare twigs and branches the weight of the accumulated snow would be more than the branches could carry, and great damage would occur.

Moss-covered humps in this Swedish spruce forest provide a wonderfully protective environment for mycorrhizal and wood-rotting fungi. The soil is light and springy, but the moss helps retain moisture during the few hot weeks of Sweden's short summer.

Even without leaves, most broadleaf trees are unsuited to the extremes of weather that occur each winter in the far north, and so broadleaf woodland is essentially a feature of the more temperate regions of Europe.

Beech woodland in the UK is mainly concentrated in southern England and south-east Wales, while oak is the dominant species further north and west. A few woods comprising mainly Ash and Sycamore remain in south-west England, while stands of poplars are invariably artificial plantations rather than relict fragments of ancient woodlands. But none of these woods are pure monocultures: pioneer species such as birches and willows invade even the most intensively managed forests, and often a few very old limes or oaks are spared when a hardwood plantation is harvested and replanted.

Mixed Woodland

In northern Europe, including Britain and Ireland, natural mixed woodland is now quite a rare habitat. In Britain there are few remaining native conifers (Yew and Scots Pine with in places also Juniper) and their distribution and abundance are very limited. Mixed plantation woodland is far more common throughout much of Britain and parts of Ireland.

Winter: semi-natural deciduous woodland on an agricultural holding. It is dangerous if not impossible to farm precipitously steep slopes, and so native broadleaf trees can live there undisturbed, their timber unharvested. In all but the driest of autumns, such places offer much to interest fungi forayers (and foragers).

In plantations, slow-growing deciduous trees such as Ash and Beech are grown for their timber amongst a faster-growing crop of typically spruces or pines. The conifers may be harvested every fifty years or so, whereas the broadleaf trees take a lot longer to reach maturity. Selective thinning and felling rather than wholesale clearance means that the ecology is more stable and better suited to the needs of low-growing plants as well as fungi.

Although still very much the dominant type of woodland, in southern Europe monocultures of citrus orchards, eucalyptus forests and pine woods are not the only kinds of plantations. Many forested areas now comprise fast-growing, drought-tolerant pines and eucalypts interspersed with Cork Oak trees whose timber is of much less value than their spongy bark. When seeking fungi, it really pays to shun monoculture plantations and focus on mixed woodlands, which are mycologically much more diverse. The management regime in mixed plantation woodland is also more fungi friendly, so that not only are there more species but also often a much greater abundance of fruitbodies. In the Algarve region of southern Portugal, for example, there is an extended ‘mushroom’ season in mixed woodland plantations running from September right through to the end of April.

Lilac Oysterling *Panus conchatus* on a Cork Oak branch in the Algarve, where even in spring the heat can cause fruitbodies to shrivel in just a few hours. This wood rotter is an occasional species in Britain and Ireland, where it occurs on decayed fallen trunks and branches of deciduous trees.

Carr woodland

Carr or wet woodland is the penultimate stage of succession in which fens and ponds become choked with aquatic vegetation and turn into swamps, marshes and boggy woodland. (The term carr is derived from the Viking word *kjarr*, meaning a marshy wood.) Pioneer trees such as alders and willows, which grow well in waterlogged soil, take over the shallower margins and grow rapidly. Maturing willows in particular have a tendency to topple over or fracture in high winds, and the fallen branches only need to touch water to begin putting down roots, thereby extending the tree coverage. By this natural process of succession wetlands and marshes become what is termed carr woodland. Downy Birch is another of the trees that often move in to add to the diversity of wet woodlands. Eventually, as carr woodland dries out, other broadleaf trees such as oaks are able to grow there, but the nature of the soil largely determines the climax tree species.

Mature carr woodland is a tangle of trees, a few more or less upright, many more leaning drunkenly, and some nearly horizontal and making access much more difficult than in open marshland. On the boggy soil, shade-tolerant flowering plants wrestle for space among sedges and rushes, ferns and mosses, lichens and liverworts.

Willows have some EM associates, but alders are mycorrhizal with dozens of fungi species; unfortunately, few of them can live in waterlogged soil. An exception is a poisonous EM mushroom *Paxillus rubicundulus* (similar to the Brown Rollrim), which is a common find in alder carr woodland. But perhaps the main interest that fungi fanciers have in wet woodland centres on the many wood-rotting species that grow on dying branches and fallen deadwood. For example Ruby Elfcup *Sarcoscypha coccinea* and Scarlet Elfcup *Sarcoscypha austriaca* are common in alder and willow carr woodland.

Carr woodland may appear dull and lifeless in early spring, but come the autumn and many of the leaning trunks and fallen branches will be bristling with colourful fungi.

Fungi as Agents in Forestry Management

Mycorrhizal fungi make nutrients available to trees, and without them the fertility of forests would decline as timber is harvested. Mycorrhizal associations are one reason why naturally regenerated tree seedlings tend to thrive even in nutrient-poor soil, whereas seedlings transplanted into recently disturbed soil sometimes wither and die.

You may have noticed how seeds from Ash and Sycamore seem able to germinate and develop into vigorous seedlings in almost any kind of soil: unlike most other broadleaf trees (and some conifers) they don't need specific EM partners and can form associations with many kinds of AM fungi. In contrast, orchids depend for germination on specific types of fungi, and their seedlings will not grow in locations lacking those particular fungi. Transplanting terrestrial orchids often results in failure, whereas with trees a lot depends on the genus concerned. Some kinds of trees require more than one fungal partner, and it can be particularly difficult to get these trees started in new locations. Other trees – willows, for example - will shoot from twigs left lying on damp soil. It's partly due to the nature of the trees but also a lot to do with fungi in the soil.

Trees with established mycorrhizal associations are generally more resistant to disease, not merely as a result of the greater supply of nutrients but also because the mycorrhizas occupy areas on the root system that would otherwise be open to invasion by pathogenic organisms. Scientists have also found evidence that certain mycorrhizal fungi may secrete antibiotics, thereby protecting roots from such killer organisms as *Phytophthora* and some *Armillaria* species as well as from nematode worms; they may even provide increased resistance against harmful bacteria.

Harvesting timber by clear felling, removal of all vegetation, and deep cultivation does more than merely remove the existing trees and 'weeds': it kills many of the fungi that were dependent on those trees and plants. (More than 95% of plant species have mycorrhizal fungus partners – poppies and cabbages are among the tiny minority that 'go it alone'.) Once a forest has been clear felled and ploughed up, it is not possible to recreate a healthy woodland ecosystem simply by planting trees. So how can such land be reforested with young trees that will grow vigorously to produce a new forest? This question worried foresters for years.

Clear-felling kills mycorrhizal fungi. If saplings are planted here in future they may have a struggle to get established.

After much research, forestry managers now know what they can do to help. They are able to add a few 'generalist' mycorrizal fungi to the nursery soil when planting tree seeds or tiny seedlings, or they can inoculate the ground around larger trees that are being transplanted. Of course, in the wild the roots of all sorts of forest plants and their associated fungi live together below the surface – indeed some trees are known to swap fungal partners as they develop from seedlings to saplings and eventually to mature trees. No inoculation process can yet recreate this level of sophistication.

Early attempts at inoculating young trees with EM fungi involved chopping up and liquidising roots from mature trees and dipping the roots of seedlings into the resulting paste prior to planting them out. Sometimes it worked, but results were not consistent. Then, in the 1980s, researchers discovered ways of growing cultures of many of the necessary fungi, and their production on a commercial scale began. Few if any of the fungi contained in inoculants in use today ring any bells with those whose interest centres on edible fungi: a few EM fungi from the genera *Pisolithus* and *Rhizopogon*, and various species of AM fungi from the *Glomus* genus.

Conifer plantations are often sited where the soil is unsuitable for other crops.

The earthball *Pisolithus arhizus* is shaped rather like a rugby ball when young. Its traditional use as a source of dye led to it acquiring the common name Dyeball. Because it forms mycorrhizas with almost any kind of root, this EM fungus is frequently used by foresters (and in recent years gardeners, too) to promote tree and plant growth.

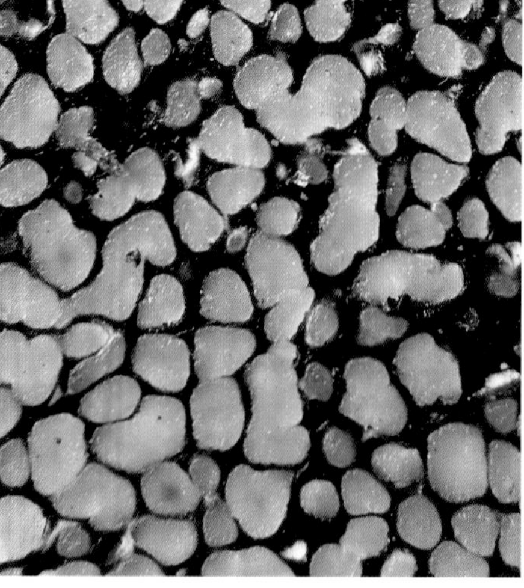

This cross-section picture (magnification 300%) of a young *Pisolithus arhizus* fruitbody shows the many separate compartments, like rice grains, within which the spores develop.

As the spores mature the *Pisolithus* earthball becomes more elongated vertically. Cracks appear in the upper surface and brown spores are dispersed by wind or rain. Progressively from the top, the whole of the fruitbody turns into a soft mass of brown spore-bearing powder. It is from this powder that mycorrhizal inoculants are produced.

Since 2000 the Royal Horticultural Society has used a blend of fungi marketed in the UK as RHS Rootgrow™ and now offers to the public tree-planting guidelines based on mycorrhizal inoculation with this product. Where soil has been severely polluted, plants with roots treated in this way can grow more vigorously, cope better with transplantation, and develop root systems that better equip them for surviving in drought conditions. Inoculation is less likely to be beneficial (and some authorities say that it might even be harmful) in soil that already contains a healthy and diverse range of mycorrhizal fungi.

Oaks, beeches, pines and other trees that cannot survive without the right kinds of EM fungal partners are said to be ‘obligately mycorrhizal’. With such trees as birches, on the other hand, the mycorrhizas are termed ‘facultative’ because the fungal associations are not absolutely necessary for the survival the trees (although they are much healthier and more vigorous with them). Trees with solely facultative mycorrhizas are generally better at colonising new territory than are the obligate trees, which is another reason that birches are so successful as pioneer species.

Brown Birch Boletes *Leccinum scabrum* on a woodland edge in central Scotland

Chapter 4 - Friends of the Forest

Ectomycorrhizal (EM) woodland fungi, their fads and fancies

The ancient Greeks and Romans were wrong: truffles are *not* the result of lightning striking damp earth. The very fact that truffles are attached to roots in woods and forests indicates that there must be some sort of relationship between these elusive underground fungi and the trees to which they are connected. We now know that this relationship is one of symbiosis – both the fungus and the tree benefit from chemicals passed across mycorrhizae that surround the fine rootlets.

The Summer Truffle *Tuber aestivum* is mycorrhizal with Beech trees and very occasionally Sweet Chestnut trees on calcareous soil. This is the best known edible truffle species that occurs in the UK, where in 2008 it fetched up to £300 per kg. That may sound a lot, but meanwhile the White Truffle *Tuber magnatum*, found only in northern Italy, was being sold for ten times that price. They are said to taste rather nice!

What is less immediately obvious is that many of the large woodland fungi, particularly cap-and-stem mushrooms, form similar mutually-beneficial relationships with trees. In fact most of these fungi not only benefit from nutrients provided by the tree but they cannot live without trees – they are therefore termed obligate mycorrhizal fungi. Some fungi can only live with trees of a particular genus, while others are able to link up with trees from several genera, and in a few instances this includes both broadleaf and coniferous trees. Ectomycorrhizal (EM) relationships between fungi and trees were discussed in Chapter 2, and now we look at the physical characteristics and habitat preferences of some of the most common EM fungi. Many of these are easy to identify right down to species level (and you certainly do need to get to species level if you intend gathering any mushrooms to eat), but there are also some very difficult groups – those from the vast and very complex *Cortinarius* genus, for example. As this book is a broad introduction to fungi rather than a formal field guide, the coverage of each group can only be partial and will concentrate on common fungi that are reasonably easy for a non-expert to identify without resorting to a microscope or chemical tests.

The Crab Brittlegill *Russula xerampelina*. Colourful but not so easy to identify to species level, all *Russula* fungi form mycorrhizal relationships with various kinds of broadleaf and/or coniferous trees.

We begin with some fairly straightforward groups, the amanitas (family Amanitaceae) and the boletes (Boletaceae) before the colourful brittlegills and milkcaps (Russulaceae – and with the brittlegills in particular colour is very variable, so the descriptive text is more important than the pictures). A small selection of *Cortinarius*, *Tricholoma* and a few other groups of mycorrhizal fungi is included to help set an agenda for further investigation via guided field trips or at least a specialist identification guide (Appendix IV).

To identify fungi with confidence always refer to the detailed descriptions and illustrations in an authoritative field guide. If in any doubt consult an expert before gathering any fungi that you (or anyone else) intend to eat.

Drop Dead Gorgeous – the Lovely Amanitas

It's difficult to imagine a more attractive sight than a group of perfect fungi from the genus *Amanita*, and as (in Europe at least) most of them live in mycorrhizal relationships with more than one tree genus it seems sensible to deal with them as a group. It's possible that their loveliness is behind the generic name *Amanita*, as the Latin word *amat* means he or she loves. Another explanation preferred by some is that *Amanita* is a reference to Amanon, a mountain range between Syria and Cilicia, and it's very likely that some *Amanita* species appear there - as indeed they do on the flanks of Ben Nevis, Snowdon, Mont Blanc and many others peaks. Worldwide there are some 600 *Amanita* species, of which about 60 occur in Europe and half that number in Britain and Ireland.

Amanita phalloides (Amanitaceae) – Deathcap

Although many people consider the *Amanita* fungi to be among the most beautiful of all the world's mushrooms, this is not the main reason for either their fame or their infamy. For that we have just two species to thank. The Fly Agaric *Amanita muscaria* is one of these. Its iconic appearance in so many aspects of culture – religion, mythology, medicine (in the loosest sense) and so on – is all pervasive. Many people believe that this is a mythical mushroom, and if they were to see one they might think it was a hallucination. More of that later… The other *Amanita*, lighter in colour but altogether darker in implications, is known throughout Europe as the Deathcap *Amanita phalloides*. In the USA, where this species is thought to have been accidentally introduced and has since spread, *Amanita phalloides* is more often referred to as the Death Cup.

Mature Deathcap fungi, their pendent rings hanging in tatters. Sometimes, as here, but by no means always there are still a few irregular chunks of the universal veil clinging to the fully-expanded caps.

This really is the Dr Crippen of the fungal kingdom. Fortunately, distinguishing Deathcaps from popular edible fungi is not at all difficult… when you know how.

Cap: young specimens are cream or light olive streaked with green or brown radiating fibres, but occasionally entirely white; smooth, sometimes with pieces of the universal veil weakly attached; convex at first, flattening; 4 to 15cm across.
Gills: white; free; crowded.
Stem: white, usually flushed with cap colour and often banded with fine scales; 5 to 12cm long and 1 to 2cm wide, thickening at base which is encased in a white bag-like volva. The pendent ring sometimes falls away at maturity leaving a bare stem.
Spore print: white.
Odour: not unpleasant when young, but as the fruitbodies mature, the sickly sweet smell of this mushroom becomes much stronger and eventually quite nauseating.

The fibrous nature of the cap surface of this Deathcap woodland toadstool is clearly visible, as also is the bag-like volva at the base of the stem.

Mainly found under oaks and Beech but sometimes occurring in conifer forests, the first fruitbodies of *Amanita phalloides* usually appear in late June or early July, but most years August to October is when they are most plentiful in Britain and Ireland. In mild weather the occasional specimen can emerge as late as November.

This young Deathcap displays only a hint of olive, and it's easy to understand how people unaware of the risks could mistake these for edible Wood Mushrooms. Checking for the presence of a volva ensures that this particular cause of confusion is avoided.

Trying to identify fungi from immature fruitbodies is fraught with difficulty, as many of the identifying characteristics become evident only at maturity.

Most of the large groups of Deathcap mushrooms I come across are under mature oak trees on slightly acid soil, and in such places I have seen more than a dozen fruitbodies beneath one tree. Deathcaps are rather more common in the southern half of Britain, while further north another equally deadly *Amanita* is likely to be waiting to trap the unwary (but why would anyone even consider eating a white-gilled mushroom?) and that is another pale-capped species, *Amanita virosa*, commonly known as the Destroying Angel.

Amanita virosa (Amanitaceae) – Destroying Angel

Just as deadly poisonous as *Amanita phalloides*, but mercifully much rarer in Britain and Ireland, the Destroying Angel really does look angelic. Containing the same toxins as Deathcaps, this northern species is an occasional find in Scotland but very common in Scandinavia; however, it can occur anywhere, and so we need to be on the alert.

Three wicked witches: even though these Destroying Angels are fully mature their caps remain convex. The rings are thin and fragile, and the caps are often perched on the stems at a jaunty angle. Veil fragments are rarely present on the caps of this species.

Cap: pure white; usually bell shaped and very smooth without veil remnants; commonly 6 to 8cm across but exceptionally up to 14cm.
Gills: white; free; crowded.
Stem: white; fragile white ring often torn or incomplete; irregularly fibrous surface; narrow bulb at base is encased in a white or pale grey bag-like volva often buried in moss and leaf litter rather than being at the surface as for many *Amanita* fungi. (This underlines the danger associated with gathering edible fungi by cutting them off at ground level!)
Spore print: white.

The egg-shaped caps of young fruitbodies of *Amanita virosa* are quite distinctive. In this young specimen a large veil fragment still adheres to the cap.

In northern Europe Destroying Angels usually appear in July, August and September. A similar species, *Amanita verna*, commonly known as Fool's Mushroom, appears in springtime. The two are almost impossible to distinguish, but if you are in to chemical testing then it is worth noting that *Amanita verna* does not react to potassium hydroxide whereas the flesh of *Amanita virosa* instantly turns yellow. For most people the different fruiting times are fairly conclusive, especially as these are not the kinds of fungi that anyone would want to collect as food.

In Britain and Ireland the Destroying Angel is often associated with Beech trees; however, this should not be used as a diagnostic feature when trying to identify this deadly poisonous species, because it can form mycorrhizas with several other broadleaf and coniferous trees.

Amanita citrina (Amanitaceae) – False Deathcap

If by chance you should mistake a Destroying Angel for a Deathcap, or vice versa, the consequences are minimal, but if you eat any of them the same cannot be said: these are the two most deadly poisonous species in the genus (and the most deadly in the world), and their common names are entirely appropriate. Unfortunately in the wild they bear no such labels, and apart from a few desperately sad accidents where toddlers pick them up and eat them, most cases of poisoning where these two killers are involved are the result of their incorrect identification as edible species. It's a help that the two *Amanita* fungi most likely to be confused with Deathcaps and Destroying Angels are either moderately toxic or at least inedible due to a bitter taste. The first of these, *Amanita citrina*, goes by the common name of False Deathcap.

Whether you visit broadleaf, coniferous or mixed woodland the chances are that you will come across *Amanita citrina* more often than most of its cousins. The specific epithet refers to a lemon tinge, but a white form (*Amanita citrina* var. *alba*) is also fairly common. This dainty-looking woodland mushroom is most common on acid soils.

Although one of the fruitbodies shown here is still immature and its cap not yet fully expanded, the veil fragments on the caps of both of these False Deathcaps are already turning ochre.

Cap: ivory or pale lemon; usually retaining veil fragments that discolour ochre (in var. *alba* the surface and veil fragments are white); convex, flattening; 4 to 10cm across.
Gills: white; adnexed or free; crowded.
Stem: ivory or white; 6 to 8cm long, 0.8 to 1.2cm dia.; persistent membranous white ring; volval remains form a gutter-like rim around swollen stem base.
Odour: strong, of raw potato.
Spore print: white.

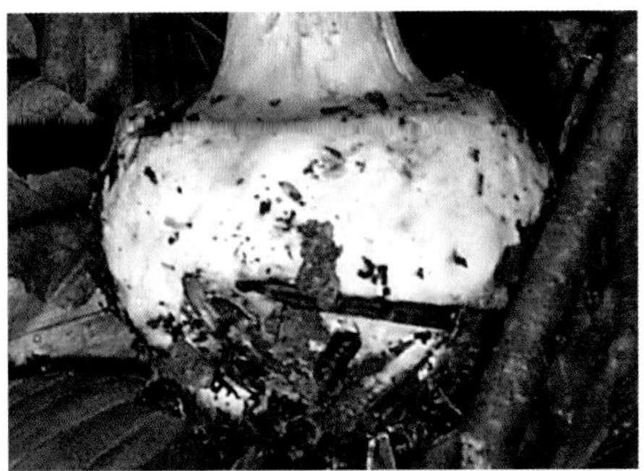

Mature fruitbodies of *Amanita citrina* do not normally retain a volval sac, but rather the volva collapses and leaves a distinct rim above the swollen base of the stem, so that the mushroom appears to be sitting in a tightly-fitting round-bottomed cup.

The lemon yellow form is the more common in most parts of the UK and Ireland. When cut, the flesh of both forms smells distinctly of raw potatoes, but the smell of the lemon form is generally stronger than that of the white form. Both are reported to taste unpleasant.

The pure white form of *Amanita citrina* shown here is sometimes denoted as a separate variety, *Amanita citrina* var. *alba*. It is found almost exclusively under Beech.

There is another very good reason for treating these woodland mushrooms as something lovely to see and nothing more. The deadly poisonous *Amanita phalloides* occasionally has a very pale cap with a few veil fragments adhering to it. To complicate matters further you may find an *Amanita citrina* whose cap has lost its veil fragments in heavy rain and occasionally with the cap surface having taken on a greenish tinge. If fruitbodies are gathered by cutting through the stems at ground level (which some mushrooming guides recommend) so that any volval remains are not visible for inspection, even an expert could be forgiven for getting these two confused… except that *Amanita phalloides* poisoning is not at all forgiving. *Amanita citrina* is inedible and definitely not a mushroom to collect along with others intended for consumption. Pass it on!

It is possible that a recently proposed new name - *Amanita bulbosa* var. *citrina* – may become the accepted way of referring to this species, although because *Amanita citrina* has been in use for a long time (and despite the fact that this mushroom was also recorded as *Amanita mappa*) many people would prefer to conserve the *citrina* specific epithet.

False Deathcaps can appear as early as June, but July to September is when they are most plentiful. In Britain and Ireland occasional specimens emerge as late as November, and in southern Europe these fungi can usually be seen at Christmastime.

***Amanita gemmata* (Amanitaceae) – Jewelled Amanita**

Although relatively small and squat, there is another pale *Amanita* species, quite similar in appearance to *Amanita citrina*, that could be mistaken for one or other of the deadly duo. *Amanita gemmata* is indeed a gem of a mushroom. Commonly referred to as the Jewelled Amanita, this rare find in Britain and Ireland is common in central and southern Europe. *Amanita gemmata* is mycorrhizal with several kinds of conifers – pines in particular – and less commonly with hardwoods.

***Amanita gemmata*. This lovely little mushroom of sandy soil usually has veil patches adhering to the pale ochre cap, which expands until flat or occasionally slightly depressed in the centre.**

Amanita gemmata is a summer and autumn mushroom, but near to the sea in all but the harshest of winters fresh specimens are still being produced at the end of November. If eaten it causes illness with symptoms similar to those that can result from severe Fly Agaric poisoning: hallucinations, nausea, vomiting, stomach pain, diarrhoea, irregular heart beat, and in exceptionally rare cases coma and convulsions. This mushroom is not generally a killer, but in one very sad case a young child's death from convulsions was traced back to eating *Amanita gemmata*.

Cap: pale ochre with darker centre; retaining white veil fragments mainly in centre; convex, flattening; 5 to 9cm across.
Gills: white; adnexed; crowded.
Stem: white, tinted ochre; 7 to 10cm long, 1 to 1.5cm dia.; short-lived ring falls away to leave indistinct mark low down on stem; short volva around slightly swollen stem base.
Spore print: white.

Of course, all these pale-capped *Amanita* mushrooms are mycorrhizal fungi, and that means they occur only under trees rather than in open fields... right? Unfortunately it's not quite that simple. Tree roots often extend a long way from the trunks of a tree. The tiny rootlets with which fungi form mycorrhizas (some mycologists prefer to use the Latin form mycorrhzae rather than the Anglicised form mycorrhizas to denote the plural) are at the tips of the roots, sometimes extending much further from the trunk than the branches do. The implications for anyone gathering field mushrooms are clear: keep well away from hedgerows and well away any trees growing in the field. It is much safer, of course, to make sure that you can identify with confidence each of the mushrooms you intend gathering, but even more importantly familiarise yourself with the key features of the most deadly fungi with which they can be confused.

Amanita pantherina (Amanitaceae) - Panthercap

Another mushroom that gets a very bad press, although probably undeserved at least in comparison with Deathcaps and Destroying Angels, is the Panthercap *Amanita pantherina*. The common name comes, of course, from the cap colouring: brilliant white scales (veil fragments) on a shiny brown or grey-brown background.

Panthercaps occur as solitary specimens or, less commonly, in small groups.

Cap: brown with small, pure-white warty veil fragments; convex, flattening; margin striate when fully expanded; 5 to 9cm (exceptionally 12cm) across.
Gills: white; free; crowded.
Stem: white; 7 to 12cm long, 1 to 1.5cm dia.; pendulous ring; volval remains form rings or sometimes a helix around bulbous stem base.
Spore print: white.

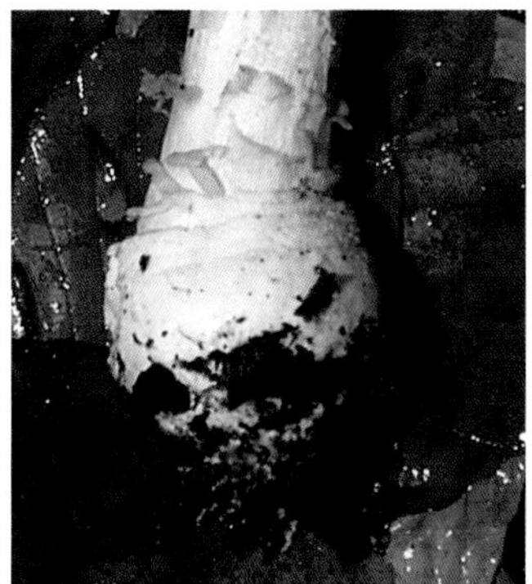

Another helpful identifying feature of *Amanita pantherina* is its stem base, which is slightly swollen and retains the white remains of the volva, usually as one or more rings or as a helix above a narrow gutter.

Panthercaps appear in summer and autumn, mainly under Beech and deciduous oaks. Beware of confusion with *Amanita excelsa*, which in Britain and Ireland is much more common than *Amanita pantherina*.

Amanita rubescens (Amanitaceae) - Blusher

This brown-capped *Amanita* mushroom is remarkably polygamous in its choice of mycorrhizal partners. In many broadleaf and conifer woods and forests Blushers are the most plentiful of all the *Amanita* species and, being large, very easy to find. The common name reflects the fact that when cut or bruised all parts of this mushroom turn pink. The colour of the caps is extremely variable, ranging from pale yellowish brown through shades of pinkish brown to a rich red-brown.

The largest of the common *Amanita* fungi, Blushers can grow up to 18cm in cap diameter.

Although edible when cooked properly, Blushers contain a haemolytic toxin (destroyed by thorough cooking) and if eaten raw or only partly-cooked they can cause anaemia. So why not abandon the idea of going on a Blusher binge?

Cap: various shades of pinkish brown; usually covered in 'roast goose skin' pinkish-grey veil fragments; convex, flattening; 6 to 15cm (exceptionally 18cm) across.
Gills: white, turning pink if damaged; free; crowded.
Stem: white, flushed with cap colour; 6 to 14cm long, 1 to 2.5cm dia.; pendent, often striate ring; swollen stem base occasionally retaining patches of volva.
Spore print: white.

Distinguished from Panthercaps by their pinkish-grey rather than white cap scales, reddening flesh and furrowed pendent stem rings, Blushers sometimes appear in early June and are most plentiful in July, August and September. In mild weather the occasional specimen can still be found in November even as far north as central Scotland.

***Amanita excelsa* (Amanitaceae) – Grey Spotted Amanita**

Amanita excelsa (syn. *Amanita spissa*) is another very large member of the *Amanita* genus. This very variable mushroom fruits in summer and autumn. It is found most often in spruce woodland and under Beech trees, although it can also form mycorrhizal relationships with other tree genera.

***Amanita excelsa* is particularly common in mature spruce forests.**

Cap: various shades of greyish brown, radially streaked; usually covered in irregular grey veil fragments; convex, flattening; 6 to 14cm (exceptionally 16cm) across.
Gills: white; almost free but with a barely visible decurrent tooth; crowded.
Stem: white; striately lined above ring, scaly pattern below; large ring lined on upper surface; 6 to 12cm long, 1.5 to 2.5cm dia.; swollen stem base rarely retains any volval remains.
Spore print: white.

Often cited as edible, this mushroom is easily confused with the poisonous Panthercap, *Amanita pantherina*, a smaller *Amanita* with pure white cap scales. Why risk it?

***Amanita excelsa*, sometimes referred to as the False Panthercap, is a very variable mushroom, especially in respect of the cap scales, as can be seen in these two immature specimens.**

Amanita crocea (Amanitaceae) – Orange Grisette

Amanita fungi whose stems do not have rings are sometimes referred to as grisettes. Way out front in terms of beauty, many would claim, is *Amanita crocea*. A smallish mushroom by *Amanita* standards, this species has a smooth orange cap and an intricately patterned stem. When seen in bright sunlight a perfect specimen of this fairly common *Amanita* must surely be one of the most wonderful of woodland sightings.

The orange coloration, snakeskin pattern on the stem, and absence of a stem ring are distinguishing features of _Amanita crocea_. It is reputed to be edible.

Mycorrhizal with birch trees and occasionally Beech trees, *Amanita crocea* is also more rarely found under oaks as well as very occasionally in spruce forests.

Cap: yellow-orange; margin radially lined; rarely with veil fragments; convex, flattening with a slight umbo; 5 to 12cm across. (The universal veil often splits into neat pointed sectors that form the volva).
Gills: creamy white; free or adnexed; crowded.
Stem: patterned regularly with scales concolourous with cap; no ring; 10 to 15cm long, 1 to 2cm dia.; swollen stem base; bag-like volva with white exterior and orange interior surfaces.
Spore print: white.

Amanita ceciliae (Amanitaceae) – Snakeskin Grisette

Less common but hardly less glamorous than the Orange Grisette, the Snakeskin Grisette is mycorrhizal with hardwoods and conifers. *Amanita ceciliae* (syn. *Amanita inaurata* and *Amanita strangulata*) is an uncommon find in Britain and Ireland but widespread in most of mainland Europe.

Cap: olivaceous fawn, darkest at the centre, margin much paler; margin with strong radial lines; irregular grey veil fragments mainly in cap centre; convex, eventually flattening; 6 to 12cm across.
Gills: creamy white, greying with age; free, with many short gills; not very crowded.
Stem: pale grey, surface developing snakeskin pattern of scales; no ring; 8 to 17cm long, 1 to 2cm dia.; stem base not swollen; bag-like white volva that soon collapses leaving patches on stem base.
Spore print: white.

Amanita submembranacea (Amanitaceae) – No Common Name

Similar to *Amanita cecilae* but usually retaining a volva, this smallish and fairly dark grisette occurs in association with fir, birch, larch and spruce. *Amanita submembranacea* is a rare find in Britain and Ireland, and it is also rather uncommon in mainland Europe, most often being found in acid areas.

Cap: olivaceous brown; margin marked with strong radial lines; sometimes with irregular grey veil fragments mainly in centre; convex, eventually flattening or even developing a slight central depression; mature caps are 6 to 10cm across.
Gills: creamy white, turning grey or brownish with age; free, with many short gills unevenly distributed; only moderately crowded.
Stem: pale grey, with scales in a regular zig-zag pattern; no ring; 8 to 15cm long, 1 to 2cm dia.; slightly swollen stem base with a thin, leathery (submembranous) white bag-like volva that greys and hardens, its surface looking like flakes of dull grey paint on a canvas background.
Spore print: white.

Amanita fulva (Amanitaceae) – Grisette and _Amanita vaginata_ (Amanitaceae) - Tawny Grisette

There are two other woodland mushrooms, also without stem rings and with furrowed cap margins, that carry the common name 'grisette'. They are both frequent finds in mixed woodlands and sometimes occur in monoculture conifer plantations.

***Amanita fulva*, the Tawny Grisette**

***Amanita vaginata*, the Grisette**

Amanita fulva (recently split into two species, *Amanita fulva* and *Amanita betulae*) is distinguished by its orange-brown volva; *Amanita vaginata* by its grey-brown cap colour. When fully expanded the caps of each of these grisettes rarely exceed 9cm in diameter - slightly smaller than a typical Orange Grisette - and the stems lack the distinctive snakeskin patterning, but in other respects they are similar to *Amanita crocea*.

Grisettes do not generally retain veil fragments on their caps… but as the picture on the right shows there are exceptions to every generalisation!

The term grisette comes from a grey woollen cloth once worn by French working-class women, to whom the name was then applied. *Gris* is a French word meaning grey. Grisettes are grey and fairly drab, but to call a Tawny Grisette (right) dull is an insult too far, surely.

Although they are generally acclaimed as edible mushrooms, the risks of confusing grisetes with other poisonous *Amanita* fungi are such that most experts counsel against gathering them to eat.

Amanita muscaria (Amanitaceae) – Fly Agaric

Now for perhaps the most famous of all mushrooms: *Amanita muscaria*. It comes as quite a surprise to many people when they discover that this is not simply a fantasy confined to children's books but a real live mushroom. Such a distinctive mushroom that once seen is never forgotten, the Fly Agaric is the classic toadstool of fairy tales, the mushroom of more myths than any other, and always such a startling find. *Amanita muscaria* fruits throughout the summer and autumn months, usually under birch trees but occasionally under conifers.

Most common on acid soil under birch and spruce, these notorious hallucinogenic mushrooms can attain a cap diameter of 20cm.

Cap: red, fading to orange; with white velar warts; convex, flattening; 8 to 20cm across.
Gills: white; free; crowded.
Stem: white; often rough with attached veil fragments; fragile floppy white ring; 8 to 18cm long, 1 to 2cm dia.; swollen stem base with volval fragments.
Spore print: white.

Amanita regalis (Amanitaceae) – Brown Fly Agaric

Quite common in Scandinavia, *Amanita regalis* is known as the Brown Fly Agaric. Apart from cap colour it is similar in size and form to the red Fly Agaric. It is also hallucinogenic.

The Brown Fly Agaric appears in summer and autumn under spruce and larch trees.

Young fruitbodies of *Amanita regalis* (left) and *Amanita muscaria* (right). In a fungal beauty contest these two mushrooms would present the judges with a very difficult decision.

Amanita caesarea **(Amanitaceae) – Caesar's Mushroom**

One edible *Amanita* species is highly recommended for its culinary value, but only if an expert has made the identification. Not yet seen in the UK but a possible immigrant as climate change progresses, *Amanita caesarea* is one of the largest of the amanitas, sometimes attaining a cap diameter of 18cm. In southern Europe and especially in the Mediterranean region the 'Mushroom of the Caesars' is collected in great numbers, the most valuable specimens being those picked, volva and all, while still at the 'button stage'.

***Amanita caesarea*. Bright orange cap, paler orange gills and stem plus a large white bag-like volva are clear distinguishing features of this prized edible mushroom.**

Cap: orange; often with irregular veil fragments; convex, flattening; 6 to 18cm across.
Gills: yellow-orange; free; crowded.
Stem: orange; often rough with attached veil fragments; large, pale orange ring; 5 to 12cm long, 1.5 to 2.5cm dia.; stem base with a white bag-like volva.
Spore print: white.

After heavy rain Fly Agarics that have lost their cap spots could be mistaken for *Amanita caesarea*, but a glance at the stem should help to resolve any uncertainty: Fly Agarics in Europe usually have white stems and retain only a vestigial volva at the stem base. The Fly Agaric shown on the right has no veil fragments adhering to its cap, and to add to the risk of confusion it is more orange than is usual; however, the stem is just visible and it is quite obviously pure white rather than the orange colour that is always associated with stems of *Amanita caesarea*.

Boletes - the Pore Relations

The Boletales constitute another important order of fungi most of which form mycorrhizal relationships with trees. The majority of the mushrooms in this group belong to the family Boletaceae, which contains more than 100 European species. They produce spores not on gills but inside tubes suspended from a cap. Sideways on they look like gilled mushrooms, but when you peer beneath the caps you can see tiny pore openings at the ends of the tubes. It is from these openings that the spores are released.

The size, shape and colour of the pores and of the spores that emerge from them are important identifying features of the boletes, whose cap colours are inconsistent and can be misleading.

Not all fungi in this group have tubes and pores. A few, including those in the families Gomphidiaceae and Paxillaceae, produce their spores upon gills similar to those found on agarics such as the *Amanita* fungi, but in other respects they are more closely allied with the pored boletes. Some earthballs and earthstars are now recognised as Boletales.

If you leave aside any boletes with red or pink pores, then all the species found in Britain and Ireland are edible. So is blotting paper, but that's no justification for putting it on the menu at your next dinner party. There are, however, one or two boletes that many fungi gatherers consider to command the heights as far as culinary value is concerned. Right at the pinnacle is a large and fairly common woodland mushroom, *Boletus edulis*.

Boletus edulis **(Boletaceae) – Cep**, or **Penny Bun**

With sometimes wrinkled brown caps, Ceps really do look like the bun-like loaves sold for a penny just after World War II. Bread has increased in price since then, and so have Ceps. In the autumn of 2008 the lowest price I could find fresh Ceps on offer for was £50 per kg. Picking your own is worthwhile!

Boletus edulis has several common English and adopted names including Penny Bun, King Bolete (in the USA), Cep (from the French cèpe) and Porcini (the Italian name for this prized edible mushroom). The specific epithet *edulis* means edible.

Cap: light brown initially, becoming darker and reddish brown, often fading to white at the rim, initially with a pale floury bloom; round at first, gradually becoming broadly convex and sometimes flat; 7 to 30cm across.
Tubes: white, yellowing with age; adnate.
Pores: white or light fawn, eventually turning greenish yellow; little or no colour change when bruised; round; 2 to 3 per mm.
Stem: light brown with a paler net pattern; 8 to 18cm long, 3 to 7cm dia.; barrel shaped.
Spore print: olive brown.

The fully-expanded cap of this Cep (left) is remarkably like the surface of a perfectly-baked homemade bread roll. Older specimens are prone to maggot infestation, and so it is important to cut through both stem and cap before storing or cooking fresh Ceps.

With *Boletus edulis* and several other mushrooms in this genus, the stem and the cap expand horizontally as well as vertically as the fruitbody matures. In the early stages of development the stem is often much broader than the cap.

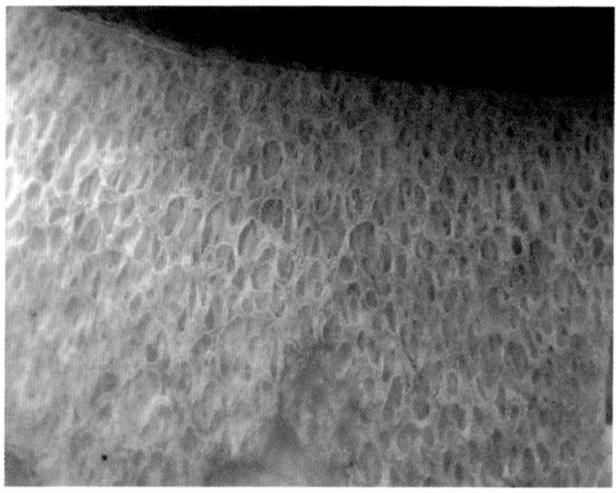

When fully developed the pale grey-brown stem, which as with other *Bolete* species (but not all members of the order Boletales) retains none of the partial veil in the form of a stem ring, is distinctly reticulated. A net pattern (stretch marks that are not visible in the early stages of development) is particularly noticeable on the upper half of the stem. Some of the inedible boletes also carry this feature, and so on its own a reticulate patterning on the stem is not sufficient for unambiguous identification.

When broken or cut, the flesh of many boletes turns blue or blue-grey. Ceps have white flesh that when cut or broken remains white or turns only slightly yellow-brown - never blue. The tubes and pores are also white or yellowish, turning greyer with age.

When you make a spore print of this bolete, the resulting pattern of dots, which mirror the pore spacing of course, is olive brown.

One of the best places to find *Boletus edulis* is beneath mature Beech trees, particularly on chalky soil with plenty of leaf litter. Often these much sought after edible mushrooms can be found with Fly Agarics – the latter being much easier to spot among the brown leaf litter of a woodland floor.

Ceps can also be found in coniferous forests, where they are most likely to be seen at the edges of footpaths and clearings. In wet woodland it's worth paying special attention to areas close to and even on the sloping sides of drainage ditches, where Ceps sometimes emerge from the drier soil.

Tylopilus felleus (Boletaceae) – Bitter Bolete

There are a few closely-related boletes that could be mistaken for Ceps, but with one notable exception they are all good edible fungi. Even that exception – *Tylopilus felleus* (syn. *Boletus felleus*) - is merely a regrettable inconvenience rather than a poisoner. Its taste is very bitter indeed: add one of these to a banquet made with a dozen good ceps and the meal will be ruined.

Despite the net-like reticulate pattern on its stem and its size and colour being similar to a Cep (it even grows in similar habitats) there is no excuse for mistaking the Bitter Bolete for a Cep. *Tylopilus felleus* is easily identified by its pores, which have a coral-pink tinge.

Cap: light brown; downy at first, becoming smooth; broadly convex; 6 to 15cm across.
Tubes: light coral pink; adnate; comprising majority of cap - up to 2cm deep.
Pores: pink, bruising brown; round; 1 to 2 per mm.
Stem: light brown with a darker brown net pattern; 7 to 10cm long, 2 to 3cm dia.
Spore print: pale pink.

The Bitter Bolete, often associated with oaks and Beech, can also occur with conifers.

Imleria badia (Boletaceae) - Bay Bolete

Another easily recognised and very fine edible member of the clan is the Bay Bolete, until recently generally recognised as *Boletus badius* (syn. *Xerocomus badius)*; it is quite a largish and conspicuous bolete with a chunky cap up to 15cm across. Bay in this context is not a reference to the Bay tree *Laurus nobilis* but to the reddish-brown or chestnut colour of the cap of this large bolete, which grows beneath spruce and pine trees and occasionally also under Beech and oaks. It occurs most commonly on acid soil with plenty of leaf litter. Although not as highly prized as a Cep, the Bay Bolete tends to fruit a little later and has one advantage over its more illustrious cousin: insects usually leave it alone for longer, so that fully developed specimens are less likely to be infested with maggots.

Cap: chestnut brown; smooth or slightly wrinkled; broadly convex; 6 to 15cm across.
Tubes: light yellow.
Pores: pale yellow, bruising blue-green; adnate; angular; 2 to 3 per mm.
Stem: light brown streaked with darker fibres, non-reticulate; 7 to 15cm long, 2 to 3cm dia.
Spore print: cinnamon brown.

Note: Bay Boletes are most plentiful in August and September, but in mild winters it is often possible to find good specimens as late as the end of November in southern parts of Britain and Ireland. When under conifers they tend to have darker caps than those found with broadleaf trees.

Xerocomellus chrysenteron (Boletaceae) – Red Cracking Bolete

Many other *Boletus* mushrooms are listed as edible, but most are no more than mediocre in flavour. Among these, abundant but often insubstantial and rather prone to maggot infestation, is *Xerocomellus chrysenteron*, whose fruitbodies often have dark reddish-brown caps when young and so might easily be mistaken for Bay Boletes. With thin flesh that blues slightly when cut or bruised, the caps of mature specimens often expand until flat, by which stage cracks in the dry surface reveal a thin layer of red flesh beneath the pellicle (the cap skin); from this feature comes the common name.

Most plentiful in summer and autumn, Red Cracking Boletes are sometimes seen in spring; however, as soon as the flail mowers have made their final summer pass along country hedgerows, and the rank vegetation has been shaved to ground level, up spring swarms of these boletes. The caps are well camouflaged against a background of oak and Beech twigs and other plant debris, but the red stems are a giveaway. Red Cracking Boletes are mycorrhizal with a wide range of broadleaf trees.

Cap: dingy sepia brown becoming paler; velvety then later smooth, surface cracking irregularly when old to reveal reddish cap flesh; broadly convex; 6 to 15cm across.
Tubes: yellow; adnate; up to 1cm deep.
Pores: pale yellow, sometimes bruising greenish; large, angular, 5 to 10 per cm.
Stem: lemon yellow, the lower part covered in red fibres. More or less constant cross section throughout length, often oval and sometimes appearing to be two stems fused together; 4 to 8cm long, 1 to 1.5cm dia.
Spore print: olivaceous tobacco-brown.

A similar species, *Xerocomellus cisalpinus* (right), also cracks but rarely displays pink sub-cuticle flesh, and its pores blue more rapidly than those of *Xerocomellus chrysenteron*. These and some other very similar boletes formerly grouped as *Boletus chrysenteron* can only be separated with certainty by a combination of cross-section images of the stems and microscopic examination of spores.

Another bolete of deciduous woodland that is easily mistaken for a young Red Cracking Bolete is *Xerocomellus pruinatus*, the Matt Bolete (pictured on the left). The felted texture of the surface of the caps is a constant feature, while young specimens have caps covered in a hoary bloom that is lost as the cap expands and the fruitbody ages. The yellow stem is finely patterned with red dots, most noticeably on the central and lower parts of the stem.

Neoboletus luridiformis (Boletaceae) – Scarletina Bolete

The stems of *Xerocomellus chrysenteron* could hardly be more different in texture from those of another edible bolete, *Neoboletus luridiformis*, known until recently as *Boletus luridiformis* (Syn. *Boletus erythropus*). Commonly referred to as the Scarletina Bolete but formerly more often referred to as the Dotted-stem Bolete, this mushroom will cause poisoning if not thoroughly cooked. It's worth noting that, despite the attractive appearance of the fresh fruitbody, the flesh turns black when it is cooked. Again, because of the mediocre flavour as well as its relative scarcity, this large woodland mushroom receives very little attention from collectors. It's a wonderful find, however, and very variable in size and shape – some with dumpy bulbous stems; others tall and straight of stem. The determining factor appears to be habitat.

Mycorrhizal but not host specific, *Neoboletus luridiformis* appears in summer and autumn in deciduous woods and conifer forests. Occasionally this colourful mushroom is found among bilberry bushes (*Vaccinium* species) on shrubby pastureland and moorland..

Cap: dull bay or snuff brown, often tinged with olive, paler brown or yellow at the margin; finely velvety at first, becoming smooth and matt; slightly greasy in wet weather; broadly convex; 8 to 20cm across.
Tubes: lemon yellow becoming greenish when old; rapidly turning dark blue when cut; free; up to 2cm deep.
Pores: orange-red fading to yellow at the cap margin, rapidly turning dark blue when bruised; small, round; 1 to 3 per mm.
Stem: yellow background densely covered in tiny red dots that are usually densest in the middle section of the stem, with more yellow visible near apex and base. A hand lens may be necessary to see the individual red dots on the stem, which distinguish it from some other reddish boletes that have net-like patterns similar to that on the stems of Ceps (but red instead of pale brown). 7 to 15cm long, 2 to 3cm dia,; more or less cylindrical or swollen slightly towards the base. (The old specific name *erythropus* means red footed, a reference to the stem colour.)
Spore print: olive brown.

Although the spores of _Neoboletus luridiformis_ are olive brown, the pores from which they emerge are orange initially, becoming bright red and then turning more of a rusty brown as the fruitbody ages.

If you cut through the stem of a Scarletina Bolete the yellow flesh instantly turns blue; however, the same occurs with many other boletes, and so on its own this is not a foolproof means of identification.

One very good reason for not eating *Neoboletus luridiformis* is the risk of confusing it with other red-stemmed boletes that *are* either suspect or known to be poisonous. Found in one of the main habitats where the Scarletina Bolete also occurs – various kinds of broadleaf woodland including oaks, Beech and limes, particularly in chalk-rich areas - *Suillellus luridus*, the Lurid Bolete, is known to be able to cause upsets. The colour-change test doesn't help a lot either, because the flesh of *Suillellus luridus* also blues rapidly when cut or bruised, and so close and thorough inspection is the only way to avoid misidentification.

Suillellus luridus **(Boletaceae) – Lurid Bolete**

Although said to be edible when cooked thoroughly, when raw or not properly cooked this bolete, known until recently as *Boletus luridus*, is certainly poisonous: it causes nausea and vomiting. The Lurid Bolete is an occasional find in broadleaf woodland, most often under oaks or Beech. Although most common in chalk and limestone areas, this is one of the few red-pored boletes that also occurs in regions with acid soil. Young caps (left) are downy and pale yellow, but as the mushrooms mature the caps turn dull olive-brown, sometimes with a pinkish tinge.

Cap: yellowish at first, turning olive-brown as the fruitbody matures; surface gradually losing its down and becoming smooth and matt; bruising blue-black; broadly convex, not flattening completely; 8 to 15cm (exceptionally 20cm) across.
Tubes: yellowish green, rapidly turning blue when cut or broken; free; up to 1cm deep.
Pores:; orange red but more yellow near the cap margin (the pores nearest to the stem are sometimes bright red in mature specimens), turning dark blue when bruised but then fading to light blue after a few minutes; 2 to 4 per mm.
Stem: background yellow, tinged orange near the apex; covered in an orange-red net; slightly swollen towards the base of the stem; 8 to 14cm long, 1 to 3cm dia.
Spore print: olivaceous.

It is very difficult to handle Lurid Boletes without leaving blue fingerprints on the mushroom and blue stains on your hands.

Rubroboletus satanas (Boletaceae) – Devil's Bolete

The name Devil's Bolete says a lot about what is reputed to be the most poisonous bolete found in Britain and Ireland. Red-pored species are uncommon but *Devil's Bolete,* known until recently as *Boletus satanas,* is particularly rare. Mycorrhizal with Beech and oak trees, in Britain this distinctive pale-capped mushroom is largely confined to a few areas with chalky soil in southern England, and it is certainly uncommon in those countries of mainland Europe where it occurs.

The Devil's Bolete also undergoes a colour change when it is cut or broken, but instead of rapidly turning blue-green or inky blue, as do most of the common red-pored boletes, the cap and stem flesh turns very gradually sky blue. Although reputed to be toxic, this is not one of the most dangerous mushrooms. Eating it is reported to cause vomiting and diarrhoea soon after its consumption, but evidence of fatalities is at best scant.

Cap: chalky white and velvety at first, eventually darkening with an olivaceous or reddish tinge as the cap expands irregularly, creating a wavy margin; surface losing its down and becoming smoother as the fruitbody matures; bruising brownish; broadly convex, not flattening; 8 to 30cm across.
Tubes: yellowish green when young becoming more olivaceous when old; turning mid blue when cut or broken; up to 2cm deep.
Pores: blood red (orange near margin) turning greenish when bruised; 2 to 5 per mm.
Stem: background lemon yellow near the apex and more orange below; covered in a fine red net; rotund, sometimes with the swelling concentrated near the base of the stem; 7 to 12cm long, 6 to 10cm dia.
Spore print: olivaceous.

Leccinum scabrum (Boletaceae) – Brown Birch Bolete

The genus *Leccinum* is another distinctive group within the Boletales. *Leccinum* species do not have stem rings but they are distinguished by the presence of scabers, small scale-like projections on the surfaces of their stems. All are mycorrhizal, forming relationships with hardwood trees and in particular with birch, oak and poplar. At least one species also occurs on heaths. Although there has long been a presumption that these are all edible fungi, some are now known to cause sickness particularly if inadequately cooked. Most of the *Leccinum* boletes are rare or at best infrequent finds, but a couple of species that are mycorrhizal with birch trees are very common. On acid soils the Brown Birch Bolete *Leccinum scabrum* is very common; *Leccinum cyaneobasileucum* , whose stem base bruises blue, is found more often in alkaline areas.

Cap: varying from reddish brown through mid brown to almost grey; smooth and matt, but sticky in wet weather; convex; 5 to 15cm across.
Tubes: white, turning ochre when old; adnate to free; up to 2cm deep.
Pores: white, turning light ochre with age or when bruised; round; 1 to 2 per mm.
Stem: White or pale grey with dark-brown scabers; 7 to 20cm long, 2 to 3cm dia. When cut the flesh in the stem base is pinkish (not blueing).
Spore print: brown.

Leccinum versipelle (Boletaceae) – Orange Birch Bolete

Similar in size to the Brown Birch Bolete, *Leccinum versipelle* has acquired the unsurprising common name of Orange Birch Bolete. Mycorrhizal with birches and with heather, this mushroom is characterised by a cap margin that overhangs the pore layer and white flesh that, when cut, turns blue-green at the stem base and dark purple throughout the rest of the stem and the cap.

Cap: orange; downy becoming smooth and matt with age; convex; 8 to 20cm across.
Tubes: white, turning ochre when old; adnate; up to 2cm deep.
Pores: white, turning buff with age and vinaceous if bruised; round; 1 to 2 per mm.
Stem: White or pale grey with woolly black scabers; 7 to 20cm long, 1.5 to 4cm dia.
Spore print: brown.

Sticky, Slimy Suillus Species

Whereas boletes in the *Leccinum* genus have dry caps and no stem rings, *Suillus* species are greasy or slimy and, at least initially, the pores are covered by a partial veil that usually leaves a distinct stem ring. All are mycorrhizal with conifers. The generic name *Suillus* comes from *sus*, the Latin for pig. Had it been realised when naming these fungi how important boletes are to Red Squirrels in cold climates, perhaps a squirrel rather than a pig would have been chosen as the generic name source. It is well known that squirrels eat fungi, but research carried out in the 1980s in Finland demonstrated that in the forests there not only do red squirrels pick and eat fungi (mainly boletes under conifers, where *Leccinum* and *Suillus* mushrooms are often the most abundant species) but they also store them in the forks of trees; there the mushrooms dry out and provide a vital source of winter food when the ground is snow covered or frozen making scavenging impossible.

The Red Squirrel shown here was photographed as it foraged for fungi beneath conifers and birches in Killarney National Park, Ireland. The most abundant fungi in the vicinity were the Brown Birch Bolete and the Larch Bolete together with several brittlegills (*Russula* species).

Suillus luteus (Boletaceae) – Slippery Jack

One of the most common *Suillus* species, known as Slippery Jack (a name that is applied to several closely-related slimy-capped boletes from the genus *Suillus*), has a brown cap that is extremely slimy during wet weather and tends to become lined and wrinkled if it dries out. This easily recognised bolete is ectomycorrhizal with pines and occasionally with other conifers. Perhaps its most distinctive visible feature is the prominent stem ring. In the specimens shown on the right (photographed during a dry spell) fragments of the partial veil cling to the cap rim; others form a stem ring.

The type species of its genus, although not highly prized, *Suillus luteus* can be cooked and eaten once the cap is peeled. (The viscid nature of the cap surface is rather more evident in the example on the left.)

Cap: chestnut brown, covered in slimy gluten; convex, often oval; 5 to 12cm across.
Tubes: lemon or straw yellow, not changing when cut; up to 10mm deep.
Pores: lemon or straw yellow, not changing when bruised; round; 2 to 3 per mm.
Stem: straw yellow, discolouring ochre; pendent white ring; 5 to 10cm long, 2 to 3cm dia.
Spore print: clay brown.

Suillus granulatus (Boletaceae) – Weeping Bolete

As early as May another very common *Suillus* species appears – also mostly under pine trees. *Suillus granulatus*, sometimes referred to as the Granulated Bolete (because the top of its stem is dotted with sugar-like granules), often occurs in groups.

The Weeping Bolete has a paler cap than Slippery Jack and is usually taller in the stem but smaller in cap diameter; it is an edible species, easy to collect in quantity and hence very popular in fungiphilic countries. The milky droplets (pictured on the next page) that form on the pore surface are responsible for its common name, Weeping Bolete.

In Britain and in Ireland the Weeping Bolete is most common and widespread in the south and east, while in Wales, western Ireland and Scotland it is found less frequently.

Cap: yellowish brown, slightly viscid when wet, shiny when dry; convex; often oval or irregularly lobed; 3 to 9cm across.
Tubes: buff to pale lemon yellow, not changing when cut; up to 8mm deep.
Pores: lemon or straw yellow, not changing when bruised; round; 1 to 3 per mm, largest near the stem.
Stem: lemon yellow, dotted with small white granules near cap; flushed pink or vinaceous towards base; no ring; 3 to 8cm long, 0.7 to 1.2cm dia.
Spore print: ochraceous sienna.

Suillus grevillei (Boletaceae) – Larch Bolete

Pine trees don't have it all their own way as far as *Suillus* species are concerned, and one such bolete, *Suillus grevillei*, is specifically mycorrhizal with larch trees. Larches are deciduous and, unlike spruce trees which block out most of the direct sunlight all through the year, grass often grows well in larch plantations, making mushrooms more difficult to find.

Fortunately the shiny caps of Larch Boletes are hard to miss. They are light brown at first, often turning much yellower as they expand. The stem ring, created when the partial veil parts from the cap margin, is clearly visible.

Cap: light brown, especially when young, but often becoming bright chrome yellow at maturity; viscid when wet, silky-matt or shiny when dry; convex; 4 to 10cm across.
Tubes: pale yellow; up to 6mm deep.
Pores: lemon yellow, turning ochre when stained by spores; bruising brownish; angular; 1 to 3 per mm.
Stem: yellow above the white ring, while below the ring cinnamon coloured, often in the form of dots but sometimes in a fine net-like pattern; base often slightly bulbous; superior (stretching upwards) ring; 4 to 8cm long, 0.7 to 1.2cm dia.
Spore print: ochre to sienna.
Odour: slight, crushed Pelargonium leaves.

Like the Slippery Jack, this bolete can be eaten once the slimy cuticle has been removed from the cap. It must be thoroughly cooked, but even then most people find it rather a disappointing mushroom.

Suillus bovinus **(Boletaceae) – Bovine Bolete**

Almost as common as the former two *Suillus* species but more restricted in its distribution is a very neat little edible mushroom, *Suillus bovinus*, the Bovine Bolete - sometimes referred to as the Jersey Cow Bolete (a reference to the cap colour, of course).

Often irregularly shaped, Bovine Boletes have attractive pink-tinged clay-coloured caps; they are found invariably under pine trees, with which they are mycorrhizal.

Cap: pinkish brown or ochraceous clay, paler at margin; viscid when wet, silky-matt when dry; convex; 3 to 10cm across.
Tubes: grey vinaceous; slightly decurrent (left); up to 5mm deep.
Pores: clay brown; angular, irregular; 5 to 10 per cm.
Stem: pale sienna; no ring; occasionally bulbous but more often of constant diameter; 4 to 6cm long, 5 to 9mm dia.
Spore print: clay brown tinged with olive.

Strobilomyces strobilaceus **(Boletaceae) – Old Man of the Woods**

Before leaving the boletes there is one other species so unusual that it deserves special mention even though it is quite rare and, for reasons that will be immediately obvious, rather difficult to spot even when you are standing right next to it. *Strobilomyces strobilaceous* (syn. *Strobilomyces floccopus*) is unique in its genus in Britain and Ireland. The pale (when young) cap is covered with large black shaggy scales that overhang the cap margin and are the reason behind its common name Old Man of the Woods.

Strobilomyces strobilaceus is not only a very rare bolete; it is also brilliantly camouflaged among the leaf litter in broadleaf woods or, occasionally, in conifer forests. The best chance of seeing these remarkable fungi is when the fruitbodies are young, since the whole mushroom becomes much darker with age (pictured overleaf) and becomes a lot harder to spot.

Cap: white or smoky grey background, darkening with age, scattered with large, ragged dark-brown scales some of which overhang the margin; the white flesh turns pink then brown if cut or broken; convex; 5 to 12cm across.
Tubes: white or pale grey, turning pinkish and then brown when cut; up to 10mm deep.
Pores: white or pale grey, turning pinkish and then brown when bruised; angular; irregularly spaced; larger near to the stem; adnate; 4 to 12 percm.
Stem: colour as cap but darker at base; covered in scales similar to those on cap; small greyish ring, often incomplete; 8 to 12cm long, 1 to 2cm dia.
Spore print: very dark brown or black with a violaceous tinge.

Please don't pick these rare mushrooms.

***Paxillus involutus* (Paxillaceae) – Brown Rollrim**
Now known to be deadly poisonous, *Paxillus involutus*, the Brown Rollrim, is a very common gilled mushroom. The Paxillaceae family of inedible mushrooms, which includes several that are known to be poisonous, belongs to the order Boletales. The Brown Rollrim was for many years considered edible, but it is now known to be a deadly poisoner. Sometimes it can be eaten frequently over a period of months or even years with no apparent ill effects, and then suddenly the victim is taken very ill, sometimes fatally.

Brown Rollrims are mycorrhizal with broadleaf trees and with conifers. They are very variable in shape and cap colour, depending on habitat and probably also the mycorrhizal partner with which they are associated.

Cap: cream to dark brown; initially downy, especially near the rim, becoming smooth; convex, developing a central depression with age; 5 to 12cm across.
Gills: ochre, turning brown when bruised; crowded; some fork near stem; decurrent.
Stem: colour as cap; fibrous; slightly clavate; no ring; 1 to 8cm long, 0.8 to 1.2cm dia.
Spore print: sienna.

Gomphidius roseus **(Gomphidiaceae) – Rosy Spike**

A Swedish-led research team published results in 2000 supporting the belief that *Gomphidius* and *Chroogomphus* species contribute to three-way relationships involving the mycorrhizae formed by *Suillus* boletes and conifers. *Gomphidius roseus* occurs with pines where *Suillus bovinus* appears (although both species don't always fruit at the same time.)

The spike caps, as *Gomphidius* fungi are sometimes called, probably give nothing either to the tree or to its *Suillus* partner, and their involvement in the mycorrhizal *ménage à trois* is now considered likely to be a parasitic one.

Cap: red, vinaceous in centre, paler at margin; convex, often with an umbo; viscid; 3 to 5cm across.
Gills: white, becoming olivaceous grey when mature; deeply decurrent.
Stem: white, tinged with red towards base; indistinct ring zone left by partial veil; 8 to 12cm long, 1 to 2cm dia.
Spore print: very dark brown or black with a vinaceous tinge.

Although it is not known to be toxic, eating this little mushroom is generally not recommended.

Chroogomphus rutilus (Gomphidiaceae) – Copper Spike

In Britain and Ireland the most commonly encountered of the spike cap mushrooms is *Chroogomphus rutilus*. Seen on a sunny day this is a most striking mushroom. Found most often beside paths, on the edges of woodland clearings, and in parks and gardens, the Copper Spike appears to be parasitically associated with the mycorrhizas that the Weeping Bolete *Suillus granulatus* forms with pines trees.

Cap: coppery-brown with a satin sheen; convex, often with an umbo; 3 to 12cm across.
Gills: buff becoming coppery when mature; deeply decurrent.
Stem: colour as cap but more yellow towards base; covered in red-brown velar remains (inset picture); fairly even but narrowing abruptly at apex; 5 to 12cm long, 0.4 to 1cm dia.
Spore print: very dark brown or almost black with a purple tinge.

Gomphidius glutinosus (Gomphidiaceae) – Slimy Spike

Much more slimy and with a greyish-fawn to purplish-brown cap, this gilled bolete is very rare in Britain and Ireland but more common in Scandinavia. It is similar in dimensions and form to the Copper Spike, *Chroogomphus rutilus*, and its spore print is also dark brown or nearly black with a purple tinge.

Within the Boletales, the spike caps are more closely related to *Suillus* than to *Boletus*, which may partly explain their preference for pine trees. The Slimy Spike has been found under pines where the only other boletes fruiting at the time were *Suillus grevillei*.

Russulas, the Dazzling but Difficult Brittlegills

To convince a sceptic of the beauty of woodland fungi, all you need do is take them to a site where there are plenty of brittlegills. The cap colours range from white through yellow, orange, red, brown, purple, green and black, and often there are regions of several colour on a single specimen. Note the use of that word often... it implies *not always*. That's the big problem with mushrooms from the *Russula* genus: with few exceptions colour is of only limited help in identification, and with some species it's almost no help at all.

***Russula rosea*, the Rosy Brittlegill**

Brittlegills belong to the order Russulales and within that group to the family Russulaceae along with *Lactarius* fungi, commonly known as milkcaps because when damaged their gills release droplets of milky latex. All brittlegills and milkcaps are ectomycorrhizal with trees or shrubs. *Russula* and *Lactarius* species are different from most other mushrooms because rather than consisting of tube-like cells they contain spherical cells called sphaerocysts, making their texture less pliable and more fragile than other mushrooms.

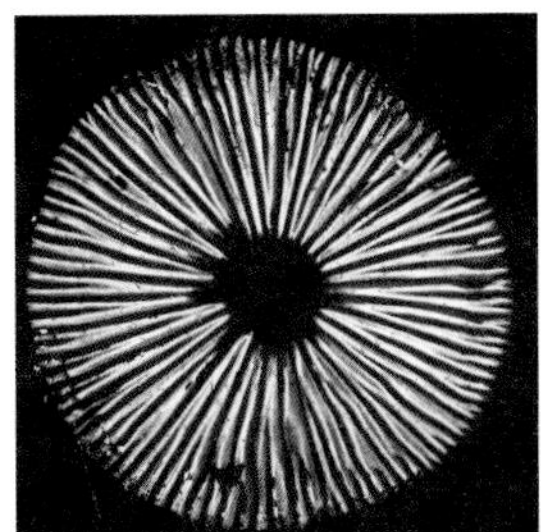

The name '*Russula'* means red, a dominant colour of many species. The spore prints are usually white or shades of cream or light ochre – and so using black card is helpful. Initially nearly all brittlegills have convex caps, sometimes flattening out or becoming concave at maturity. They have white or yellowish gills that are usually attached to the stem (which has neither ring nor volva) rather than free as, for example, they are in the *Amanita* fungi described earlier. With few exceptions the gills are brittle and snap off if you try to bend them, and only rarely are there intermediate gills.

With many features either common to all brittlegills or varying only slightly between species, plus the variability in cap colour between individuals of the same species, identification is a nightmare for beginners and a continuing challenge even for experts. Size is a poor discriminator with most fungi, and the brittlegills are no exception. The majority of brittlegills found in Britain and Ireland are accommodated within the cap diameter range 4 to 10cm when fully developed with just one or two unusually small or exceptionally large, when size does help to eliminate some of the possibilities.

The taste of a small piece broken from a brittlegill is a useful in-the-field clue to identification. (It's a good idea not to swallow any of these samples when taste testing, as some *Russula* fungi cause sickness.) While some species have a mild taste, others are instantly hot on the tongue, and one or two are deceptively mild at first and then leave an intense burning sensation on the tongue. In a few instances the gill material tastes a lot hotter than the stem flesh; and at least two common brittlegills have such a distinctive smell that once you get to know them you could recognise one even if you were blindfolded. Writers of field guides have the unenviable task of trying to describe these odours. We may find the flesh of some brittlegills inedible because they taste bitter or extremely hot; or, as with *Russula emetica* (as if the specific epithet isn't warning enough, its common name of the Sickener further underlines the threat) because they are poisonous to humans and cause serious stomach upsets. Other creatures are not so easily deterred. It can be very difficult to find perfect specimens of some kinds of brittlegills because they are such popular snacks for many woodland creatures.

Mice, slugs, bugs and other small creatures are not alone in feeding on brittlegills; many larger animals, including deer, are partial to them, and as they forage for fungi their trampling feet can do almost as much damage as our own!

Because brittlegills are mycorrhizal, they appear only under or near to trees – but as the finest of tree roots can extend up to 100 metres from the trunk of a large tree, in anything but a tree monoculture it is very difficult to determine with certainty which of several nearby tree species a particular mushroom is attached to. And to make matters worse, not all brittlegills are specifically mycorrhizal to one tree genus, although there are some that invariably stick either with pines or with Beech, for example, and all good field guides provide this kind of information.

To be confident of the identification of many of the brittlegills found in Britain and Ireland, the sad reality is that chemical tests - and in many instances also microscopic examination - are necessary. Whether you go down this track or not, you will find that this genus of neat, colourful woodland mushrooms contains some stunningly beautiful fungi.

If all the difficulties in identifying brittlegills sound like a charter for despair, fear not: several of the most common and widespread species can, with a little care, be identified in the field with a high degree of confidence provided you work through each of the identifying characters in the description. Once you have seen and identified several examples of a particular species in various stages of development and under different conditions (particularly in prolonged wet weather and after a dry spell) quite a few of the brittlegills can be identified with confidence at a glance.

Russula ochroleuca (Russulaceae) – Ochre Brittlegill

One of the most abundant and widespread of the brittlegills, *Russula ochroleuca* can be found in all kinds of woodland throughout summer and autumn.

For many years this mushroom was known as the Common Yellow Russula; its more recent common name refers to (somewhat variable) cap colour and the brittle nature of the gills.

Cap: ochre-yellow, sometimes with a green tinge; initially convex, then flat or slightly depressed; margin becomes striate; cuticle peels 70% to centre; 4 to 12cm across.
Gills: white or cream. Greying slightly with age; narrow and brittle; adnexed or adnate.
Stem: white, greying; tapering towards apex; 4 to 8cm long, 1.5 to 2.5cm dia.
Taste: not a very useful test, as some specimens are mild and others peppery hot.
Spore print: pale cream.

Although Ochre Brittlegills can sometimes be found in damp woodlands, they are far more common and plentiful in dry forests and woods. Well shaded banks on woodland edges are sometimes peppered with these long-lasting fruitbodies. Although considered edible, there are not highly valued and fought over by mushroom gatherers.

Russula claroflava **(Russulaceae) – Yellow Swamp Brittlegill**
Similar in size to the Ochre Brittlegill but associated with birch trees in wet grassy or mossy places, the Yellow Swamp Brittlegill can appear in late spring and summer but is most common in the autumn. This is generally considered to be a good edible mushroom.

Cap: shiny and chrome yellow when young, becoming ochre tinged; cuticle peels halfway to the centre; initially convex, then depressed; extreme margin becomes striate; 4 to 10cm across.
Gills: pale ochre, darkening with age; brittle; adnexed or free; fairly crowded.
Stem: white, greying; tapering in towards base ; 2 to 6cm long, 2 to 4cm dia.
Taste: mild.
Spores: cream with an ochre tinge.

Russula farinipes (Russulaceae) **– No Common Name**
A less common find than other yellowish brittlegills, and most often on calcareous soil in broadleaf woodland, this beautiful mushroom is quite distinctive. Oaks, Beech and birches are common mycorrhizal partners with this species.

The specific epithet refers to the surface of the stem, the upper section of which is covered in a flour-like powder. The cap and stem flesh is also distinctive, being much tougher and more elastic than is normal for a brittlegill.

Cap: rufous yellow, becoming russet brown with age; margin sulcate (furrowed); convex, sometimes developing a central depression; grainy, esp. at margin; cuticle peels very little; 3 to 6cm across.
Gills: pale straw yellow; quite distant; arching upwards; slightly decurrent.
Stem: white or very pale straw yellow; powdery towards apex; with cavities; 3 to 7cm long, 1 to 1.8cm dia.
Taste: very acrid (inedible).
Odour: slightly fruity.
Spore print: white.

Russula fellea (Russulaceae) – Geranium Brittlegill

Very common in Beech woodland in Britain and Ireland, but on mainland Europe also quite frequent in spruce plantations on acid soil, this honey-coloured brittlegill smells like stewed apples (although some insist that the scent is more reminiscent of geraniums – hence the common name).

Cap: usually honey yellow but sometimes tawny-buff or orange towards cap centre; smooth; convex, soon developing a central depression; margin not lined or with only very short lines; cuticle peels 30% to the centre; 4 to 9cm across.
Gills: paler than cap, turning buff with age; moderately crowded; adnate.
Stem: colour as cap or slightly paler; sometimes slightly clavate; 4 to 6cm long, 1 to 2cm dia.
Taste: very hot and bitter (inedible).
Odour: of geraniums or of stewed apple. **Spore print**: pale pinkish cream.

Many other brittlegills occur sometimes in yellow forms, but the distinctive odour of the Geranium Brittlegill makes it one of the few that can be identified with a high degree of certainty in the field.

Russula delica (Russulaceae) – Milk White Brittlegill

A large and truly ground-breaking brittlegill, *Russula delica* pushes up through compacted soil in mixed woodland. It is one of the largest of the brittlegills found in Britain and Ireland.

There are at least two milkcap species with which this mushroom could easily be confused, but to check all that you need to do is simply score across the gills: unlike the milkcaps (but like all other *Russula* species), *Russula delica* releases no latex.

Cap: creamy, matt; often tipped to one side; soon developing a deep central depression and discolouring brownish; does not peel to any significant extent; 10 to 18cm across.
Gills: white, darkening with age; decurrent; crowded.
Stem: white, greying; 4 to 10cm long, 1 to 2cm dia.
Spore print: white.
Taste: bitter and hot.
Odour: sometimes has a slight fishy smell.

Russula chloroides is almost identical but has a narrow blue-green zone at the stem apex.

A pair of stinkers

Two smelly ochre-capped brittlegills that occur quite frequently in both coniferous and broadleaf woodlands are almost impossible to separate on characteristics visible in the field, but they can be distinguished easily by an odour test. *Russula foetens* (right) has an oily, rancid smell, whereas *Russula grata* smells strongly of bitter almonds or marzipan. *Russula foetens* caps are up to 14cm across; those of *R. grata* rarely exceed 9cm. *Russula foetens*, the Stinking Brittlecap, produces cream spores from cream-coloured gills often spattered with brown spots; so does its slightly smaller lookalike *Russula grata*.

Russula nigricans **(Russulaceae) – Blackening Brittlegill**

Initially the Blackening Brittlegill has a white cap and a white stem, but it soon develops reddish-brown patches before turning entirely black. The distant gills are very distinctive.

Cap: dingy white, turning brown and then black; flesh reddens then blackens if cut; finely felty; convex, then depressed; margin inrolled until old; 5 to 20cm across.
Gills: white or cream, blackening as cap; adnate; very widely spaced; extremely brittle.
Stem: white or cream, blackening as cap; often tapering towards base; 4 to 7cm long, 2 to 4cm dia.
Taste: mild.
Odour: slight, fruity.
Spore print: white.

Unless eaten by slugs or parasitic fungi, the jet-black remains of these brittlecaps can persist through the winter and into the following spring.

Russula densifolia **(Russulaceae) – Crowded Brittlegill**

Another persistent, blackening brittlegill found in all kinds of woodland (it is mycorrhizal with broadleaf trees and with conifers), the Crowded Brittlegill also turns red-brown before blackening. Unlike the Blackening Russula, the cap of the Crowded Brittlegill is smooth rather than felty.

Cap: white or cream, blackening; peeling half-way to centre; cut flesh reddens then blackens; smooth convex, then depressed; margin not inrolled; 6 to 12cm across.

Gills: white, blackening as cap; adnate; crowded; interspersed with short gills near cap margin.
Stem: cream, gradually blackening as cap; 4 to 7cm long, 1.5 to 3cm dia.
Spore print: white.

Note: *Russula anthracina* is very similar to *Russula densifolia* but its cap does not peel, and when cut the flesh turns black without first reddening.

***Russula nobilis* (Russulaceae) – Beechwood Sickener**
Having started by saying how beautiful most mushrooms of the *Russula* genus are, it's surely time now to move on to some of the more colourful species. How about red?

Russula nobilis, (syn. *Russula mairei*) is one of the few brittlegills that cause sickness if eaten. The caps are usually a gorgeous red, although occasionally you may find a much paler pink form or even an entirely white specimen. As the common name suggests, this brittlegill is associated with trees of the *Fagus* genus.

Cap: red or pink, sometimes with white areas; occasionally pure white; peels 30% to centre; flesh is pink beneath cuticle; smooth; convex, becoming flat or with the margin uplifted with age; 3 to 9cm across.
Gills: white, turning pale cream; adnexed; crowded.
Stem: white; cylindrical, base sometimes clavate; 2.5 to 5cm long, 1.0 to 1.5cm dia.
Taste: very hot.
Spore print: white.

***Russula emetica* (Russulaceae) – Sickener**
Another 'red for danger' brittlegill very similar in appearance to the Beechwood Sickener, this very common and widespread species is found mainly beneath conifers (pines and spruces in particular) and occasionally also on heathland. When cut it has a distinctive fruity smell.

Cap: scarlet, fading in wet weather; peels almost to centre; flesh is pink beneath cuticle; smooth convex, becoming depressed; margin striate; 3 to 10cm across.
Gills: white turning pale cream; adnexed or free; crowded.
Stem: white; cylindrical, base slightly clavate; 4 to 9cm long, 0.7 to 2cm dia.
Spore print: very pale cream.
Odour: fruity.
Taste: very hot and peppery.

Note: The species epithet *emetica* needs no explanation. As long as you spit out a sample of any of the red brittlegills, taste testing will not result in sickness. When such a test proves that you have found one of the hot species, however, not only will you have eliminated numerous identification possibilities but you may have disabled a lot of your taste buds, making other more subtle tastes undetectable for quite some time.

Russula paludosa (Russulaceae) - Hintapink

Despite being easily mistaken for the poisonous Sickener and growing in the same habitat – coniferous woodland – *Russula paludosa* is a popular edible mushroom in Scandinavia, where it is very common in spruce plantations.

In Britain this is an occasional find in the uplands of Scotland, while reports of it being sighted in England, Wales or Ireland are very few and far between.

Cap: red, purplish bay brown or ochre; occasionally with pale patches; peels 50% to centre; flesh is pink beneath cuticle; hemispherical then convex, becoming flat with a central depression; margin becoming striate; 5 to 15cm across.
Gills: cream, turning light ochre; adnexed; crowded.
Stem: white, often with just a hint of pink (hence the common name); cylindrical, occasionally swollen in centre or with a slightly clavate base; 4 to 15cm long, 1 to 3cm dia.
Spore print: deep cream.

There are many other brittlegills with reddish or pinkish caps, and several whose caps are red sometimes but not always. Visually, several other changelings in the *Russula* genus can be just as puzzling, but the odour when mature (not decaying) specimens are cut or broken in the field can be a help in sorting many of them out. Good field guides therefore include Odour and Taste characters of those species where they are distinctive.

Russula aurea (Russulaceae) – Gilded Brittlegill

A rather uncommon brittlegill of deciduous woodland, *Russula aurea* (syn. *Russula aurata*) is an attractive but also - and this is a notorious *Russula* trait - very variable mushroom. It forms mycorrhizal relationships with various oaks, and with Beech and Hazel. Neither taste nor smell are distinctive, but the striking cap colouration is often an indicative feature; when it is not, chemical tests and microscopic examination are necessary for a confident identification.

Cap: patchy mixture of red, orange and yellow – occasionally all yellow; peels 50% to centre; hemispherical then convex, with a central depression; margin sometimes becoming striate at maturity; 5 to 10cm across.
Gills: cream, turning ochre with bright yellow edges; adnexed or free; crowded.
Stem: white or pale yellow; cylindrical, occasionally with a slightly clavate base; 3 to 8cm long, 1 to 2.5cm dia.
Spore print: ochre.

If reddish brittlegills are a challenge, then purple ones are even more difficult, and newcomers to the identification process are advised to admire them and then look for something a bit easier. That said, one or two of the common ones are quite distinctive.

Russula atropurpurea (Russulaceae) – Purple Brittlegill

The blackish-purple centre and wine-red margin of this very common brittlegill can hardly be described as distinguishing features on their own, because so many other *Russula* species have purplish caps that are darker in the centre and paler near the rim; however, taken with other macroscopic characters the (remarkably consistent for a brittlegill) cap colouration is a good starting point for making an identification.

Cap: purple or wine red shading to almost black in the centre, sometimes with yellow mottling near rim; peels 50% to centre; hemispherical then convex, becoming flat with a shallow central depression; shiny; sticky when wet; 4 to 10cm across.
Gills: pale cream, turning ochre; adnexed; crowded.
Stem: white; cylindrical, occasionally swollen in centre or with a slightly clavate base; 3 to 6cm long, 1 to 2cm dia.
Odour: slight, of apples.
Spore print: whitish.

Russula xerampelina (Russulaceae) – Crab Brittlegill

Whereas being colour blind creates problems for a few people (mostly men), our lack of an agreed odour dictionary is a problem for us all. Most people agree on the odour of this very common and widespread woodland mushroom, however: young specimens smell slightly fishy, while older ones stink of boiled shellfish.

The Crab Brittlegill occurs mainly with deciduous hardwood trees and in particular under Beech. It is sometimes seen also in coniferous forests.

If you fancy trying a chemical test, rub iron sulphate ($FeSO_4$) on to the cut flesh: it very quickly turns dark green. Most common brittlegills turn salmon pink initially (but if you wait long enough some turn pink and then change to green much later).

Cap: various shades of reddish purple, wine, cinnamon, brown or ochre, often in blotches, usually darker towards centre; peels 25% to centre; irregularly convex, developing a shallow central depression; margin eventually striate; 7 to 15cm across.
Gills: cream, turning ochre; adnexed; crowded.
Stem: white flushed with red, discolouring brown when bruised; cylindrical, occasionally with a slightly clavate base; 4 to 10cm long, 1 to 3cm dia.
Odour: cooked crab.
Spore print: deep cream.

Rarely infested with maggots, Crab Brittlegills are considered to be among the best of the edible brittlegills. Be prepared for a kitchen smelling of fish if you cook them indoors!

Russula caerulea (Russulaceae) – Humpback Brittlegill

This is one of the very few purplish brittlegills which can usually be identified in the field without resorting to chemical tests. Its umbonate (humpbacked) brownish-purple cap is quite distinctive. The specific epithet *caerulea* suggests that this mushroom is deep blue, but purple is usually its dominant colour component.

This distinctive brittlegill is mycorrhizal with conifer trees and is a fairly common find in pine plantations.

Cap: 4 to 8cm across; various shades of glossy purplish brown or vinaceous brown; convex, with a low central umbo; peeling typically 50 to 70% to the centre.
Gills: cream, becoming ochre with age.
Stem: 3.5 to 6cm tall and 0.7 to 1.4cm dia; white.
Odour: not distinctive
Taste: cap cuticle tastes bitter, but the taste of the flesh of the cap, gills and stem is mild.
Spore print: Dark yellow.

Russula parazurea (Russulaceae) – Powdery Brittlegill

A powdery bloom and overall greyish appearance distinguish the caps of young Powdery Brittlegills. Some have a blue-grey tinge, while others show hints of purple, but something about this brittlegill usually betrays its identity even at a distance.

The Powdery Brittlegill is mycorrhizal with broadleaf trees and common under oaks.

Cap: Grey and matt with a (often uniform) blue, blue-green or occasionally purple tinge and, when young and fresh, with a powdery bloom that eventually washes off; older caps flatten out and may become slightly depressed, and the margins often become striate and sometimes slightly toothed. Caps are rarely perfectly round but more often irregularly oval, 4 to 9cm across the major diameter. The cap flesh is white, and the cuticle (surface skin) peels between 50 and 70% towards the centre.

Gills: Pale cream, turning light ochre; adnexed; crowded.
Stem: white, often with rusty spots mainly towards the base; cylindrical or slightly tapering towards the base; 3.5 to 7cm long and 0.8 to 2cm diameter. The stem flesh is pale brownish pink.
Odour and taste: mild and pleasant but not distinctive.
Spore print: cream.

Russula cyanoxantha (Russulaceae) – Charcoal Burner

Colour, odour and taste can all be key factors in identifying members of the *Russula* genus, but with the Charcoal Burner texture is the thing to check. It is a brittlegill whose gills are not brittle: they bend quite a long way without snapping off.

The name Charcoal Burner is a reference to the remarkable range of colours seen in a single cap of this edible mushroom; similar colours can be seen in the flames coming from burning charcoal.

Cap: usually a mixture of various shades of grey, purple, lilac, wine, olive and green; peels 50% to centre; convex, flattening with a shallow central depression; greasy when moist; margin ribbed with branching veins; 7 to 15cm across.
Gills: white or pale cream, turning ochre; adnexed or slightly decurrent; narrow; flexible, unlike most *Russula* fungi whose gills are brittle. Often (again unusually for a *Russula* species) some of the gills are forked.
Stem: white, sometimes flushed with purple or red; cylindrical, sometimes tapering in at base; 5 to 10cm long, 1.5 to 3cm dia.
Spore print: white.

Look out for these chunky brittlegills in broadleaf woodland, where they are particularly common under Beech trees.

Russula aeruginea (Russulaceae) – Green Brittlegill

Few fungi have green caps, and among the brittlegills there are just two common ones; their identification is therefore not usually a problem. The Green Brittlegill has a grass-green cap, sometimes with yellowish tints but never vinaceous. Knowing that makes life a bit easier for those of us who find the many red, purple and pink brittlecaps confusing!

Cap: grass green, paler towards margin; peels 50% to centre; convex, flattening only in the centre, sometimes with a slight depression; greasy when moist; margin sometimes faintly grooved; 4 to 9cm across.
Gills: white, turning yellow with age; adnexed; crowded.
Stem: white, sometimes flushed with purple or red; cylindrical, sometimes tapering at base; 4 to 8cm long, 0.7 to 2cm dia.
Spore print: cream.

Also commonly referred to as the Grass-green Russula, this inedible mushroom is often found on the edges of pine forests but always under birches.

Russula virescens (Russulaceae) – Greencracked Brittlegill

Less common, slightly larger, but otherwise similar to the Green Brittlegill and sharing the same habitat, this species is distinguished by a dry, velvety cap surface that breaks up into a 'crazy-paving' pattern. The spore print is darker than that of the Green Brittlegill.

Cap: grass green, paler towards margin; peels 50% to centre; convex, flattening only in the centre, sometimes with a slight depression; greasy when moist; margin sometimes faintly grooved; 4 to 9cm across.
Gills: creamy white, turning more yellow with age; adnexed; crowded.
Stem: white or cream, browning with age; cylindrical, sometimes slightly fusiform, or tapering at base; 4 to 8cm long, 1.5 to 4cm dia.
Spore print: cream.

So much depends on the weather...

Before leaving the *Russula* genus it may be helpful to add a few words about how weather affects the appearance, disappearance or non appearance of these mycorrhizal woodland mushrooms.

Dawn Brittlegills. In the hot sun the gill edges of even the immature specimen on the left are wrinkling at the edges as the cap pellicle becomes dry and shrinks slightly.

Brittlegills seem to love warm summer weather followed by early autumn rains, whereupon they produce lots of fruitbodies that can push up through the soil without damage or distortion of their caps. Finding perfect specimens at such times ought to be easy... but that's also just the kind of weather that brings out hordes of hungry slugs. In contrast during hot dry spells, especially where the soil is heavy or has become compacted, caps sometimes split under the pressure of breaking through the soil surface; those that do emerge without damage are often covered in sand, soil or debris, and it's not long before the cap pellicles wrinkle and shrink, distorting the gills into wonderfully wavy shapes.

Primrose Brittlegills have purple-flushed stems and primrose gills that turn golden yellow with age. One of the many woodland creatures partial to brittlegill mushrooms has been nibbling at the cap of this one.

The Dawn Brittlegill *Russula aurora* appears under deciduous broadleaf trees; its cap edge distorts in dry weather. Like most brittlegills of damp conifer forests the Primrose Brittlegill *Russula sardonia* is a magnet for slugs. These are just two of the reasons why finding perfect brittlegills is never likely to be easy.

Meet the Milkcaps

Lactarius is a large genus, with over 400 known species worldwide. The genus was originally described by the South-African born botanist Christian Hendrik Persoon at the end of the eighteenth century. (When you see the abbreviation Pers. after a botanical or mycological name, Persoon is being cited as the author.) *Lactarius* is derived from the Latin word *lac*, meaning milk.

All mushrooms in the genus *Lactarius* lack stem rings. Most have slightly decurrent gills, and nearly all of them exude white or coloured latex (commonly referred to as 'milk' – hence the name 'milkcaps') from cut or broken flesh. The initial colour of the latex and any colour change as it dries are important identification features for this large group of mushrooms many of which are of similar size, shape and colour.

As with their relatives the brittlegills, all milkcaps are mycorrhizal. The Coconut Milkcap *Lactarius glyciosmus* is an EM associate of birch trees.

Fortunately, several of the most common milkcaps are easy to identify in the field, although microscopic examination of spores and chemical testing of cap or stem material may be necessary if you want to be certain of the identification of some of the more difficult ones. All are EM fungi, but only a few are specific to one tree genus.

Most milkcaps become funnel shaped as they mature. Unlike their close relatives the brittlegills, which have smooth caps most of which are slightly greasy when wet, milkcaps vary greatly in their surface texture. This, too, is feature that helps with identification. Some are woolly, a few are fleecy and others have smooth cap surfaces, either dull and matt or shiny and greasy.

Features that help make some of the milkcaps identifiable without recourse to chemical tests or microscopic examination of spores include:

- the presence or absence of furrows on the cap margins
- circular colour zones on the cap surface
- whether the cap surface is matt, greasy or velvety
- whether the rim is overhung with shaggy or woolly hair-like fibres
- whether the cap or stem surface has oval pits (strobicules)

As with brittlegills, the caps of *Lactarius* species contain a high density of sphaerocysts, rounded cells that make the flesh brittle; however, the gills of most milkcaps contain few sphaerocysts and so they are nowhere near as brittle as the gills of most *Russula* species.

***Lactarius torminosus* (Russulaceae) – Woolly Milkcap**
Let's start with one of the most beautiful and easily identified milkcaps, *Lactarius torminosus*, which appears in summer and autumn, often in small groups beside footpaths in wet woodland. It is most often mycorrhizal with birch trees.

Cap: buff, pale pink and salmon often in faint concentric zones; shaggy, inrolled margin; convex, later depressed and occasionally quite deeply funnelled; 6 to 15cm across.
Gills: cream or pink; crowded; adnate or slightly to moderately decurrent.
Latex: sparse, thick, white; tasting hot and peppery.
Stem: cream flushed salmon pink; cylindrical; 4 to 8cm tall; 1 to 2cm dia.
Spore print: creamy yellow.
Odour: slight, pungent like turpentine.

***Lactarius pubescens* (Russulaceae) – Bearded Milkcap**
The woolly milk-cap is not alone in having a fluffy margin. *Lactarius pubescens* is smaller, paler and slightly less hirsute than the woolly milk-cap. It, too, is associated with birch trees, but generally in drier, often sandy habitats.

Cap: creamy white with a pale salmon pink blush; faint concentric zoning; slightly shaggy, inrolled margin; convex, becoming depressed; 4 to 10cm across.
Gills: white or pale salmon pink; crowded; slightly decurrent.
Latex: creamy white, sparse; tasting immediately hot and acrid.
Stem: cream flushed salmon pink; cylindrical; 3 to 6cm tall; 1 to 2cm dia.
Spore print: creamy yellow.
Odour: of crushed pelargonium leaves.

There are still conflicting views about which of the milkcaps are good edible species. Some of the hot, peppery ones are unpopular simply because people find the taste unpleasant. There is no doubt about these rather uncommon but visually very attractive mushrooms: they are known to cause stomach upsets even when thoroughly cooked, and so they should definitely be considered as poisonous fungi.

***Lactifluus* (formerly *Lactarius*) *vellereus* (Russulaceae) – Fleecy Milkcap**
A cap surface that is velvety rather than woolly has earned this, the largest of the milkcaps commonly found in Britain and Ireland, its common name. Fleecy Milkcaps are found most often with broadleaf trees, but they are also fairly common in spruce plantations.

Cap: white, velvety; convex, developing a deep central depression; greasy when moist; margin sometimes faintly grooved; 12 to 30cm across.
Gills: pale cream, turning creamy ochre with age; brittle; decurrent; moderately crowded.
Latex: white, abundant, mild or only slightly bitter tasting.

Stem: white; slightly velvety; cylindrical, tapering towards the base; 4 to 7cm long, 2 to 4cm dia.
Spore print: white.

Although on its own the latex from this milkcap tastes quite mild, when it is tasted with the flesh of the mushroom it is very hot and peppery. For this reason the Fleecy Milkcap is generally considered to be inedible. (Bugs and slugs disagree with this point of view: you will come across plenty of their luncheon leftovers!)

***Lactifluus piperatus* (syn. *Lactiarius piperatus*) (Russulaceae) – Peppery Milkcap**

Somewhat smaller in cap diameter and yet often with a much taller stem than the Fleecy Milkcap but otherwise visually quite similar, the Peppery Milkcap also has a matt cap surface. Its white milk quickly turns creamy, and after a few moments delay it tastes extremely hot and acrid. Fortunately, there is no real need to suffer the discomfort of a taste test: a glance beneath the cap at the extremely crowded gills of the Peppery Milkcap immediately distinguish it from the Fleecy Milkcap.

Cap: creamy white; matt; convex, developing a central depression; 6 to 16cm across.
Gills: pale cream, turning creamy ochre with age; rather more brittle than is usual for a milkcap; decurrent; thin and very densely crowded.
Latex: white, sparse; mild. (NB the flesh taste gradually becomes hot and peppery.)
Stem: white; slightly velvety; cylindrical, tapering towards the base; 6 to 10cm long, 2 to 3cm dia.; no ring.
Spore print: white.

Another much less common large white milkcap, *Lactarius controversus*, is mycorrhizal with willows and occasionally poplars. This hot-tasting mushroom has no generally-accepted common name. In stature it is similar to the Peppery Milkcap (but with less crowded gills) with a cap up to 15cm across. A good place to look for these milkcaps is in coastal dune slacks, where they usually occur in scattered groups with Dwarf Willow.

***Lactarius deliciosus* (Russulaceae) – Saffron Milkcap**

Continuing with the larger milkcaps, two orange species whose individual fruitbodies vary rather a lot in appearance are not always easy to tell apart. The first of these, fairly common in acidic parts of Britain and Ireland, is the Saffron Milkcap, which is mycorrhizal with pine trees. As its specific epithet implies, this is a highly-prized edible mushroom, but its similarity to less delectable and even doubtful species poses a problem. In mixed spruce and pine woodland it is possible to find Saffron Milkcaps and their lookalikes side by side. Rings of dark orange strobicules (inset picture, overleaf) on the cap of the Saffron Milkcap are accompanied by similar indents running down the stem (inset picture, overleaf). Stems of its common lookalikes are generally smooth.

Cap: bright orange; convex, developing a slight central depression; matt surface pitted with carrot-coloured strobicules in circular zones; 6 to 15cm across.
Gills: orange; slightly decurrent; narrow, crowded.
Latex: carrot-coloured; sparse; mild tasting.
Stem: (inset) orange, with carrot-coloured strobicules as cap; pale yellow flesh turns orange (after about 40 minutes) when cut, cylindrical; 3 to 6cm long, 2 to 3cm dia.
Spore print: pale ochre.

Lactarius deterrimus (Russulaceae) – False Saffron Milkcap

Superficially similar to Saffron Milkcaps - hence the recently acquired common name False Saffron Milkcap - *Lactarius deterrimus* is nearly always associated with spruce trees, although very occasionally it grows with pines. It is also known as the Spruce Milkcap. The caps and stems of this mushroom can turn greenish (inset picture, below) as they age, and broad depressions invariably form in the centres of the caps.

Cap: dull buffish salmon pink or dull orange, not strongly zoned; convex, developing a broad central depression; flesh turns slowly wine-red (after about 20 minutes) when cut; 6 to 14cm across.
Gills: orange-buff; adnate or slightly decurrent; crowded.
Latex: reddish orange; sparse; bitter tasting.
Stem: colour as cap with pale collar at top; smooth, rarely pitted; cylindrical; 3 to 6cm long, 2 to 3cm dia.
Spore print: white.

Lactarius camphoratus (Russulaceae) – Curry Milkcap

Fancy a curry? If you dry out caps of this mushroom they give off a strong odour reminiscent of curry – the reason for common name for this pine-forest fungus. (Very occasionally this little milkcap is also found in broadleaf woodland.) In some European countries its dried fruitbodies are crushed and used for flavouring soups and sauces. The Curry-scented Milkcap usually occurs in groups rather than singly.

Cap: red-brown, darker towards centre; convex, developing a central depression usually with a slight umbo; surface smooth and matt; margin slightly furrowed; 3 to 6cm across.
Gills: ochre, turning red-brown with age; adnate or slightly decurrent; crowded.
Latex: watery; abundant; mild.
Stem: colour as cap margin, darker towards base; cylindrical; 3 to 10cm long, 4 to 8mm dia.
Spore print: cream.

Rather disconcerting to some of us is the much-quoted assurance that fresh Curry Milkcaps smell like bed bugs or like boiling laundry – not odours everyone experiences nowadays. If you are not an expert on bed bugs, you may detect a weak 'chemical' odour, a bit like liquorice or perhaps moth balls; this ambiguity underlines the difficulty of describing odours. Nevertheless, as there are many small brownish milkcaps, taste and smell can be useful identifying factors. Noting the habitat is often just as important.

Lactarius quietus (Russulaceae) – Oakbug Milkcap

Although small and with ground-hugging brown caps that blend in with a background of dead oak leaves, once you have spotted one of them Oakbug Milkcaps are hard to miss because they usually occur in such great numbers. It is unusual among milkcaps in having a stem colour darker than its cap. This edible mushroom is specific to oak trees, and for many years it was simply referred to as the Oak Milkcap.

Cap: dull cinnamon-brown with indistinct darker concentric bands or spots; matt; convex, developing a shallow central depression; 3 to 8cm across.
Gills: ochre, turning red-brown with age; adnate or slightly decurrent; crowded.
Latex: white, drying cream; abundant; mild or slightly bitter.
Stem: colour similar to cap but usually somewhat darker; cylindrical; 4 to 9cm long, 1 to 1.5cm dia.
Spore print: cream, tinged salmon-pink.

Lactarius chrysorrheus (Russulaceae) – Yellowdrop Milkcap

This small milkcap is mycorrhizal almost exclusively with one genus of trees, and again it is *Quercus* (oaks). The cap blends in well with a background of dry leaves, but its white milk dries bright sulphur yellow on any damaged gills, and these spots of colour are the tell-tale signs to look for, especially on sunny days.

Cap: salmon pink with rings of darker watery blotches or bands; convex, becoming shallowly funnel-shaped; 3 to 8cm across.
Gills: orange-buff; adnate or slightly decurrent; crowded.
Latex: initially white, quickly turning sulphur yellow when exposed to air; tasting mild then rapidly becoming bitter and hot.
Stem: cream or buff, pinker towards base; cylindrical with a slightly swollen base; 3 to 8cm long, 0.9 to 2cm dia.
Spore print: creamy white with a salmon pink tinge.

Note: In some field guides the specific epithet is spelt *chrysorheus* (with just one 'r').

Despite its attractive appearance, the Yellowdrop Milkcap is known to be poisonous, even when cooked thoroughly. This is a great pity because it is a widespread species and, in oak woodland on acid soils, it usually fruits in vast numbers.

***Lactarius blennius* (Russulaceae) – Beech Milkcap**

Not all milk-caps are attractive; some have drab or even leaden colours. Among the most common and uninspiring of these is *Lactarius blennius*, a rather slimy milkcap found mainly, as the common name declares, under Beech trees.

Cap: drab greenish-grey or olive-grey with rings of darker watery blotches; convex, developing a slight central depression; 4 to 9cm across.
Gills: white, gradually becoming cream, turning grey-buff when cut, adnate or slightly decurrent; crowded.
Latex: white, drying grey; abundant; tasting bitter and hot.
Stem: pale grey; cylindrical or tapering slightly towards base; 3 to 7cm long, 0.9 to 2cm dia.; no ring.
Spore print: cream.

For those who feel the urge to gather milkcaps to eat, this is a species that is not only widespread and abundant but also reportedly edible, if mediocre, when cooked thoroughly.

The Good, the Bad, and the Ugly

Having mentioned that some milkcaps are good to eat and others bad, it should come as no surprise that one of them is known as the Ugly Milkcap. It is sometimes big, usually common, and always inedible.

***Lactarius turpis* (Russulaceae) – Ugly Milkcap**

Although this is a decidedly dull olive-brown mushroom, it is helped just a little by the fact that it is mycorrhizal with birch trees in wet woodland, so that when you come across these inconspicuous fungi they do make an effort by glistening whenever the sun shines. Even so they can be difficult to spot until you ‘get your eye in’.

Cap: dark olive-brown with a paler margin; slimy when wet; convex, centre becoming depressed; 7 to 18cm across.
Gills: cream to pale buff, becoming sepia tinged when bruised (inset picture, right); decurrent; narrow and crowded.
Latex: white, drying olivaceous; abundant; hot, acrid tasting.
Stem: colour as cap or lighter; cylindrical tapering near base; 4 to 7cm long, 1 to 2.5cm dia.; no ring.
Spore print: cream with a slight salmon-pink tinge.

In some northern European countries there was a tradition of boiling these milkcaps and then using them to spice up other mushroom dishes; however, there is now some worrying evidence that the Ugly Milkcap may be carcinogenic, and so it should most certainly be considered as poisonous.

Lactarius subdulcis (Russulaceae) – Mild Milkcap

Another of the small milkcaps commonly found in broadleaf woods, *Lactarius subdulcis* is most often associated with Beech trees. This is a difficult milkcap to identify with certainty because is has so many lookalikes. Caps of *Lactarius subdulcis* store abundant, sweet-tasting white milk.

Cap: variable from reddish-brown to dark cinnamon with a paler buff margin; convex, centre becoming depressed with a small umbo; 3 to 7cm across.
Gills: white maturing to a pinkish buff; adnate or slightly decurrent; moderately crowded.
Latex: white, unchanging; abundant; taste initially mild, becoming slightly bitter.
Stem: slightly paler than cap but much lighter at apex; cylindrical, base slightly clavate; 4 to 7cm long, 0.6 to 1.3cm dia.; no ring.
Spore print: cream with a slight salmon-pink tinge.

Not all milkcaps are dull and boring…

It is true that most milkcaps are generally drab compared with many of their more showy relatives the brittlegills. Before leaving the *Lactarius* genus here is a large and flamboyant species whose brilliance, particularly in wet weather, rivals any woodland mushroom.

Lactarius rufus (Russulaceae) – Rufous Milkcap

Like so many of the red-brown and tawny milk-caps, the colours of the Rufous Milkcap vary with location, weather and age. These very common milkcaps are mycorrhizal with conifers; they are also known to form EM associations with birches in acid heathland. Young caps have inrolled margins and slight central bumps, features which are usually retained (picture, below) as the caps mature and develop a central depression.

Cap: brick-red to orange-brown, margin paler; matt or slightly velvety; convex then flat or funnel shaped with a slight umbo; 4 to 12cm across.
Gills: yellowish becoming red-brown; adnate or slightly decurrent.
Latex: white; tasting mild, then (after a minute or two) very hot.
Stem: colour as cap, but much paler at apex and base; cylindrical; 4 to 8cm long, 0.6 to 2cm dia.; no ring.
Spore print: creamy white with a slight salmon-pink tinge.

The Tricky Tricholomas

Although many fungi once included in the genus *Tricholoma* have since been moved to other genera within the huge family Tricholomataceae – *Lepista nuda*, the Wood Blewit, and *Calocybe gambosa*, St George's Mushroom are two examples – those remaining (more than 50 in Britain and Ireland) still constitute quite a sizeable group. Commonly referred to as 'knights' these woodland fungi have chunky fruitbodies with fleshy stems to which their gills are attached either adnately or sinuately (with a notch near to the stem), and they all produce white or nearly white spores. All *Tricholoma* fungi known to occur in Britain and Ireland are ectomycorrhizal, some specifically with pines or other conifers and others with various broadleaf trees. There are also a few mycorrhizal fungi within other genera in the family Tricholomataceae, and a selection of the more common and conspicuous of these is included at the end of this section.

A few *Tricholoma* species are quite distinctive, either because of their size, colours and growing habits or because they have unique and strong odours; quite exceptionally for this genus, one or two species have stem rings. Unfortunately many more are various shades of grey or brown and frustratingly difficult to differentiate without resorting to chemical tests and microscopic examination, and so for anyone with a passion for wild mushroom dishes, tricholomas pose a problem. Some, such as *Tricholoma equestre* are known to be poisonous, but edible species including *Tricholoma terreum* are easily confused with other grey inedible or poisonous species. Anyone who is not an expert would be taking a big risk in gathering any of these kinds of fungi for food.

Tricholoma sulphureum (Tricholomataceae) – Sulphur Knight

You might have thought that the terrible smell of *Tricholoma sulphureum (*syn. *Tricholoma bufonium)*, which has secured for it the delightful alternative common name of Gasworks Mushroom, would be enough to put anyone off frying it for their supper. Unfortunately not so; however, since this bright yellow mushroom is *known* rather than merely suspected to be poisonous, the inference is that someone, perhaps suffering from a very bad cold at the time, must have made a meal of it. Surprisingly, despite its extremely pungent odour, this mushroom does not have a distinctive taste.

Cap: sulphur yellow, often with reddish-brown or olive tints; convex, usually with a wavy margin, sometimes flattening or becoming slightly depressed, but retaining an umbo; matt; 3 to 8cm across.
Gills: bright sulphur yellow; broad; distant; sinuate.
Stem: yellow, lined vertically with reddish fibres; cylindrical; 3 to 5cm long, 0.6 to 1cm dia.; no ring.
Spore print: pure white - despite what you might expect from the colour of the gills!
Odour: very strong, of coal gas.

This distinctive mushroom is found under deciduous trees - mainly oaks and Beech - and just occasionally in coniferous woodland. Although the main fruiting season is late summer and autumn, Sulphur Knights appear as early as the end of springtime.

Tricholoma equestre (Tricholomataceae) – Yellow Knight

Despite a visual similarity to the Sulphur Knight, this chunky mushroom is distinguished by its smell: there is none. *Tricholoma equestre* (syn. *Tricholoma flavovirens*) is sometimes referred to as the Man on Horseback, but why that should be seems to have become lost in the mists of time. Fairly common in northern Scotland, where it is most often mycorrhizal with Scots Pine in sandy areas but also occasionally with birches and with oaks, this late season mushroom is rarely seen either in southern Britain or in Ireland.

Cap: bright yellow, with a fibrous or scaly olive-brown central area; convex, often with a wavy margin and a slight central umbo; 5 to 9cm across.
Gills: bright yellow; adnexed.
Stem: pale yellow; lined vertically with brown fibres; cylindrical; 5 to 10cm long, 0.8 to 1.5cm dia.; no ring.
Spore print: white.
Odour: none - a feature that clearly distinguishes it from the visually very similar Sulphur Knight.

Several cases of severe poisoning have been confirmed as being the result of eating, over a period of several days, meals each containing moderate portions of these mushrooms.

Tricholoma fulvum (Tricholomataceae) – Birch Knight

Another large and very distinctive mushroom that is mycorrhizal with birch and sometimes spruce is *Tricholoma fulvum* (syn. *Tricholoma flavobrunneum*), the Birch Knight. This very common mushroom, which is considered edible but of rather poor quality, is mycorrhizal with birch trees. Often it occurs in large numbers on wet woodland edges, but also keep an eye open for these atypical knights where birches have sprung up as pioneer trees on the disturbed boggy land beside low-lying forestry tracks.

Cap: reddish-brown centre, margin yellow with radial brown streaks; convex, flattening with a small umbo; matt and finely fibrillose; sticky when wet; 5 to 12cm across.
Gills: yellowish buff, developing brown spots with age (pictured on the right); sinuate; crowded.
Stem: yellow-brown, paler at apex; fibrous; cylindrical; 5 to 10cm long, 0.8 to 1.4cm dia.; no ring.
Spore print: white.
Odour: slight, farinaceous.

Most of the fungi in the genus *Tricholoma* fruit quite late in the season, but the Birch Knight appears early – from late June onwards. It is arguably the most distinctive member of this tricky group of mushrooms.

Tricholoma saponaceum (Tricholomataceae) – Soapy Knight

Few tricholomas have truly descriptive common names, but the Soapy Knight, *Tricholoma saponaceum*, thoroughly deserves the one it has been given. Not only is this a rather greasy-capped mushroom but it also smells like unperfumed soap.

Cap: very variable - yellow, olive and green tints, darker towards the cap centre, are most common; convex, flattening with a wavy margin and a broad umbo; margin splitting with age; greasy when moist, silky when dry; 5 to 10cm across.
Gills: pale cream tinged with green or olive; thick; fairly distant; sinuate.
Stem: white, tinted red or olive; cylindrical; 5 to 10cm long, 0.6 to 1.2cm dia.; no ring.
Spore print: white.

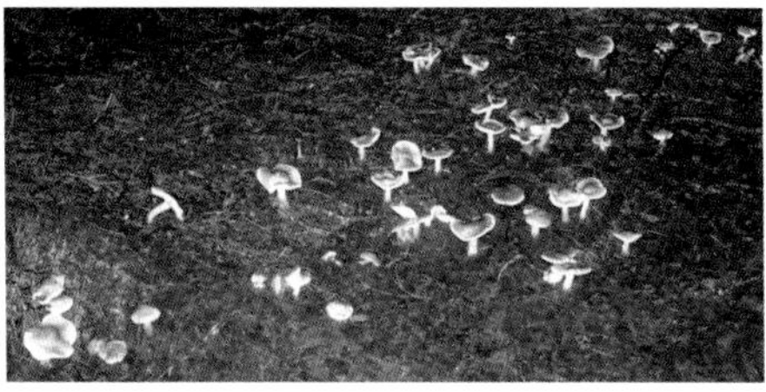

The Soapy Knight is fairly common in dark conifer forests, and it also occurs in some deciduous broadleaf woods. Often these gregarious knights gather in great crowds (right). Unfortunately, not only is this abundant mushroom regarded as inedible but it may even be poisonous. In any case, who would want to eat soap?

Tricholoma album (Tricholomataceae) – White Knight

Although not always a pure white knight (and never in shining armour), this is a very pale mushroom and therefore easy to find against the dark background of a forest floor… unless it has been snowing. (White Knights can appear as late as November and December) . This substantial mushroom can be found in both broadleaf and coniferous woodland. In Britain and Ireland it is rather a rare find, but in Scandinavia it is common in the spruce forests that dominate the landscape.

Cap: initially conical with an inrolled margin, later convex or flattened with small umbo; white or with a pale yellow tinge, ochre-yellow towards the centre when mature; smooth; 4 to 10cm across.
Gills: white or pale yellow; with coarsely toothed edges; of uneven lengths and quite distant; sinuate (notched very close to the stem).
Stem: white to yellow-brown often with fine fibrils near base; cylindrical; 3 to 6cm long, 0.8 to 1.5cm dia.; no ring.
Spore print: white.

Note: *Tricholoma stiparophyllum* is very similar in macroscopic characteristics.

Tricholoma columbetta **(Tricholomataceae) – Blue Spot Knight**

Another white knight, *Tricholoma columbetta*, is very common in Britain and Ireland. This beautiful (are reportedly edible) mushroom is often pure white with a silky umbonate cap much the same size as those of *Tricholoma album*; however, its gills are attached to the stem without the significant notches that are characteristic of *Tricholoma album*. The Blue Spot Knight is mycorrhizal with broadleaf trees rather than with conifers.

Cap: pure white, becoming cream when old, sometimes with a bluish flush or blue spots on cap (and on stem base); convex, flattening with a slightly wavy margin; smooth; greasy when wet; 5 to 10cm across.
Gills: white; crowded; sinuate.
Stem: white, sometimes with a blue-green area at base; cylindrical; 4 to 10cm long, 1 to 2cm dia.; no ring.
Spore print: white.

Tricholoma virgatum **(Tricholomataceae) – Ashen Knight**

One of the more common of the many greyish *Tricholoma* species, the Ashen Knight is an easy-to-miss mushroom. It is mycorrhizal mainly with conifers on acid soil, where it usually occurs in small groups. The gills are very light grey at first, darkening gradually as the fruitbody matures.

Cap: grey, often with a hint of violet, and with darker radial fibrils or very fine scales; conical then bell-shaped, sometimes flattening with a broad umbo with a conical pip at the centre; margin slightly incurved; dry and silky; 4 to 9cm across.
Gills: pale grey, darkening with age; crowded; sinuate.
Stem: white or pale grey; smooth, cylindrical or slightly clavate; 4 to 10cm long, 1 to 1.8cm dia.; no ring.
Spore print: white.
Odour: of radish.
Taste: hot and peppery.

Tricholoma terreum **(Tricholomataceae) – Grey Knight**

Of the many similar knights with which the Ashen Knight could be confused, *Tricholoma terreum* is the one most commonly encountered in Britain and Ireland. It is mycorrhizal with conifers, mainly pines – a helpful habitat clue to its identification. The common name Grey Knight is not a reference to the cap colour (that would be unhelpful, as so many other tricholomas have grey caps) but rather to the dull grey colour of the gills. Although edible and lauded by some, this is a risky mushroom for anyone but an expert.

Cap: light grey to dark grey, sometimes slightly tinged with brown; convex with a broad umbo; felty, becoming finely scaly; 4 to 7cm across.
Gills: pale grey; free or sharply sinuate at stem; distant.
Stem: white or pale grey; silky smooth; cylindrical; 3 to 8cm long, 1 to 1.5cm dia.; no ring.
Spore print: white.

Tricholoma focale (Tricholomataceae) – Booted Knight

Tricholoma focale is quite distinctive, with its orange-brown colouring and cottony collapsing stem ring. It is also quite a large mushroom albeit not found throughout most of Britain and Ireland. One of its strongholds is in Scotland's Caledonian Forest.

Cap: orange-brown to reddish-brown, cracking as it ages; convex, developing a flat top, margin inrolled; 7 to 12cm across.
Gills: white, browning on gill edges with age; adnexed to free; moderately distant.
Stem: white and smooth above shaggy ring, patterned with bands of large brown scales below; tapering continuously towards base; 4 to 8cm long, 2 to 4cm dia.
Spore print: white.

Calocybe gambosa (Tricholomataceae) – St George's Mushroom

Worldwide more than 200 *Tricholoma* species have been described, but their relationships to other white-spored fungi may not be as close as was once considered the case. Within the family Tricholomataceae currently reside the saprophytic funnels, *Clitocybe* spp., and the blewits, *Lepista* spp., as well as a fine edible spring mushroom, *Calocybe gambosa* (syn. *Tricholoma gambosum*) commonly known as St George's Mushroom. (St George's Day is 23rd April, by which time this mushroom can often be found.)

Cap: white, tinged with brown when old; irregularly convex; 5 to 15cm across.
Gills: white; sinuate; very crowded.
Stem: white; often swollen at base; 2 to 4cm long, 1 to 2.5cm dia.; no ring.
Spore print: white.
Odour: farinaceous.

The art of deception

Among the most variable of woodland fungi, and mycorrhizal with a wide range of coniferous and broadleaf trees, is a group of small mushrooms commonly referred to as 'deceivers'. The name is fully justified. Although sometimes found singly, *Laccaria* fungi often provide splendid group displays. The deceivers have long been included in the Tricholomataceae, but based on DNA sequencing some authorities now place them in the Hydnangiaceae. In any event, they are ectomycorrhizal fungi and will be discussed next.

Laccaria laccata (Hydnangiaceae) – Deceiver

Although *Laccaria laccata* is easily recognised as a member of the *Laccaria* genus, others in that group (for example *Laccaria proxima*) look so similar that the only way to be sure is to resort to a microscope. However, in most areas *Laccaria laccata* is by far the most common of the half a dozen 'deceivers' found in the British Isles, and so if the caps fits...

Cap: hygrophanous, orange-brown when wet, drying to pinkish beige and eventually pale buff; slightly scurfy; convex, flattening often with a slight central depression; 2 to 5cm across.
Gills: flesh pink to pinkish brown, drying almost white; distant, often crinkly; adnate or slightly decurrent.
Stem: colour as cap but streaked with pale fibrils; cylindrical or slightly flattened, often twisted; tough, fibrous; 6 to 10cm long, 0.6 to 1cm dia.; no ring.
Spore print: white.

Laccaria amethystina (Hydnangiaceae) – Amethyst Deceiver

In size, shape and habitat preference the Amethyst Deceiver is identical to the Deceiver, with which it often occurs (left) - indeed in the fairly recent past these were treated as one and the same species. Usually the deep purple colouration of *Laccaria amethystina* (syn. *L. amethystea*) is enough to identify it, but its common name comes from an ability to shake off its coloured overcoat during hot weather and turn buff.

Cap: hygrophanous, deep amethyst when wet, drying to lilac beige and then buff; slightly scurfy; convex, flattening; 2 to 5cm across.
Gills: flesh amethyst, drying pale lilac-buff; distant; adnate or slightly decurrent.
Stem: colour as cap but streaked with pale fibrils; cylindrical or slightly flattened, often twisted; tough, fibrous; base downy with lilac fibres; 6 to 10cm long, 0.6 to 1cm dia.; no ring.
Spore print: white.
Always a joy to find (in wet weather!) the

Amethyst Deceiver must surely rank as one of the most beautiful of all our woodland fungi. Once it has had a few days of hot dry weather, this memorable mushroom begins to lose its lustre, and in time it is not easy to distinguish it from common Deceivers that have also become dry and buff coloured.

The Amethyst Deceivers (above left) are becoming progressively more buff coloured as they dry out. Eventually they may become almost indistinguishable via their macro characteristics from dry common Deceivers (above right). Spore features provide conclusive identification regardless of the degree of dryness of the caps. (The spores of *Laccaria amethystina* are significantly larger than those of *Laccaria laccata*.)

Although the caps of both of these deceivers (but not the tough stems) are considered edible, those in the know say that these fiddly little mushrooms are nothing to get excited about. If that's so then the next member of the clan *Laccaria* is certainly not going to feed the world...

Laccaria tortilis (Hydnangiaceae) – Twisted Deceiver

This tiny and often rather squat deceiver has an irregularly wavy and torn margin and a top that is flat or more often slightly depressed; it is found mainly in damp woodlands and on the banks of drainage ditches or small streams. Often small groups of Twisted Deceivers spring up in otherwise bare soil.

Cap: hygrophanous, orange-brown when wet, drying to pale flesh pink; flattened or centrally depressed with a very wavy margin; 0.5 to 1.5cm across.
Gills: pink; broad and more widely spaced than other deceivers; adnate.
Stem: colour as cap but with a white downy base; cylindrical or slightly flattened, often twisted and bent; tough, fibrous; 0.5 to 3cm long, 1 to 2mm dia.; no ring.
Spore print: white.

For those with access to a microscope, *Laccaria tortilis* is distinguished from most other *Laccaria* species found in Europe by its basidia, each having just two sterigmata on which its huge spores develop. The two larger deceivers described above have 4-spored basidia.

Cortinarious Consternation

Within the order Agaricales, the family Cortinariaceae contains a huge number of fungi (well over 2000 species), the majority of which are ectomycorrhizal and hence commonly found in or on the edge of woods and forests. All fungi in the *Cortinarius* genus are best considered inedible because several are known to be deadly poisonous; so unless you are ready to die (or perhaps to dye) these are fungi for enjoying visually but nothing more. Spore prints are of limited value in separating species within this genus, as they all have brown spores that tend to vary slightly between samples of the same species depending on the age of the fruitbody. Spore prints taken from immature caps can be very misleading.

Apart from the many large and conspicuous but superficially similar *Cortinarius* fungi (the 'webcaps'), there are also several hundred little brown mushrooms, few of which have any distinguishing features discernable without using a microscope. Amateur mycologists (and many professionals) tend to shrug, shake their heads and move on from these LBMs. Let's do that, too. But among the larger webcaps are some very beautiful mushrooms, and sometimes they pose in wonderfully photogenic groups.

Cortinarius armillatus (Cortinariaceae) – Red Banded Webcap

One of the tiny minority of webcaps that has a widely used common name, *Cortinarius armillatus*, the Red Banded Webcap, is also one of the few instantly recognisable species in this frustratingly difficult genus. This elegant mushroom has distinctive reddish veil girdles on its stem.

The specific name comes from the Latin *armilla*, meaning a collar (as in 'armlet'). The bands on the stem are remnants of the cobweb-like veil that covers the gills of the fruitbody as it emerges from below ground.

Cap: rusty brown in centre, paler at margin; dry; developing fibrous scales with age; hemispherical or bell-shaped, flattening with a broad umbo; 4 to 12cm across.
Gills: pale cinnamon, turning dark rust-brown; adnate or free; cortina (veil remnants) white with a pink tinge.
Stem: whitish with 2 to 4 orange-red belts; 5 to 12cm long, 1 to 2.5cm dia.
Spore print: rust-brown.
Odour: radish (when the gills are crushed).

The Red Banded Cortinarius is fairly common in areas where the soil is acidic. It fruits from July until the first winter frosts and is most often found growing through leaf litter in mixed woodland containing birch, with which *Cortinarius armillatus* is mycorrhizal.

The spruce forests of Scandinavia are in places peppered with these colourful mushrooms, which are suspected of forming mycorrhizal associates with not only spruce trees but also several other kinds of conifers.

Cortinarius bolaris (Cortinariaceae) – Dappled Webcap

The Dappled Webcap is another very distinctive and beautiful cort; it can be found from late summer through to early winter mainly in Beech woods on acid soil. The colourful cap is its most distinguishing feature, especially in older specimens where the cap surface breaks up into rings of orange or red scales on a pale background.

Cap: covered in small red scales on a white or yellow-pink background; hemispherical or convex, flattening with a broad umbo; 3 to 7cm across.
Gills: yellow-ochre, turning rusty brown as spores mature; adnate; the cortina is white with a pinkish tinge.
Stem: pale buff, patterned with pinkish-buff or brown veil fragments; often bowed; cylindrical sometimes with a slightly swollen base; 4 to 8cm long, 0.8 to 1.2cm dia.
Spore print: rust-brown.

The dappled effect is more clearly evident in this mature specimen (right). Despite its uniqueness and its habit of growing in clumps, *Cortinarius bolaris* can be hard to spot in autumn because it is quite well camouflaged among the fallen red-brown Beech leaves.

If in doubt about an identification, cut through the stem: the odourless flesh gradually turns yellow, particularly near the base.

Cortinarius cinnamomeus (Cortinariaceae) – Cinnamon Webcap

Conifer forests contain many large *Cortinarius* species, some of which are also mycorrhizal with one or more broadleaf trees and so can be found in all kinds of woodland and under trees in parks. One of those that is most often found in dark woods and forests is *Cortinarius cinnamomeus*, a species that is also seen occasionally under birch trees on heathland.

The caps sometimes develop wavy-edges reminiscent of swirling ball gowns – they seem to have a flair for that sort of thing.

Cap: olive-yellow, paler towards margin; convex, flattening with an umbo; smooth or radially fibrilose; 0.5 to 1.5cm across.
Gills: yellow turning golden brown; distant; adnate; pale, fleeting cortina.
Stem: lemon to chrome yellow, with irregular brown fibres below ring zone; cylindrical; 3 to 10cm long, 0.4 to 1cm dia.
Spore print: rust-brown.

Favouring acid soil, *Cortinarius cinnamomeus* is a sombre-coloured mushroom and easily overlooked, even though it appears in groups more often than singly. Reddish-brown dyes can be produced from the caps of this mushroom, which may be listed in some field guides under its synonym *Dermocybe cinnamomea*.

Cortinarius trivialis (Cortinariaceae) – Girdled Webcap

The Girdled Webcap is an infrequent find in boggy broadleaf woodland, mainly under poplars, willows and birches. Young fruitbodies sometimes exhibit beautiful blue or mauve tinges that quickly disappear from the cap surface as it turns brown, but a bluish tinge usually persists on the gills until they become stained by ripe rusty-brown spores.

Cap: 3.5 to 11cm in diameter; conico-convex at first, expanding until almost flat or with a shallow central depression but retaining a slight umbo; tawny to bay brown sometimes with a central bluish flush that is soon lost, paler towards the margin; extremely viscid.
Gills: initially covered by a bluish glutinous cortina; pale grey, turning rust-clay; adnate.
Stem: pale near apex; below a rusty ring zone brown and belted with pale scales; cylindrical; 5 to 12cm long, 1 to 2cm dia.
Spore print: rust-brown.

Cortinarius caerulescens (Cortinariaceae) – Mealy Bigfoot Webcap

As close to blue as can be found in its genus, chunky, and with an incurved margin that is sometimes elegantly rippled, it's not hard to spot these spectacular show offs. Unfortunately this webcap is not common and tends to be localised in its distribution. Appearing in late summer and autumn, these substantial fungi are reported as being edible, but I would not take that even *with* a pinch of salt, as there are several other cyan-coloured webcaps of very dubious edibility. For many years this autumn mushroom, found mainly with Beech on chalky soil, was better known by its synonym *Cortinarius caesiocyaneus*.

Cap: blue-mauve, turning rufous-brown from centre; convex; fibrillose at incurved margin; flattening in centre and becoming smooth; 4 to 9cm across.
Gills: blue-violet, turning clay-buff then rust-brown; adnate.
Stem: white with pale mauve fibrils, turning rust-brown when spores mature; cylindrical with a broad-rimmed basal bulb; 3 to 7cm long, 1 to 2cm dia.
Spore print: rust-brown.
Odour: earthy when cut or crushed.

Cortinarius stillatitius **(Cortinariaceae) – Purple Stocking Webcap**
Common in deciduous woodland and occasionally under conifers, *Cortinarius stillatitius* (syn. *Cortinarius pseudosalor*) often fruits through moss; then the stems can very long.

Cap: ochraceous brown with a tawny centre; smooth and shiny; viscid when wet; conical, expanding to become umbonate; margin may be either smooth or faintly striate; 4 to 9cm across.
Gills: clay-brown then ochre-rust-brown; free or adnate; cortina pale violet or almost white.
Stem: White above ring zone; slimy and covered in violaceous veil material below; cylindrical; 7 to 10cm long, 1 to 2cm dia.
Spore print: rust-brown.

Several other smallish slimy-capped webcaps have ochre, brown or red-brown caps, and separating them with certainty is not something to take on lightly unless you have access to testing chemicals and a microscope. Among these are *Cortinarius collinitus*, which is common in coniferous forests on acid soil and *Cortinarius livido-ochraceus* (syn. *Cortinarius elatior*), the Wrinkled Webcap. All produce rust-brown spore prints.

Cortinarius rubellus **(Cortinariaceae) – Deadly Webcap**
Beauty and a beast: that's *Cortinarius rubellus* (syn. *Cortinarius speciosissimus*). Aptly known as the Deadly Webcap, this visually attractive toxic toadstool has been the cause of several deaths and many more close shaves – including some in Britain, where it is an occasional find from late summer to early winter in coniferous woodland. Rarely seen in the south of England and Wales, but becoming increasingly more common as you go further north, this webcap is much more common in conifer plantations in mainland Europe.

Despite its very different form, the orange cap of this webcap has resulted in it being mistaken for *Cantharellus cibarius*, the highly prized edible Chanterelle mushroom, with serious and in several instances fatal consequences. The Deadly Webcap contains the toxin orellanine, which if eaten can destroy the kidneys and liver.

Cap: orange to tawny-brown; convex, flattening with a shallow umbo and with a narrow down-rolled margin; surface dry and finely scaly; 3 to 8cm across.
Gills: pale yellow, turning rust-clay with paler edges; adnate; fairly distant.
Stem: colour as cap but slightly paler; fibrillose; irregularly banded with reddish-brown veil remnants; fibrous; cylindrical, often bowed; 5 to 10cm long, 0.7 to 1.5cm dia.
Spore print: rust-brown.
Taste: of radish - but why would anyone want to risk it with such a toxic toadstool?

Cortinarius orellanus (Cortinariaceae) – Fool's Webcap

Very similar to *Cortinarius rubellus* and just as deadly, *Cortinarius orellanus* is rather more common in Britain and Ireland, where it is found most often in deciduous woodland.

Cap: orange, darkening with age to foxy brown, the centre darker than the rim; convex, flattening with a shallow umbo and with a narrow down-rolled margin, often wavy; surface dry and finely scaly; 3 to 7cm across.
Gills: pale yellow, turning rust-clay with paler edges; adnexed; fairly distant.
Stem: colour as cap but slightly paler; fibrillose, irregularly banded with reddish-brown veil remnants; fibrous; cylindrical, often curved and slightly clavate; 4 to 9cm long, 0.5 to 1.2cm dia.
Spore print: rust-brown.
Odour: (when gills are cut or crushed) faintly of radish or turnip.

A middle-aged lady, on holiday in Ireland, picked some Fool's Webcaps and made and ate mushroom soup from them, unaware that they were poisonous. Ten days later she was admitted to hospital with acute kidney failure. After a lengthy period of dialysis and months of medication she recovered; not everyone is so fortunate. Beware the Fool's Webcap!

Cortinarius semisanguineus (Cortinariaceae) – Surprise Webcap

The pale colour of both cap and stem lead you to expect the gills to be pallid. Not so! The gills are blood red - hence the rather fanciful common name given recently to this species. (The specific epithet *semisanguineus* means half blood-red; a related species, *Cortinarius sanguineus,* has blood-red cap *and* gills and is known as the Bloodred Webcap).

The Surprise Webcap is common in coniferous woodland but also occurs with birch trees.

Cap: yellow or pale olive-brown; convex, flattening with a distinct umbo; surface dry with fine fibrils or tiny scales; 3 to 6cm across.
Gills: blood red turning red-brown with age; adnate.
Stem: olive-yellow with pale brown fibrils; cylindrical, often curved; 4 to 9cm long, 0.5 to 1.2cm dia.
Spore print: rust-brown.
Odour: (when crushed) faintly of radish.

Cortinarius violaceus **(Cortinariaceae) – Violet Webcap**
This rare webcap is entirely purple and, at up to 12cm in diameter, a very striking species indeed. It grows under broad-leaf trees (seldom with conifers) in summer and autumn. Cut the flesh and you will find that the Violet Webcap is violet all the way through.

Cap: deep violet, sometimes blue-black; hemispherical then convex, expanding to become umbonate; margin incurved; surface dry and granular; 5 to 12cm across.
Gills: deep violet, turning violet-brown; adnate; cortina pale violet.
Stem: deep violet, covered in woolly fibrils; cylindrical with a bulbous base; 8 to 15cm long, 1 to 2cm dia.
Spore print: rust-brown.
Note: This beautiful webcap is the type species of its genus.

Introducing the Inocybes

While a few large fungi get lots of bad press, many other poisonous mushrooms - some containing toxins as deadly as the most notorious of the *Cortinarius* and *Amanita* killers - hide within the genus *Inocybe* (family Inocybaceae). Some *Inocybe* species are known to be hallucinogenic, while others contain the toxin muscarine (in lethal quantities in *Inocybe erubescens*), and the genus contains no mushrooms that are considered safe to eat.

Worldwide, *Inocybe* is a large and complex genus of mycorrhizal mushrooms many of which are quite selective in their choice of tree partners. The caps are small and initially conical, although in many species they flatten with age but generally retaining a sharp central umbo. Because most of the common species in this group have fibrous caps that tend to split as they expand, the genus has been given the common name of fibrecaps.

Inocybe rimosa **(Inocybaceae) – Split Fibrecap**
Typical of the genus, *Inocybe rimosa* (syn. *Inocybe fastigiata*) is difficult to distinguish with certainty from several other members of the group without resorting to detailed microscopic examination – and even then the task is far from easy. (It is by no means the only member of its genus whose cap splits as it expands.) This poisonous mushroom is mycorrhizal with hardwood trees, particularly Beech but also deciduous oaks.

Cap: straw yellow or buff to yellowish brown, paler towards rim; conical, becoming broadly bell-shaped with a distinct umbo; margin splitting radially; surface dry and silky; fibrous; 3 to 8cm across.
Gills: clay coloured with white edges; adnate or adnexed sometimes separating from stem at maturity.
Stem: white at apex, pale yellow-buff below; smooth or silky; cylindrical; 3 to 9cm long, 4 to 10mm dia.
Spore print: tobacco-brown.
Odour: slight, farinaceous.

***Inocybe geophylla* (Inocybaceae) – White Fibrecap**

There are very few white *Inocybe* species and this is the only one commonly seen in Britain and Ireland. They are most likely to spring up beside forest footpaths, but I also find them quite often on verges beside country roads. Its colour makes this little white mushroom reasonably easy to identify, once you are quite sure that what you have found is an *Inocybe*. If it looks pretty much like the ones pictured here, and you found it in Britain or Ireland rather than in some exotic location, then almost certainly it *is Inocybe geophylla.*

This mushroom is poisonous and unfortunately also very common. It has been mistaken for small Field Mushrooms *Agaricus campestris* with tragic results: because they contain a high concentration of the poison muscarine, eating these little monsters can be fatal. The White Fibrecap is mycorrhizal with hardwood trees, particularly Beech, and less frequently with conifers. A lilac form of this toxic toadstool, *Inocybe geophylla* var. *lilacina*, known as the Lilac Fibrecap, is equally common although, because of its colour, less likely to be mistaken for an edible mushroom.

Cap: white, turning ochre-brown from the centre as the fruitbody ages; conical, soon flattening and developing a pointed umbo; silky smooth with streaky radial fibres that tend to tear in dry weather; 1.5 to 3.5cm across.
Gills: cream darkening to clay-brown; sinuate or adnexed; crowded.
Stem: white; silky; cylindrical; 2 to 6cm long, 3 to 6mm dia.
Spore print: tobacco-brown.
Odour: slight, earthy or mealy.

Right: cap of *Inocybe geophylla* var. *lilacina*.

Most *Inocybe* species are very difficult, even for expert mycologists. Let's call the rest of the bunch LBMs (most are brown, after all) and quit while we are on top (of just two, admittedly). We will continue the ordeal with yet another challenging genus.

Hopeless with Hebelomas?

If so you are certainly not alone in finding these close relatives of the *Cortinarius* fungi difficult to identify. *Hebeloma* fungi (Hymenogastraceae) form EM relationships, usually with more than one tree genus. Some favour deciduous hardwoods on either chalky soil or in acid areas, while others are found in coniferous forests. Habitat is a clue to identity.

Hebeloma crustuliniforme (Hymenogastraceae) – **Poisonpie**
The most infamous of these toxic toadstools, which occasionally forms fairy rings in broadleaf or coniferous woodland, goes by the name of Poison Pie. As for its culinary value, enough said! Whoever thought 'pie' was a good name may have mistaken 'nasty' for 'tasty'. In the past this species was commonly referred to as the Fairy Cake Mushroom – now how irresponsible is that?

Slightly larger and stouter, usually with a darker ochre-brown cap but otherwise very similar, *Hebeloma sinapizans*, Bitter Poisonpie, favours chalky soil. It, too, is poisonous.

Cap: pale buff to ochre, darker in centre; convex, becoming broadly umbonate; slightly greasy when wet; margin often wavy, sometimes lobed; 4 to 11cm across.
Gills: white turning clay-brown with white edges; when damp exuding watery droplets that dry as brown spots; adnate; crowded.
Stem: white or very pale yellow; mealy towards apex; cylindrical; 4 to 8cm long, 1 to 2cm dia.
Spore print: rust-brown.
Odour: (from cut gills) of radish.

Hebeloma mesophaeum **(**Hymenogastraceae**) – Veiled Poisonpie**
Nearly always associated with conifers on sandy acidic soil, *Hebeloma mesophaeum* is a relatively small and very common mushroom; it is also poisonous and yet another that gives off a radish-like odour when cut or crushed.

Cap: pale buff with a date-brown centre; ephemeral velar fragments cling to rim; convex, becoming almost flat; greasy when wet; 2 to 4.5cm across.
Gills: clay-brown turning dark brown; usually adnate or adnexed, but occasionally free.
Stem: white or pale cream, darker towards base; faint fibrous ring zone soon disappears; cylindrical; 3 to 6cm long, 3 to 4mm dia.
Spore print: rusty clay-brown.
Odour: strong, of radish.

Rotters that buck the saprophytic trend
Many kinds of fungi that occur in woodland are also found in grassland well away from trees. The *Entoloma* genus is one such group, several of which are either known to form or are strongly suspected of forming ectomycorrhizal relationships with trees of the family Rosaceae, and in particular with fruit trees of the genus *Prunus*. Within this group are *Entoloma saepium, E. clypeatum, E. aprile* and *E. saundersii*. Here's another:

Entoloma sinuatum **(Entolomataceae) – Livid Pinkgill**
Found in deciduous woodland, this poisonous pinkgill is synonymous with *E. lividum*.

Cap: ivory white, darkening with age; conical then convex to plane with a blunt umbo; slightly sticky when young; 6 to 15cm across.
Gills: white turning pink; sinuate; crowded.
Stem: ivory white; smooth; cylindrical; 3 to 10cm long, 0.6 to 1.5cm dia.; no ring.
Spore print: pink.

Note: this deadly poisonous pinkgill, also known as the Lead Poisoner, is reported to be able to form mycorrhizas with willows.

Many more *Entoloma* mushrooms occur mainly in meadows, on moorland, or on mountain slopes, and so they are discussed under the heading of Grassland Fungi, in Chapter 8. There is also evidence that the Buttercap *Rhodocollybia butyracea* may occasionally be ectomycorrhizal with pines, but as it is nearly always a saprophyte it is covered in Chapter 6. Quickly leaving the Entolomataceae, let's try something easier...

Woodland Waxcaps (known as Woodwaxes)
Indicators of the quality of grassland habitats, waxcaps have won the title 'the orchids of the fungal world', but it is to the *Hygrocybe,Gliophorus and Humidicutis* species that this title truly belongs. Another group, the genus *Hygrophorus*, consists mainly of woodland fungi. Most of them are quite rare in Britain and Ireland, and with few exceptions they are duller than their grassland cousins. Another big difference between these two groups is that *Hygrophorus* species are known to be ectomycorrhizal with forest trees.

***Hygrophorus hypothejus* (Hygrophoraceae) - Herald of Winter**
A mushroom of pine forests and mixed pine and broadleaf woodland, *Hygrophorus hypothejus* is a late-season species. It has a bright yellow stem and a distinct ring zone, and so you might expect to spot this mushroom without any difficulty; but looking down on caps that are various shades of brown and olive against a background of dead leaves and pine needles they are all too easy to miss. The trick is to stand still and look carefully at a smallish area of the forest floor before moving on and trying another. Once you have found one Herald of Winter, the rest of the gang seem to throw off their camouflage and surrender without too much of a struggle.

This late-autumn mushroom favours the compacted earth beside forest walks, and so wandering off the beaten track is rarely an advantage; it is mycorrhizal with pines.

Cap: various shades of olive brown, margin paler; convex, flattening, sometimes centrally depressed; slimy when wet; margin sometimes wavy at maturity; 3 to 6cm across.
Gills: pale yellow, turning browner with age; distant; adnate or decurrent.
Stem: pale yellow, sometimes tinged with orange; cylindrical; 4 to 7cm long, 0.7 to 1.4cm dia.
Spore print: white.

***Hygrophorus eburneus* (Hygrophoraceae) – Ivory Woodwax**
Often seen on woodland edges, the Ivory Woodwax is mycorrhizal with Beech and oaks.

Cap: white or ivory; convex, becoming flat; very slimy; 3 to 7cm across.
Gills: white; distant; decurrent.
Stem: white; tapering slightly towards base; usually curved; 4 to 7cm long, 0.5 to 1cm dia.
Spore print: white.
Odour: said to resemble that of injured larvae of the Goat Moth, *Cossus cossus*, from which this woodwax's synonymous name *Hygrophorus cossus* originated! (Some experts consider *H. cossus* to be a separate species.)

EM Fungi without Gills

Chanterelles, hedgehogs, fairy clubs and corals belong to the taxonomic order Cantharellales. Most of the fungi within this order are known to form EM relationships with trees in woodland and parkland settings. Several of the most common *Cantharellus* species are also highly prized as edible fungi, and in Scotland in particular there is a significant amount of commercial collecting during the summer and autumn fruiting season.

Cantharellus cibarius **(Cantharellaceae) – Chanterelle**

With wavy-edged funnel-shaped caps, these summer-fruiting mushrooms come close to the top of the fungi list in terms of economic value. Despite the fact that Chanterelles have forked wavy ridges rather than gills, there have been several instances where people have eaten poisonous gilled fungi such as the Fool's Webcap *Cortinarius orellanus,* mistaking them for similarly coloured Chanterelles.

Cap: light yellow to deep egg-yolk yellow; funnel-shaped with a wavy, irregular margin that is sometimes inrolled and lobed; 2 to 12cm across.
Fertile surface: colour as cap; deeply decurrent forked veins, sinuous towards the cap edge.
Stem: colour as cap or paler; cylindrical or tapering towards base; 2 to 8cm long, 0.5 to 1.5cm dia.
Spore print: pinkish white or very pale buff.
Odour: faint, of apricots.

Known as Girolles in France, these edible (and delicious) golden nuggets appear in groups in mixed woodland, notably under birches, oaks, Sweet Chestnut or Hazel and often beside paths. Year after year they recur in the same locations.

Craterrellus tubaeformis **(Cantharellaceae) – Trumpet Chanterelle**

Another very good edible mushroom of the same genus, mycorrhizal with broadleaf and coniferous trees mainly in acid soil regions, is *Craterellus tubaeformis*, the Trumpet Chanterelle. This swarthy, gregarious mushroom fruits much later than the Chanterelle.

Cap: thin fleshed; brown with a pale wavy margin; funnel-shaped; margin, sometimes lobed; 2 to 5cm across.
Fertile surface: yellow turning grey; decurrent forked veins, with some cross-veins; sinuous towards the cap edge.
Stem: yellow; often slightly club-shaped or bulbous at the base; 2 to 8cm long, 0.5 to 1.5cm dia.
Spore print: pinkish-white.

From late summer through autumn and even into November if the first winter frosts are delayed, these tough-stemmed chanterelles are plentiful, and they rarely attacked by slugs. In form they are very similar to *Cantharellus cibarius*. Easily mistaken for dead leaves when seen from above, look for these mushrooms from a distance and their bright-yellow oval stems will give them away.

***Craterellus lutescens* (Cantharellaceae) – Golden Chanterelle**

The key identifying feature of this mushroom is the underside of its cap, which is smooth or only very slightly wrinkled with sometimes a few very broad veins rather than the deep false gills that characterise the much larger and more commonly seen *Cantharellus cibarius* and *Craterellus tubaeformis*.

I have found these little mushrooms mainly under oaks, and invariably in small groups rather than singly. *Cantharellus aurora* and *Craterellus aurora* are among the many synonymous scientific names that have been given to the Golden Chanterelle.

Cap: brown scales cover a golden background that shows through more as the cap expands; funnel-shaped with a wavy, irregular margin that is often multi-lobed; 2 to 5cm across.
Fertile surface: cream or pale pinkish-yellow; smooth and matt; with very few shallow veins.
Stem: yellow; cylindrical or tapering towards base; becoming hollow; 2 to 5cm long, 0.5 to 1cm dia.
Spore print: white or pale yellow.

***Craterellus cornucopioides* (Cantharellaceae) - Horn of Plenty**

A sombre-looking mushroom, known in France as *Trompette de la Mort* (trumpet of death), the Horn of Plenty is a good edible species. It is frequently listed as being mycorrhizal, although it is probably much more commonly a saprophyte.

Cap: dark grey-brown or almost black when moist, drying scurfy and lighter grey-brown; deeply funnel-shaped with a flared, wavy inrolled margin; 2 to 5cm across. Flesh very thin and leathery.
Fertile surface: ashen grey; smooth and matt; undulating but without veins.
Stem: hollow continuation of horn without demarcation; 4 to 10cm tall.
Spore print: white.

The Horn of Plenty appears usually in large tufts among leaf litter beneath deciduous broadleaf trees, but its dark colouring makes it one of the most difficult of all fungi to spot even when you are standing right on top of it (unfortunately sometimes quite literally).

In Greek mythology, the cornucopia was the horn of the goat Amalthea to which Zeus, having accidentally broken its horn, bestowed supernatural powers. The horn filled up with whatever food its owner requested; hence it became the symbol of plenty.

Several other fungi from the order Cantharellales are of uncertain mycorrhizal status, including some of the coral-like fungi of the genera *Clavaria, Clavulina, Clavulinopsis* and *Ramaria* that are found in broadleaf woods and among conifers, while others are found in grassland habitats. A small selection of the latter has been included in Chapters 8.

Clavulina rugosa **(Clavulinaceae) – Wrinkled Club**
Sometimes occurring singly but more often in large, scattered groups, these very common (and edible, although not greatly prized) club fungi are found in all kinds of woodland. They are particularly abundant in conifer forests on acidic soil, where they are generally thought to be mycorrhizal.

Fruitbody: white or cream; simple upright club without branches or with very few side branches; surface usually wrinkled and often irregularly flattened; spores are produced on the club surface; usually 4 to 8cm tall, but occasionally stretching to 12cm tall, and 3 to 8mm dia.
Spore print: white.

So often these sepulchral fruitbodies emerge from the damp mossy floor in the densest woodlands, and in the gloomy light they bring to mind (to some of us, at least) childhood fears of ghosts wearing white shrouds and drifting about slowly, silently in an eternal search of something they forgot to take with them into the afterlife.

Ramaria stricta **(Gomphaceae) – Upright Coral**
Although most *Ramaria* species are thought to be mycorrhizal, this fairly common coral fungus often grows on buried wood, under Beech trees in particular but also in coniferous forests. It's possible that Upright Coral has a Jeckyll and Hyde lifestyle and that it may be either mycorrhizal or saprophytic.

The specific epithet *stricta* is used a lot in botany and mycology. It simply means upright, and although *Ramaria stricta* branches (in the form of repeated dichotomous forks) all of the branches turn quite sharply to point upwards.

Fruitbody: white or pale cream turning buff with age; tough and rubbery coral-like structure with a short base often 'rooted' in buried wood, repeatedly forking with slender upright branches ending in sharp tips; surface smooth, often flattened; spores are produced on the club surface; turns wine-red when bruised; 4 to 10cm tall and up to 8cm across the whole fruitbody.
Spore print: rusty yellow.
Odour: faint, of aniseed.

Further evidence that *Ramaria stricta* can sometimes be saprophytic rather than mycorrhizal comes from its frequent appearance in flowerbeds and other areas that have been mulched using wood chippings.

Ramaria formosa (Gomphaceae) – Salmon Coral
A rare coral fungus of broadleaf woodland, *Ramaria formosa* is very variable in colour. Some specimens have more of an orange tinge, but perhaps the most attractive is the pink form pictured here. Unfortunately the delicate colouring of young fruitbodies soon fades. This poisonous fungus is occasionally mycorrhizal also with conifers.

Fruitbody: pinkish-ochre to orange-pink, paler at tips of branches, turning ochraceous with age; tough and rubbery coral-like structure with a pale stout base, repeatedly forking; surface smooth, often flattened; spores are produced on the club surface; turns dark wine-red or black when bruised; 7 to 20cm tall, and up to 15cm across the whole fruitbody.
Spore print: yellow-orange.

EM Species among the Gasteromycetes

Grouped for convenience as 'stomach fungi' the motley crew known as the gasteromycetes includes both saprophytic and ectomycorrhizal species – further evidence if it were needed that this is an artificial division with no real scientific justification for its existence.

Puffballs are saprophytes, whereas earthballs and some earthstars and earthstar-like fungi are known to form EM relationships with trees. In Britain and Ireland the tree genus most commonly associated with all of these fungi is *Pinus*, the various kinds of pines.

Scleroderma citrinum – (Sclerodermataceae) – Common Earthball
The Common Earthball, has a thick scaly outer skin within which a purple-grey spore-laden gleba ripens. From late summer through to the onset of winter these poisonous fruitbodies (which some unscrupulous mushroom gatherers used to mix in with truffles – guaranteed at least to ruin such delicacies!) are easy to find on woodland paths. In mossy areas they can be harder to spot.

Fruitbody: yellow or light ochre; covered in coarse scales; globose with no significant stem; attached to soil surface by pale ord-like threads of mycelium; interior initially white, turning purple-black before becoming brown and powdery; breaking open with a ragged aperture on upper surface when spores are mature; 3 to 10cm across and up to 8cm tall.
Spore mass: dark brown.

Note: Not all Common Earthballs are quite as deep lemon-yellow as those that are illustrated here.

Hydnoid Fungi

Many but by no means all hydnoid (toothed) fungi are mycorrhizal – further evidence that the physical characteristic of a toothed hymenial surface has evolved in parallel within fungal genera that are not closely related.

Phellodon niger (Bankeraceae) – Black Tooth

This tough hydnoid fungus could easily be mistaken for the charred end of a post standing slightly proud of the forest floor. Black Tooth is its common name, but don't be fooled: the teeth on the underside of the caps are not black but a pallid blue-grey when young and mid grey later. If asked to give this species a more descriptive common name I would suggest that Charcoal Hedgehog is an appropriate label for this spiny fungus of pine woodland.

Cap: Flat topped or occasionally with a shallow depression, the upper surface is blue-black becoming black but with a white rim. The cap surface is rough, often gnarled and pitted, and most often concentrically zoned with a sharp, slightly striate margin. Ranging from 3 to 8cm across, larger specimens tend to have lobed and wavy margins. Fruitbodies usually appear in small groups so that several caps become fused together.
Fertile surface: pale blue-grey decurrent spines (inset picture), up to 3mm long.
Stem: 2 to 5cm long and 1 to 2cm in diameter, more or less cylindrical, black and tomentose; often entirely buried in moss or leaf litter.
Spore print: white.

Hydnellum concrescens – (Bankeraceae) – Zoned Tooth

This rare woodland fungus often engulfs conifer needles on the forest floor; it can so easy be overlooked. Variable in cap shape, the fruitbodies have brownish tones and usually occur in small groups that tend to merge and become fused.

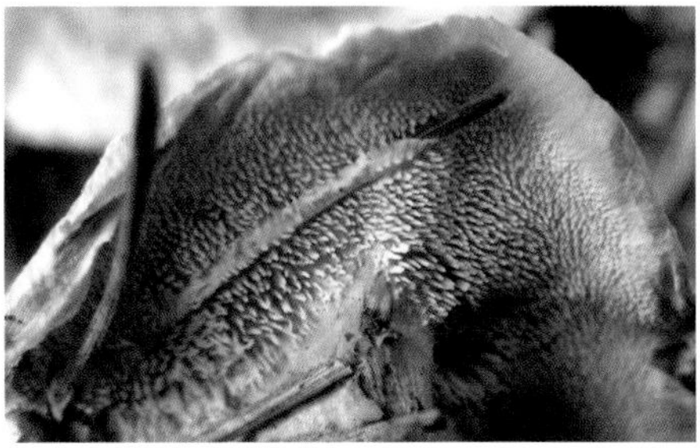

Cap: 2 to 5cm across, often oval or multi-lobed; initially shallowly domed or flat topped but with a finely velvety bumpy surface, becoming slightly funnel-shaped; white or very pale brown to pinkish-buff with a paler margin, eventually turning brown from the centre before blackening and decaying. The cap flesh is tough and fibrous. Total height of a fruitbody ranges from 3 to 6cm.
Fertile surface: pinkish buff, covered in decurrent spines up to 3mm long.
Stem: up to 4cm long; 0.5 to 2cm dia.; buff; tough, but more spongy towards the base.
Spore print: white.

Hydnum seek (or Hunt the Hedgehogs)

It is well known that hedgehogs live in woods. Less well known is the fact that some hedgehogs become very attached to certain trees, so much so that their relationship can only be described as... mycorrhizal. The hedgehogs in question belong to the genus *Hydnum*, within the order Cantharellales; however, whereas Chanterelles produce spores on wavy gill-like ridges, hedgehog fungi do so on spines - hence their common name.

Hydnum repandum – (Hydnaceae) – Wood Hedgehog

This is the larger of the two common hedgehog fungi found in Britain and Ireland, and it occurs usually in groups or arcs in coniferous and broadleaf woodland in autumn. It is a good edible mushroom and unlikely to be confused with any poisonous species.

Cap: cream, pale yellow or pale flesh-pink; finely velvety; irregularly convex, flattening with an incurved slightly undulating margin, sometimes developing a shallow central depression; 4 to 15cm across.
Fertile surface: white or pale pink decurrent spines (inset, left), 2 to 6mm long.
Stem: white, tinged as cap towards base; often eccentrically positioned; 3 to 7cm long, 1.5 to 4cm dia.
Spore print: white.

Hydnum rufescens – (Hydnaceae) – Terracotta Hedgehog

Darker and smaller than the more highly-prized hedgehog mushroom described above, *Hydnum rufescens* occurs in much the same kinds of habitats, often in scattered groups. Like the Wood Hedgehog, this edible mushroom is rarely infested by maggots. In coniferous woods and forests the Terracotta Hedgehog is generally the more common.

Cap: bright orange-brown; finely velvety; irregularly convex, flattening, sometimes developing a shallow central depression; 2.5 to 8cm across.
Fertile surface: white or pale buff-pink adnate spines, 2 to 5mm long.
Stem: white, becoming orange-tinged with age; centrally positioned; 3 to 6cm long, 1.5 to 2cm dia.
Spore print: white.

Sarcodon squamosus (Bankeraceae) – Bitter Tooth

Distinguishing between *Sarcodon imbricatus* (Scaly Tooth) and *Sarcodon squamosus* (Bitter Tooth, the only one of this pair known to occur in Britain) has taxed mycologists for years. Although macroscopically similar, molecular analysis supports the view that Bitter Tooth is an obligate mycorrhizal partner of spruces, while Scaly Tooth is associated with pines. The Bitter Tooth fungi shown overleaf are under pines.

Cap: pale brown background covered with dark-brown overlapping scales, larger near centre; convex then irregularly flattish with an undulating margin, usually developing a shallow central depression; 6 to 18cm across.
Fertile surface: spines (below, right) 4 to 10mm long, white or pale buff, turning purple-brown with age. (Just as with most boletes, the fertile layer of *Sarcodon* fungi can be separated easily from the rest of the cap flesh, which is said to be edible but rather bitter in taste.)
Stem: white, becoming brown at maturity, and with a blue-green base; centrally positioned; 4 to 8cm long, 1 to 3cm dia.
Spore print: brown.

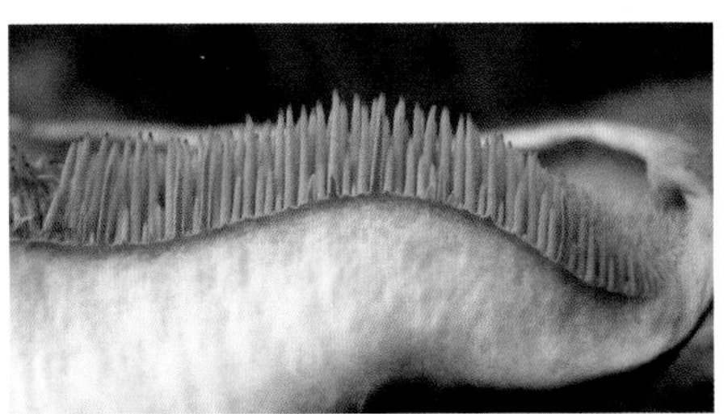

Earthfans

Some of the earthfans (*Thelephora* species) are half hearted about forming mycorrhizal relationships with trees, and you are likely to see as many on rotting wood as among mosses on the forest floor. It seems that as far a creating a mycorrhizal association is concerned, many of these inedible fungi can either take it or leave it.

Bird's-nest Orchid, *Neottia nidus-avis*, and several other wild orchid species are known to form mycorrhizal relationships with some earthfan species.

Thelephora penicillata (Thelephoraceae) – Urchin Earthfan

Thelephora penicillata (syn. *Thelephora spiculosa*), forms rosette-like fans in clusters among mosses on the forest floor, most often under spruce trees. These short-lived fruitbodies can be found from late summer through to the end of autumn.

Fruitbody: short-lived rosette-like fans lying low on the forest floor looking as though they have been trodden on, even when they have not; purple at the base and white or cream towards the branched and pointed tips; 4 to 15cm across; individual spines 2 to 7cm long.
Spore print: purplish-brown.

Note: When growing on the forest floor, even a 'good' specimen has rather a downtrodden appearance.

Rare saprophytic orchids including the Ghost Orchid *Epipogium aphyllum* and the Coralroot Orchid *Coralorhiza trifida* are reported to parasitise the mycorrhizas that are formed between coniferous trees and the Urchin Earthfan.

Thelephora terrestris (Thelephoraceae) – Earthfan
This strange fungus is well camouflaged on the floor of needle-strewn conifer plantations. It is nearly always found on dry sandy soil, where it forms mycorrhizae with pines and with spruce trees, but it also occurs in mossy coastal dune slacks, even where there are no obvious large plant associates. (*Thelephora terrestris* has also been shown to form ectomycorrhizal associations with certain kinds of Eucalyptus.) The saprophytic capacity of this fairly common fungus is evident from the fact that a resupinate (crust-forming) variety is sometimes found lightly attached to rotting conifer wood.

Fruitbody: rosette-like fans; reddish brown to dark chocolate brown, sometimes paler at margin and often with faint darker circular banding; no stem; petals splitting irregularly at margin; covered in radial fibres; 6 to 15cm across, with individual petals 2 to 6cm long.
Fertile (lower) surface: clay brown to mid brown or reddish brown; wrinkled but less fibrous than the upper surface.
Spore print: purplish-brown.

In China a related species, *Thelephora vialis,* is highly valued as a gourmet mushroom.

Earthstars and their Lookalikes

Most earthstars (*Geastrum* species) are not mycorrhizal; however, a lookalike species *Astraeus hygrometricus,* commonly known as the Barometer Earthstar, is known to form mycorrhizal associations with trees. This just underlines the point that in the kingdom of fungi appearances can be very deceptive. Molecular studies indicate that the Barometer Earthstar is more closely related to the earthballs, and indeed it is included in the same order (Boletales) as, for example, the Common Earthball *Scleroderma citrinum*, which is also an EM fungus.

Astraeus hygrometricus – (Diplocystidiaceae) – Barometer Earthstar

What makes this earthstar-like fungus particularly interesting is the way that its 'arms' open out in wet weather but close in again to protect the spore-bearing bulb, called a peridium, in dry conditions. (Some true earthstars, *Geastrum* species, are slightly hygroscopic in the behaviour of their rays; however, none reacts to weather changes so much and so rapidly.) A hole appears in the top of the peridium when the spores are mature, and when raindrops fall on to the bulb puffs of spores are emitted. Empty fruitbodies can persist for a year or more.

The Barometer Earthstar forms EM associations with pines and occasionally with hardwoods, nearly always in sandy places.

Fruitbody: ochre, tan or brown outer skin, splitting into six or more pointed rays that open when moist and close over the peridium when dry; grey, globose spore sac, 1 to 3cm across, thin walled and bursting at top to form a small irregular pore via which spores are released; spore-bearing gleba changes from white to brown as spores mature; no significant stem; whole fruitbody 2 to 5cm across when rays are extended.
Spore mass: cinnamon brown.

Is that the lot?

Quite definitely not! This has been a far from complete run through some of the most common basidiomycetes EM fungi that produce large fruitbodies. So far there has been no mention of any of the ascomycetes. That is because most of them produce fruitbodies so tiny that they are not likely to be seen on a woodland foray, and the few that do produce large fruitbodies are, for the most part, not ectomycorrhizal with trees. There are, however, some notable exceptions

Saddle Fungi

Among the EM fungi within the phylum Ascomycota is a group known as the saddle fungi. Like the delicious and much sought after morels (*Morchella* genus) they belong to the order Pezizales.

Helvella crispa **(Helvellaceae) – White Saddle**

Stark white against a dark brown background of earth and dried leaves, this large saddle fungus is easy to spot beside paths in deciduous woodland, where it is commonly found beneath Beech and oaks.

Cap: creamy white; irregularly lobed with a smooth fertile upper surface and a slightly downy buff or light ochre infertile lower surface; flesh thin and brittle; 4 to 8cm across and 2 to 5cm in height.
Stem: white or pinkish; ornately ribbed and grooved; hollow; 4 to 10cm tall, 1 to 2.5cm diameter at base; tapering towards apex.
Spore print: white.

Helvella elastica **(Helvellaceae) – Elastic Saddle**

With a stem as rubbery as the common name implies, this inedible saddle is a fairly frequent find beside footpaths through conifer forests and sometimes in deciduous woods.

Cap: grey-brown to yellow-brown; smooth fertile upper surface usually twin lobed; buff or light grey-brown; paler matt infertile lower surface; flesh thin and rather brittle; 2 to 4cm across and 1 to 2cm in height.
Stem: white or light grey; smooth or slightly wrinkled but not grooved; solid; 5 to 12cm tall, 4 to 8mm diameter at base, tapering slightly towards apex.
Spore print: white.

***Helvella lacunosa* (Helvellaceae) – Elfin Saddle**
The leaden shades of this saddle fungus suggest that it has come through an inferno, and indeed it is particularly common in mixed woodland around the edges of bonfire sites.

Cap: lead grey fertile upper surface; lighter grey infertile lower surface; multi-lobed, sometimes so contorted that parts of the infertile surface face upwards; 2 to 5cm across and 2 to 4cm in height.
Stem: light grey; hollow, deeply grooved; 4 to 10cm tall, 1 to 2cm diameter at base, tapering towards apex.
Spore print: white.

Note: The specific epithet *lacunosa* means 'with holes', a reference to the slots on the sides of the stems.

The Morel Maze

Like the saddle fungi, morels (family Morchellaceae) belong to the order Pezizales, within the Ascomycota. Morels often fruit in greatest abundance in forest areas that have suffered fire, disturbance or tree disease resulting in an abundance of dead organic material. They also spring up in new locations that have been mulched with woodchip. All this would suggest a saprophytic lifestyle; however, there have been scientific studies indicating that morels also go through a mycorrhizal phase during their lifecycles and enter into EM associations with trees, notably pines. That's just one of many morel mysteries...

Physically, various kinds of morels look very different one from another. Some have pale caps, others almost black; some produce tall conical caps, others are more or less spherical; some have caps much broader than their stems, others have tiny caps as narrow as or even narrower than the stems on which they perch. And when you look at the patterning of the multiple cups that make up a morel cap, some types are neatly aligned in rows, while others are randomly scattered. Based on combinations of these features numerous morel 'species' have been described in the past, but it has not been possible to confirm the separation of all of these species based on their microscopic characteristics which, in many instances appear to be minimal. DNA analysis may eventually reveal more, but in the meantime I am going to describe two fairly common morel species (or possibly species complexes) plus a dangerously toxic imposter known as the False Morel.

***Morchella esculenta* (Morchellaceae) – Morel**
Nowhere near as common as its former name Common Morel suggests, this highly prized edible (when cooked!) mushroom - *esculenta* means 'edible', of course - is found mainly on chalky soil under deciduous trees, and only in springtime. If you are really lucky you may come across a small group, but more often they fruit as singletons so that each specimen has to be earned by lots of searching for yellowish-brown irregular shapes among the yellowish-brown irregularly-shaped remains of last year's autumn leaves. Sunshine helps!

Many people are keen on eating morels, but strangely the rest of the animal world is less impressed. The flesh of morels is rarely ruined by insects or other small creatures, but the stems are often pierced by bugs that find the cosy cavity within the cap and stem a handy hideout. Before cooking, slice vertically through each morel to check for occupants.

Cap: sometimes conical, often globular, or an elongated vertical oval; flesh waxy; hollow; covered in an irregular array of pits separated by narrow ridges; pale cream, ochre, yellowish brown or mid brown, with the ribs along the ridges often a slightly darker shade than that of the pits; cap margin inrolled and fused to stem; 3 to 8cm across and 5 to 12cm tall.
Stem: white or pale cream, sometimes marked with brown blotches near base; flesh tough; hollow; smooth; 3 to 12cm tall and 1.5 to 6cm diameter at base, usually tapering towards apex.
Spore print: creamy white or pale ochre.

Morchella elata (Morchellaceae) – Black Morel

More reliably conical, the Black Morel is now far more common than the erstwhile Common Morel, and this is entirely due to the increased use of woodchip mulch on flowerbeds, herbaceous borders and the edges of parkland paths. Again it is a spring mushroom. In lowland Britain and Ireland it fruits in March, April and May, depending on the spring weather; however, in mountainous areas of mainland northern Europe morels answering to this description are known to fruit in summer; whether they are *Morchella elata* or another species is, like so much to do with these enigmatic mushrooms, as yet unclear.

Cap: usually conical but occasionally globular; flesh waxy; hollow; covered in an array of pits generally aligned in vertical columns separated by narrow ridges; pit surfaces smoky-grey, mid brown or dark brown; ribs a darker shade of brown or even black; cap margin inrolled and fused to stem; 2.5 to 5cm across and 5 to 10cm tall.
Stem: white or pale cream; surface finely granular; flesh tough; hollow; 3 to 10cm tall and 2 to 5cm diameter at base, usually tapering towards apex.
Spore print: creamy white.

Gyromitra esculenta (Discinaceae) – False Morel

On no account should you let the specific epithet fool you: this is not an esculent. Far from being edible, it is a poisoner whose dastardly deeds can go unnoticed for many years. Most often False Morels are found on sandy soil under conifers, particularly pines. Potentially fatal if eaten raw, this distant relative of the saddle fungi has long been a popular delicacy in many European countries (although its sale is now prohibited in Spain, for example). Even when properly cooked it has been shown that the False Morel can cause damage to the liver, kidneys and central nervous system.

Cap: irregularly globose, sometimes multi-lobed, with a brain-like outer surface (rather than the pits typical of true morels); surface smooth; reddish-brown to dark brown; cap margin inrolled and fused to stem; interior consisting of several separate chambers (the head and stem of a true morel encloses a single chamber); 5 to 15cm across and 5 to 10cm tall.
Stem: white; often longitudinally furrowed; surface finely felty; flesh tough; hollow - stem chamber separate from those within head; 1 to 5cm tall and 2 to 4cm dia.
Spore print: creamy white.

Note: The False Morel fruits in spring and early summer, overlapping the period when enthusiasts are gathering other morels.

Trouble with Truffles

Very few people who wander through woodlands find truffles. You might say that this is hardly surprising because truffles live through their entire life cycle under the ground (their lifestyle is therefore termed hypogeous). That's not strictly true, however; if it were, how could they distribute their spores and produce fresh colonies elsewhere when the trees they were attached to eventually died?

Truffles do not rely on earthquakes to distribute their spores; they have developed a more reliable strategy. Their fruitbodies smell and taste nice to a host of animal species (not just us), and when these creatures dig up and eat truffles the spores pass through their guts undamaged and are deposited wherever the animals pause to poo, and quite often enough that is under another tree. Rain then washes the spores into the ground, where with luck germination and development of mycelia may ensue. (Usually it does not ensue, of course, but truffles produce quite a lot of spores, and this ups their chances considerably.)

Hunting for truffles

People are not well equipped for truffle hunting. Their favourite technique is to use a rake, tearing back the dead leaves and the upper layer of soil from beneath a tree suspected of harbouring truffles among its roots. The method works, but it can do great damage to the woodland ecology, evicting many small creatures from their homes and disturbing other fungi species that might otherwise have fruited among the leaf litter. It does not work well, however, for two reasons. The first of these is that truffles are very well camouflaged and may be simply torn from their partner's roots and discarded with the leaf litter. The second problem is even more difficult to overcome: truffles have to ripen to be really good to eat (or to sell - many truffle hunters operate as commercial enterprises), and ripping up immature truffles guarantees that they will never reach maturity.

The answer is to find truffles by their scent, which they emit only when they are mature. We are not good at detecting the scent of an underground truffle, but other animals have noses much better equipped for the task. Hunting truffles by smell, animals do far less damage. Some gourmet truffles, including a French speciality known as the Périgord Truffle *Tuber melanosporum* and its Italian white rival the Piedmont Truffle *Tuber magnatum* have scents that mimic a male pig's sex hormone. That is why female pigs have been used to help find truffles. In recent times, dogs have become the truffle hunter's preferred companion, because they can be trained to find but not eat the truffles (and they don't make so much mess on the back seat of the car en-route between truffle forests!).

Tuber magnatum (Tuberaceae) – Piedmont Truffle

To try to describe the shape of these shapeless lumps seems futile. The knobbly exterior is light brownish-yellow and the flesh inside is whitish. All truffles are extremely variable in size. The Piedmont Truffle (right) usually ranges between 3 and 12cm across, but exceptionally large ones do occur and are sometimes auctioned for vast sums of money. (The Summer Truffle, *Tuber aestivum*, which occurs in Britain and Ireland mainly under Beech trees on chalky soil, is dark brown and warty with a white interior that becomes a marbled grey-brown at maturity.)

A woodland display of Fly Agarics *Amanita muscaria* is an unforgettable sight.

Chapter 5 - Parasites, Brackets & other Hangers-on

Forest Fungi on trunks, branches and twigs of standing trees

Over thousands of years a balance of power has been established between trees and the many kinds of fungi that feed upon them. Most trees provide fungi with occasional snacks in the form of fallen twigs and branches, finally delivering a great feast when the trees die of old age or are toppled in a storm. That's fine for the majority of fungi, which seem quite content to nibble at canapés while awaiting the banquet. Parasitic fungi do not wait for the grim tree reaper to deliver the goods, and most of them appear to be insatiable, sustaining a healthy appetite at least into the early courses of the banquet. As a consequence, there is no clear dividing line between the fungi that grow on trees and those that you will find on felled trunks or large branches broken off during gales.

Parasites are not necessarily killers. Many fungi are only weakly parasitic on their hosts, extracting nutrients at the expense of the vigour of the tree without causing fatal injury. Of course, when a tree grows old, is infected by some other ailment, or suffers seriously from drought or physical damage (for example losing large limbs in stormy weather) a parasitic fungal attack can then be 'the last straw'; otherwise a tree may live on for many years or even decades despite the presence of fungal parasites. These vampire-like fungi generally produce annual fruitbodies rather than perennial ones.

Plant and Fungi parasites – a double-whammy

Parasitism of trees and bushes is not restricted to fungi. Occasionally a host must contend with the weakening effects of attack by other plants as well as fungi. For example, mistletoe (*Viscum album* is the native European species) is hemiparasitic most commonly on poplars and on cultivated apple trees, taking nutrients and water from the host tree but also contributing nutrients via photosynthesis. In southern Europe many of the cistus bushes are host to *Cytinus* root parasites. For example, the pink-flowered *Cistus albidus* is attacked by a bizarre-looking parasitic plant *Cytinus hypocistis* that frequently surrounds the stems. As if in compensation for carrying such burdens the same bushes are frequently supported by several mycorrhizal fungi of the *Boletus* and *Russula* genera.

The attractive wildflower *Cytinus hypocistis* is parasitic on cistus plants. Here it has latched on to a pink-flowered *Cistus albidus*, whose roots are simultaneously benefiting from the mycorrhizal support of the Powdery Brittlegill *Russula parazurea* (inset).

Some parasitic fungal infections cause damage so serious that the host trees die quickly, often within a season or two. These necrotrophic fungi are usually also able to feed on dead wood, often colonising the stumps of fallen trees. They are really saprophytes with a killer streak. Honey Fungus *Armillaria mellea* is one of these optional parasites.

Other fungi are only weak parasites, living with their host tree and drawing nutrients from it without killing it. Many of these are biotrophic species unable to live on dead wood, and so they are termed obligate parasites. Once the host tree has died, the biotrophic mycelium dies soon afterwards and so no more fruitbodies appear.

And then there are saprophytic fungi - species that consume only the wood of dead trees. They may create an impression of parasitism when actually they are feeding on dead parts of otherwise healthy living trees. It's not easy, therefore, to separate the true parasites from other 'hangers on', and so in this chapter you will find information about the various kinds of fungi you are likely to see growing on living trees. Most of these can also be found on fallen or felled trunks and on stumps. (Crusts, cups, clubs and other fungi that feed mainly on old stumps, rotten trunks and branches, or on fallen leaves and dead wood within the litter of the forest floor are described and illustrated in Chapter 6.)

Bracket fungi

Looking from a distance like shelves attached to the trunks of trees (and hence sometimes referred to as 'shelf fungi'), many bracket fungi are large, colourful and hard to miss. Their spore-bearing surfaces are usually on the underside of the fruitbodies, and most of them release their spores from pores at the ends of vertical tubes or irregular maze-like slots rather than gills. Unlike most boletes, whose spongy tube layers can be detached quite easily from the rest of the cap material, the bracket polypores are tougher (some of the perennial types can only be removed from their host tree with the help of a saw or a chisel) and the tube layer does not peel away from the rest of the material.

All tough bracket fungi that release their spores via pores on the underside of the cap used to be included in one very large genus, *Polyporus*. Latterly, mycologists have sorted many of them into several families and dozens of genera based on a range of macroscopic and microscopic characteristics, including features of their hyphae and their spores. Families of particular interest are Bondarzewiaceae, Fistulinaceae, Ganodermataceae, Hymenochaetaceae and Polyporaceae, and examples from each are illustrated and described in this chapter. Some of the families concerned contain numerous species most of which are not often seen, either because they are very rare or very small. The bracket fungi illustrated and described in this chapter are either fairly common or they are so conspicuous that they are difficult to miss.

Even today, the true relationships of most polypores with the other taxonomic groups of fungi remain uncertain. This is reflected in scientific texts on the taxonomy of these kinds of fungi, where you will see the Latin phrase *insertae sedis*, meaning 'of uncertain taxonomic placement'. We must expect more changes. Plenty of new synonyms have already been created and, as with so much of this complex kingdom, the taxonomy of bracket fungi is still in a state of flux, as species that on visual inspection seemed such obvious close relatives and were placed in the same genus are later found to be but distant cousins.

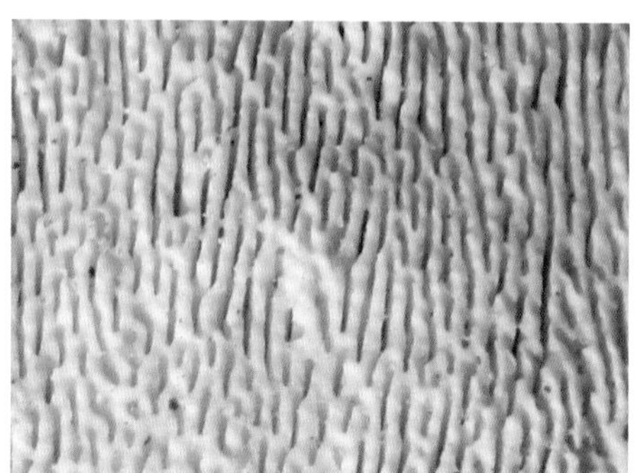

The slot-like pores of the Lumpy Bracket fungus *Trametes gibbosa*

Not all bracket fungi have tubes and pores; a few have slots or maze-like labyrinths, one or two have spines, many more produce their spores on smooth fertile surfaces, and there are even bracket-like species with true gills and others with grooved structures that look very much like the gills of agaric mushrooms. The nature of the fertile surface may not be obvious at first glance: some brackets have such tiny, densely-packed tubes that their pores can only be distinguished using a magnifying lens – a very handy thing to have with you when out on a fungus foray.

Early symptoms of parasitic fungal attack, such as thinning of a tree's crown, often go unnoticed. By the time brackets appear on the trunk it is too late to avert damage: the mycelium will already have spread into either the sapwood or the heartwood or both (depending on the fungus species concerned) and the tree will at least be weakened if not mortally wounded. All too frequently people knock off the fruitbodies in the belief that they are killing the fungus and protecting the tree, but of course it is far too late for that.

Cap-and-stem assassins and grave robbers

Only a tiny minority of agaricoid fungi are parasitic on trees – Honey Fungus (*Armillaria* spp.) is quite the most notorious of these – and in many instances the fruitbodies form only after the parasite has killed its host. Several other gilled fungi feed on the dead parts of living trees, often competing with brackets and gilled parasites for the first course of the post-mortem banquet.

Many more cap-and-stem mushrooms join the feast after a tree has fallen (or been felled); and once its valuable timber has been harvested the decaying stump provides food for a great variety of other fungal species. They are included with the 'Rest of the Rotters' in Chapter 6 along with various disc, club and jelly fungi that are also found occasionally on standing dead trees.

The brackets and cap-and-stem fungi mentioned in this chapter belong to the phylum Basidiomycota and produce large, readily visible fruitbodies; however, trees, and indeed plants generally, suffer far more from the ravages of fungal foes that do not produce fruitbodies (or in some instances their fruitbodies are so tiny that they cannot be seen without the help of a microscope).

Within the Basidiomycota are many rusts and smuts that can only survive as parasites on living plants. While rarely killing their host plants they reduce the vigour and, in the case of food crops such as cereals and fruit trees, the yield.

In 1845 and 1846 the potato crop failure resulted in a million Irish people dying of starvation. Only mass emigration saved the lives of millions more, and Ireland's population was halved in just a couple of years. The culprit was the blight *Phytophthora infestans*, a fungus-like water mould belonging to the oomycetes. Tree-specific species of *Phytophthora* cause serious and often fatal damage. One such example is *Phytophthora alni*, which as the specific epithet implies attacks alders (*Alnus* spp.), causing root rot. In Britain and Ireland this disease has spread along many river corridors, leaving bare riverbanks that are more prone to soil erosion once they lose the protection of the tree roots.

Alder killed by *Phytophthora alni*

Parasitic and pathogenic ascomycetes

A few saprophytic fungi of the phylum Ascomycota produce compound fruitbodies large enough to be visible to the naked eye, and some of the significant and common ones are described and illustrated in Chapter 6. However, most of the ascomycetes that are parasitic on trees and other plants produce fruitbodies so small that they are difficult if not impossible to see in any detail without the aid of a strong magnifying lens or a microscope.

Within the relatively small order Ophiostomatales are the notorious Dutch elm disease fungi *Ophiostoma ulmi* and *Ophiostoma novo-ulmi*, whose spores are carried from tree to tree by bark-boring beetles. The devastation caused by *Ophiostoma* is out of all proportion to the microscopic size of its fruitbodies.

Brackets on Trees

The majority of bracket fungi are saprophytic on dead or dying trees or on rotting stumps, but some parasitic species are also included in the group. Most but not all are in the order Polyporales and belong to the families Polyporaceae, Fomitopsidaceae and Meripilaceae. There are a few surprises, however...

Daedalea quercina (Fomitopsidaceae) – Oak Mazegill

Specific to trees of the oak genus (*Quercus*), in Britain this common bracket fungus consumes dead standing and fallen trunks and large branches; elsewhere it has also been found on living oaks and occasionally on other kinds of broadleaf trees. (Despite its preference for oaks in the wild, in laboratory conditions the mycelium of this fungus has been shown to attack timber from almost any kind of broadleaf tree.) The Oak Mazegill occurs throughout Europe as well as in Asia, North Africa and North America, and there are recent reports of it in Australia. It is a brown-rot fungus that attacks the heartwood.

This old oak stump supports a large colony of Oak Mazegill brackets.

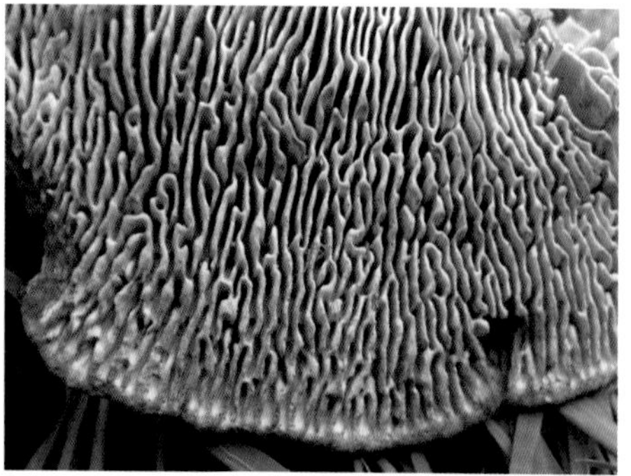

The maze-like pores, which do not change colour when bruised, release white spores.

This fungus was valued by beekeepers, who used the smoke from smouldering fruitbodies to anaesthetise bees. Once the bees had been calmed by the dense smoke, the beekeeper could open a hive and work on it without triggering painful panic reactions by the occupants.

Fruitbody: tough annual brackets; buff; fan-shaped; 1 to 10cm thick, 10 to 20cm dia.
Fertile surface: buff; mazelike channels, 1 to 3cm deep, 1 to 3mm wide.
Spore print: white.

The generic name refers to Daedalus, who according to legend designed the maze in which Queen Pasiphae hid her offspring the Minotaur, half man and half bull. After Theseus had slain the Minotaur and run off with King Minos's daughter, the king turned his anger on double-dealing Daedalus and locked him and his son Icarus in the labyrinth; however, they escaped using wings, but Icarus flew too close to the sun and his wings melted.

Such mythical tales may be a bit hard to swallow, but no more so than this common and extremely tough bracket fungus.

The deep, hard-wearing channels make these tough and durable brackets very handy as combs for grooming horses – one of their traditional uses.

Phaeolus schweinitzii (Fomitopsidaceae) – Dyer's Mazegill

Parasitic on the roots of conifers, the fruitbodies of this unusual and colourful fungus rarely occur singly, but when they do the spinning-top shape and golden yellow margins with faint concentric zones are very distinctive.

Arising from near-surface roots of an old pine, the fan-like brackets of _Phaeolus schweinitzii_ cause serious brown rot damage.

Initially yellow and downy, the cap surface becomes browner at maturity, when it releases pale spores with a yellow tinge.

The genus name *Phaeolus* means dark - a reference to the dark brown mature fruitbodies. (Those that survive the winter eventually turn black.) This species was named after Lewis David von Schweinitz (1780-1834), who is generally recognized as the father of American mycology. Von Schweinitz, a cleric, gathered and studied fungi in the eastern states of the USA and published many of his findings in *Synopsis Fungorum Carolinae Superioris* (in 1822) and *Synopsis Fungorum in America Borealis* (in 1832). As well as describing some 3000 species of fungi, the majority new to science at the time, von Schweinitz produced beautiful illustrations of fungi, lichen, wildflowers, ferns and mosses.

Fruitbody: Individual caps 10 to 30cm diameter; often several caps are fused together along the line of a tree root; no clear demarcation between stem and cap; overall height of mature fruitbody ranging from 4 to 10cm.
Tubes: yellow; 3 to 6mm deep.
Pores: angular, of very variable shape; usually spaced at 0.5 to 2mm on a greenish-yellow background that turns brown with age or when bruised.
Spore print: white or very pale yellow.

Larches, pines and firs can be infected, but this fungus is most common on spruce. *Phaeolus schweinitzii* is widespread throughout Europe (and in the USA), producing fruitbodies annually from early summer through to late autumn. Because of the woody nature of these polypores, old fruitbodies can sometimes be seen alongside new ones.

A fungus to dye for

With a few notable exceptions, bracket fungi are so tough and bitter tasting that even if they were poisonous it would require a considerable feat of endurance to chew and swallow sufficient to cause problems. Some of these fungi do have their uses, however. There are records going back many centuries showing that certain species have been used for dyeing wool and other fabrics. One of these is *Phaeolus schweinitzii*, whose young fruitbodies provide a bright yellow dye, while various shades of brown can be extracted from older specimens. Because of this use and its very variable and misshapen pores, this attractive polypore is commonly known as Dyer's Mazegill.

Piptoporus betulinus (Fomitopsidaceae) - Birch Polypore
Also known as the Razorstrop Fungus because its hard surface was used to hone the edges of cut-throat razors, this common bracket of broadleaf woodlands is found almost exclusively on birches. *Piptoporus betulinus* causes a yellowish-brown cubical rot, and it is a powerful decomposer of dead wood. Fruitbodies can be seen throughout the year, but in wet or frosty weather they soon decay and fall to the ground.

This annual polypore may be parasitic on weakened birches, but without doubt its fruitbodies are most commonly seen when the host tree is already dead.

Fruitbody: Up to 20cm in diameter and 6mm thick, with a brownish top that is initially rounded but later flattens, often with a wavy margin.
Tubes: white; 1.5 to 5mm deep.
Pores: white; spaced at 3 to 4 per mm.
Spore print: white.

Inonotus hispidus (Hymenochaetaceae) – Shaggy Bracket
This bracket fungus acquired its common name because the upper surface of its fruitbodies is finely velvety. It is a serious pathogen with a particular liking for Ash trees. Apple trees and other hardwoods can also be infected by this colourful polypore. The white rot caused by this parasite results in brittle fracture, where large branches or even trunks of Ash trees suddenly snap, with potentially disastrous results. In common with other parasitic fungi, timber infected with the mycelium of this bracket fungus continues to produce fruitbodies long after the host tree has died.

The Shaggy Bracket can be distinguished from the superficially similar Beefsteak Fungus *Fistulina hepatica* not only by the texture of its upper surface – velvety rather than smooth – but also by the cap flesh, which is creamy brown. (The bloody droplets that exude from all but the oldest of Beefsteak Fungi provide another clue that is difficult to miss.)

Fruitbody: rust-brown on top with concentric zoning on a distinctive, downy surface that is usually wrinkled at the edges; up to 30cm across; broadly attached to the substrate (no stem).
Tubes: buff; 6 to 10mm deep.
Pores: initially cream, later turning buff then brown; round; spaced 2 to 3 per mm.
Spore print: yellow.

Fortunately for Ash trees in particular (but unfortunately for anyone interested in hunting for this bracket fungus) *Inonotus hispidus* is a rare species in Britain and Ireland.

Pseudoinonotus dryadeus (Hymenochaetaceae) - Oak Bracket
Another parasitic fungus, this annual bracket attacks mainly oaks, although occasionally it is reported on other broadleaf trees including Beech and alders.

Initially fruitbodies occur singly, but in time they spread all around the base of the tree.

Beneath the honey-coloured cap with its caramel droplets is a grey pore-bearing surface that releases pale yellow spores.

The genus suffix *-inonotus* comes from *ino*, meaning fibrous, and *ot* meaning ear. 'Fibrous ear fungus' is not a particularly descriptive name for something which more closely resembles a 'thick ear' with a rather nasty skin complaint.

The *dryadeus* specific epithet is easier to understand: it is a particular reference to oaks rather than a more vague reference to a dryad, or wood nymph.

Fruitbody: light brown; usually 20 to 30cm across but exceptional specimens can attain a diameter of 60cm; stemless; attachment to the trunk is typically half the width of the fruitbody.
Tubes: brown; 5 to 20mm deep.
Pores: 3 to 5 per mm; buff; exuding drops of amber liquid when young; turning brown when old or bruised.
Spore print: yellow.

What makes this such a striking polypore are the amber teardrops that ooze from the upper surface. With droplets of 'runny honey' on a 'set honey' background, this fungus looks as if it really belongs inside a beehive! Despite it's delectable appearance, this polypore is inedible.

Look out for this not-so-common bracket fungus on the boles of old oak trees, where it causes white rot of the tree's base and major buttress roots. Note, however, that this species can also infect the stumps of recently-felled trees, where it feeds as a saprophyte sometimes for as long as two or three years. Oak Brackets can be seen throughout the year, but attractive young fruitbodies are produced during late summer and autumn.

Pseudoinonotus dryadeus enters via bark wounds on the lower trunk and buttress roots – damage often caused by power mowers, tractors encroaching too close to the trunk, road traffic accidents and even fencing wires or notices nailed to trees. Whether this fungus is a strong enough parasite to kill otherwise healthy trees is questionable, but it certainly affects not only the timber but also the growth of its host. Oak trees carrying this polypore show a thinning of the crown, and since this reduces the leaf area available for photosynthesis the functioning of the tree's respiratory and feeding systems must inevitably suffer. There is, of course, no cure, and so prevention of bark damage is the only effective management strategy... but perhaps it is worth losing just a few oaks so that occasionally we can see these gorgeous bracket fungi.

Fistulina hepatica (Fistulinaceae) - Beefsteak Fungus

Edible it may be, but even when young and soft this beautiful bracket is just too good to be true: a mediocre meal at best and to most palates rather bitter compared with the sirloin steak (or, as some say, ox tongue or liver) that it mimics in appearance.

Fistulina is a monotypic genus, meaning that it contains only one species. The generic name *Fistulina* means 'having small tubes'.

The specific epithet *hepatica* means 'liver' - a reference to the appearance of mature fruitbodies. It's strange, therefore, that this bracket, so common throughout Europe and reported also from the eastern side of the USA, is not generally known as the Liver Fungus!

Young Beefsteak Fungus fruitbodies emerging from a dead Sweet Chestnut trunk

Fruitbody: Emerging from trunks either singly or in small groups, these narrowly-attached brackets have little or no obvious stems and, while initially globose, are very variable in shape at maturity. Typically 10 to 20cm across but exceptionally expanding to 25cm, the caps have at first sticky pink and later blood-red upper surfaces that gradually become dry and fibrous, turning purplish brown with age.
Tubes: light ochre; densely packed; separate (not bonded together in a solid mass as is more usual with polypores); tube length does not vary much across the surface of the fruitbody and is typically 10 to 15mm.
Pores: spaced 1 to 3 per mm. Seen from below, mature fruitbodies have creamy white pore openings that gradually turn fawn and eventually reddish brown. When scratched or handled roughly, the pore surface bruises and turns at first red and then brown within a few minutes.
Spore print: white or pale yellow when taken from young fruitbodies, but usually pale brown from older specimens.

A mature fruitbody at the base of an old oak

Slice through a fruitbody and the resemblance to raw meat is quite remarkable; young fruitbodies even exude 'blood'!

Most often seen on oaks and Sweet Chestnut, the Beefsteak Fungus is a weak parasite and a saprophyte. Fruitbodies appear in summer and autumn and attack mainly the cellulose and hemicellulose in the wood, causing the timber of the host tree to darken and develop an attractive pattern that is greatly valued as a material for making furniture as well as for producing carved and turned decorative artefacts.

Ganoderma australe (Ganodermataceae) – Southern Bracket
Of the seven genera in this family – *Amauroderma, Ganoderma, Haddowia, Humphreya, Lazulinospora* and *Thermophymatospora* – *Ganoderma* species are the only ones commonly found in Europe. The ability of *Ganoderma* fungi to break down cellulose and lignin has also triggered interest in their use for bioremediation (restoring contaminated land to a usable state) and in paper making. Medical treatments extending back into early Chinese folklore use *Ganoderma* fungi. All of these brackets produce clouds of brown spores that coat the trees to which they are attached and often discolour the tops of the brackets. That brown staining is all you need to see to identify these fungi to genus level.

Ganoderma australe (syn. *Ganoderma adspersum*) is parasitic on hardwood trees, notably Beeches, and the fruitbodies usually appear on the lower trunk or on buttress roots.

Three layers of growth are visible as ridges on the cap of this Southern Bracket.

Fruitbody: stemless; up to 30cm thick and typically 25cm across, but occasionally growing to 60cm across. The upper surface becomes ridged, as a new layer of tubes grows on the underside each year. The brackets can be seen throughout the year, but spores are produced in autumn.
Tubes: brown; 7 to 20mm deep; annual layers are added to the lower surface.
Pores: white bruising brown; round; 3 to 5 per mm.
Spore print: brown.

Ganoderma applanatum (Ganodermataceae) - Artist's Bracket
This perennial bracket is found on Beech trees and less frequently on other hardwoods. Artistic etchings can be made by scratching the pore surface – hence the common name.

Fruitbody: stemless; perennial; thinner (typically 2 to 8cm thick) than *G. australe.*
Tubes: brown; 7 to 20mm deep.
Pores: white, bruising brown; round; 4 to 5 per mm.
Spore print: brown.

Cinnamon-brown spore deposits have discoloured these originally grey caps.

The almost flat fertile surface makes an excellent medium for drawing or writing on.

Ganoderma lucidum (Ganodermataceae) - Lacquered Bracket

Ganoderma species are notoriously difficult to identify with confidence because of their great variability, and *Ganoderma lucidum* is no exception. Before it matures and begins releasing clouds of brown spores, which attach themselves to the upper surface of the cap (and the bark of the tree to which it is attached), thereby masking its lacquered appearance, this is one of the most attractive of large bracket fungi.

Ganoderma lucidum on the base of an oak. Although the sample shown here has a broad rudimentary stem, this is not always a feature of Lacquered Brackets; some are sessile.

The Lacquered Bracket is seen mainly at the bases of oak trees (or on the stumps of recently felled oaks) but is occasionally found on other broadleaf trees. The young fruitbody pictured on the right was also on an oak but, unusually for this species, sited up at head height. At this stage soft, the fruitbody hardens through autumn and decays during the following year.

An immature Lacquered Bracket

Fruitbody: to 35cm across; to 4cm thick.
Tubes: brown; 5 to 20mm deep.
Pores: creamy-white turning brown when old or bruised; round; 2 to 3 per mm.
Spore print: brown.

Polyporus squamosus (Polyporaceae) - Dryad's Saddle

Many of the annual brackets produce spectacular displays in summer and autumn, and Dryad's Saddle, which is parasitic on broadleaf trees, is one of the best. Fruitbodies can appear on the same host tree for many years, so that once you have found a good site you can return to it time and again with a high probability of the visit being worthwhile.

Polyporus simply means having many pores, while the specific epithet *squamosus* is a reference to the squamous or scaly upper surface of the brackets. *Polyporus squamosus* digests lignin in wood and so it results in white rot. (Many other fungi consume only the cellulose and leave the remains as rectangular blocks of brown lignin.)

Fruitbody: upper surface cream with concentric bands of brown scales; fan shaped sometimes with a short cream stem that darkens at the base; 10 to 50cm across.
Tubes: white, becoming cream; 5 to 10mm deep.
Pores: cream; irregular and angular; no colour change when bruised; 3 to 5 per cm.
Spore print: white.

Fomes fomentarius (Polyporaceae) - Hoof Fungus

Tinder Fungus is another of the common names given to this persistent and very tough perennial polypore. The pale leather-brown flesh was used for lighting fires. (It smoulders and so burns very slowly.) The fruitbodies are seen in Britain and Ireland mainly on birch trees but also occasionally on Beech and Sycamore. Uncommon or rare in the south, this polypore becomes increasingly more plentiful the further north you go. In northern Russia nearly every Silver Birch has Hoof Fungus brackets on its trunk. This parasitic fungus sometimes gains a hold via clefts in the trunks of older trees.

Fruitbody: grey; typically 10 to 20cm across but exceptionally growing to 40cm, usually as solitary specimens; occasionally two or more tiers of brackets are produced.
Tubes: brown; 2 to 7mm deep.
Pores: light grey, often tinged ochre; becoming brownish-grey with age and darker when bruised; 2 to 3 per mm.
Spore print: very pale lemon. Spores are emitted in late summer and autumn.

***Fomes fomentarius* (above) and *Fomitopsis pinicola* (below)**

The similar Red-belted Bracket ***Fomitopsis pinicola*** (right) is rare in Britain and Ireland but common in parts of mainland Europe. This pale-spored polypore (family Fomitopsidaecae), found on living or dead conifers, has an orange or red line between the older annual layers and the current layer.

Phellinus igniarius (Hymenochaetaceae) - Willow Bracket

Mostly you are likely to come across old, blackened, gnarled and cracked fruitbodies of this bracket (which experts believe is probably a 'complex' of several species rather than a single species). That's because fruitbodies can continue growing for many years, feeding on the remains of the host tree long after it has died. Willows are the preferred victims of this very tough (when mature) bracket, which looks quite similar to the Hoof Fungus. One of the many synonyms of *Phelinus igniarius* is *Fomes igniarius.*

Fruitbody: upper surface grey at first, turning black and developing vertical cracks; outer margin remaining brown and velvety even on very old fruitbodies; up to 40cm across and as much as 20cm thick; hoof-like and concentrically ridged in annual layers.
Tubes: brown, 3 to 5 mm deep.
Pores: light-brown, sometimes with a purple tinge; 4 to 6 per mm.
Spore print: white or creamy-yellow.

This inedible polypore causes white rot.

Laetiporus sulphureus (Polyporaceae) – Chicken of the Woods

With its strident orange or sulphur yellow colour, this flamboyant bracket is hard to miss. Also known as the Sulphur Polypore, this parasite grows on Beech, oaks, Sweet Chestnut and Yew. (Never eat Chicken of the Woods gathered from Yews.) The fruitbodies are usually annual but sometimes survive winter and continue fruiting the following year.

Fruitbody: upper surface varies from egg yellow to pale creamy yellow with pink and orange tinged bands, and the flesh is also yellow-orange when moist, drying paler; wavy-edged young brackets are soft and spongy with broad margins, but as they age the margins become thinner and paler; individual brackets range from 10 to 40cm across and are 3 to 12cm thick.
Tubes: yellow; 1.5 to 4mm deep.
Pores: pale yellow; round when young, then angular; 2 or 3 per mm.
Spore print: white.

Young caps taste rather like chicken; old ones taste more like the wood!

Chicken of the Woods is considered a good edible species, but very young caps are best.

Heterobasidion annosum (Bondarzewiaceae) - Root Rot

This really is one of the most serious parasites of conifers, and it is the cause of major economic loss to the forestry industry. Occasionally this root-rotting perennial bracket infects Beech trees and once in a while birches too. The tough fruitbodies of 'Fomes Rot', as many forestry managers still call it (an earlier synonym for this species was *Fomes annosus*), occur low down on the buttress roots.

Trees become infected via wounds to the bark, where the sapwood of buttress roots is exposed. Stumps of freshly felled trees are an open invitation to this fungus, whose mycelium spreads from one tree to another where the roots of adjacent trees rub against one another.

Fruitbody: brown, corrugated upper surface blackening with age; narrow, round-edged brackets 5 to 30cm across and 1 to 2cm thick; sometimes in tiers and occasionally resupinate; downy when young, then smooth but uneven or knobbly.
Tubes: off-white; a new tube layer 2 to 5mm thick grows each year.
Pores: creamy white; round; spaced at 2 to 4 per mm.
Spore print: cream or pale yellow.

Although a spruce tree was felled here several months earlier, brackets of *Heterobasidion annosum* have now appeared on its stump and may infect other trees in the forest.

Daedaleopsis confragosa (Polyporaceae) – Blushing Bracket

Despite its common name, this kidney-shaped polypore is often found without the reddish warts on its upper surface. Bruise the pore layer, however, and the justification for its nickname soon becomes apparent: the pale pore surface turns pink.

Blushing Bracket fruitbodies often occur in tiers.

Fruitbody: concentrically-lined, laterally-attached stemless brackets 5 to 20cm across and 1 to 4cm thick.
Fertile surface: cream; mostly closed slits, 5 to 10mm deep, but a few of the slits form maze-like patterns, clearly distinguishing the Blushing Bracket from the Oak Mazegill, whose pores are all in the form of a maze.
Spore print: white.

Willow is the most common host for this perennial bracket fungus, but it can also occur on other hardwoods including Hazel, poplars, birches and alders.

Waterside Goat Willows are particularly prone to infection by this common polypore, whose brackets persist through the winter months and can continue growing for several years.

Postia caesia (Polyporaceae) – Conifer Blueing Bracket

Only a tiny minority of fungi are blue and most of those are cap-and-stem fungi, so a blue polypore comes as quite a surprise. *Postia caesia* is also known as the Blue-cheese Polypore, although the resemblance is solely visual: it smells very strange and is generally considered inedible. This relatively uncommon bracket fungus occurs mainly on conifers, usually in damp and shady locations, although very occasionally it can be found on deciduous broad-leaf trees.

***Postia caesia* on a mossy conifer trunk**

Fruitbody: laterally attached to the substrate, typically 3 to 8 cm across and roughly semicircular, sometimes with a rudimentary stem. Even when fully mature the fruitbodies are rarely more than 2cm in thickness.
Tubes: white; 4 to 6mm deep.
Pores: white; round; 2 to 4 per mm.
Spore print: off-white.

Because of its particular type of hyphal structure, this annual polypore is soft and soon decays once the frost arrives. As it ages, the whole of the fruitbody takes on a bluish tinge. Even the off-white spore print then sports a noticeable hint of blue.

Postia stiptica **(Polyporaceae) – Bitter Bracket**
The Bitter Bracket is fairly common but often very well hidden, so that despite being big and brilliant white it is easily missed. Synonyms include *Tyromyces stipticus* and *Oligoporus stipticus* (plus at least another dozen!). The watery droplets that in all but the driest of weather exude from the margin and the pores on the fertile (lower) surface help distinguish this bracket from several other related pallid polypores.

Fruitbody: irregular bracket; up to 10cm across; sometimes roughly semicircular but more often shell shaped; 1 to 3cm thick; upper (infertile) surface velvety, uneven; white, becoming light ochre with age; margins rounded in young specimens, more acute as fruitbodies age; lower (fertile) surface with tubes; watery droplets exuded mainly from margin region and from tubes.
Tubes: white; 2 to 6mm deep.
Pores: white; round or angular, spaced at 1 to 2 per mm.
Spore print: white.

Nearly always found on dead conifer logs and stumps, although it smells like field mushrooms this inedible bracket is so bitter that it is definitely worth getting to know it so well that you can identify it at a glance without the need for a taste test!

Pycnoporus cinnabarinus **(Polyporaceae) – Cinnabar Bracket**
This very rare and beautiful polypore is saprophytic on hardwood trees, including Beech, birches and Cherry. Only once have I seen this species, and that was in Bulgaria. If you think that you have found one, check again: often a Beefsteak Fungus *Fistulina hepatica* is mistaken for this cinnabar polypore. (Both are beautiful fungi, so it's no cause for tears.)

Fruitbody: bright orange; up to 10cm across and projecting typically 4 to 6cm from substrate; usually between 1 and 2cm thick; upper (infertile) surface rough or wrinkled, orange-red, fading with age; margins are rounded (left) in young specimens, which are downy or finely hairy on the upper surface; margin becomes more acute as fruitbody ages; lower (fertile) surface with tubes.
Tubes: pale orange; 2 to 6mm deep.
Pores: cinnabar red; round or angular, spaced at 2 to 4 per mm.
Spore print: white.

If you come across this bracket in Britain or Ireland count it as the find of a lifetime. It is rather more likely to turn up in foray records on mainland Europe, but even there it is a rare species and so it should never be picked.

***Trametes gibbosa* (Polyporaceae) – Lumpy Bracket**
This saprophytic polypore is found on most kinds of hardwood trees but particularly on Beech; it causes white rot. Often the pale upper surface is discoloured by green algae, the more so in the zones further from the margin. That and the slot-like pores (other whitish *Trametes* species have round or oval pores) makes this a very easy polypore to identify.

Fruitbody: white with leathery flesh; typically 5 to 20cm across and roughly semicircular, varying greatly in thickness but usually between 1 and 6 cm; margins are rounded in young specimens, which are downy on the upper surface, whereas the upper surface loses its down and the margins become more acute as fruitbodies age.
Tubes: light grey; 3 to 15mm deep.
Pores: cream turning ochre with age; irregular, elongated and maze-like.
Spore print: white.

***Trametes gibbosa* produces brackets on standing trunks and occasionally, as above, attractive rosettes on stumps.**

This is yet another of the many inedible bracket fungi that produce visually attractive perennial fruitbodies.

Just because we cannot enjoy eating a fungus doesn't necessarily mean it has no food value: the fruitbodies of *Trametes gibbosa* are frequently attacked by boring beetle larvae.

***Trametes hirsuta* (Polyporaceae) – Hairy Bracket**
Very few of the polypores can be described as beautiful, but when you come across young fruitbodies of *Trametes hirsuta* on a nice sunny day you may well agree that they look absolutely gorgeous in their silvery velvet gowns. Unfortunately these brackets soon lose their pristine appearance, developing brown radial lines and deep furrows near the margin on the upper surface and a yellowish tinge to the fertile underside. Aged specimens are sometimes devoid of the downy coating to which the specific epithet refers.

Fruitbody: white or cream, downy with tough, cork-like flesh; semicircular, up to 10cm across and typically 5mm deep; often tiered, adjacent caps are occasionally fused laterally.
Tubes: white; 4 to 6 mm deep.
Pores: white; angular, often varying randomly in size and sometimes merging; typically 3 to 4 per mm (see inset picture, right).
Spore print: white.

***Trametes hirsuta* on the standing trunk of a dead Wild Cherry tree**

Note: *Trametes hirsuta* can be seen on many kinds of broadleaf trees. It is a saprophytic fungus causing white rot.

Trametes versicolor (Polyporaceae) - Turkeytail

In the past this very common bracket fungus was generally referred to as the Many-zoned Polypore, but the American common name Turkeytail is now widely accepted. *Trametes versicolor* (syn. *Coriolus versicolor*) fruits in autumn and early winter but the brackets take a long time to decay and so can be found all through the year. Tough and inedible, this fungus grows mainly on dead hardwood. The wide range of colour variations has resulted in the dried brackets having many ornamental uses - even as hat decorations.

Turkey tails form rosettes or tiers of brackets.

Fruitbody: colour forms are many, with concentric zones of red, yellow, green, blue, brown, black and white on the upper surfaces; individual leathery, fan-like brackets are up to 10 cm across and 1 to 3mm thick, frequently overlapping in layers to form a large compound fruiting mass.
Tubes: white; 0.5 to 1mm deep.
Pores: white or cream, not staining when bruised; spaced at 3 to 5 per mm.
Spore print: white.

There is no distinctive odour to these bracket fungi and no particular taste either, but that hardly matters because they are far too tough to eat. This does seem rather a shame because, unlike some of the best edible brackets, Turkeytail can easily be collected without the need for climbing!

Daedaleopsis tricolor (Fomitopsidaceae) – No Common Name

There are so many colour variations in *Trametes versicolor* that it is almost forgivable to assume that any fan-shaped thin bracket with concentric, many-zoned bands on its upper surface must be yet another Turkeytail. No so! Easily misidentified as *Trametes versicolor* is another thin and leathery fan-like bracket, again with many concentric colour bands but predominantly wine red; however, there is one very important feature distinguishing it from Turkeytail. To spot the difference you have to look on the underside of a bracket. *Daedaleopsis tricolor* has gills rather than pores. They aren't merely very long magegill slots but structures very similar to the gills of an agaric mushroom… but nevertheless, this white-rot producer is a polypore – taxonomically, that is!

If not Turkeytail, it must be a mazegill…

…but to be quite sure just look underneath.

Fruitbody: many-zoned, often reddish fan-like brackets, up to 10 cm across and 1 to 2 cm thick at the point of attachment; usually in tiers.
Gills: white at first, turning brown with age; well-spaced or fairly close; sharp-edged; tough; up to 1 cm deep.
Spore print: white.

Genetic analysis suggests that in evolutionary terms the *Daedaleopsis* genus is close to other polypores, which must have split from the Agaricales a very long time ago. The fact that agarics *and* one or two polypores now have gills may be an example of convergent evolution – or simply that the capacity to grow gills had remained latent in the polypores and re-emerged in *Daedaleopsiss* (and in *Schizophyllum commune* too – see below).

***Schizophyllum commune* (Schizophyllaceae) – Split Gill**
Often seen on sickly hardwood trees, but equally common on dead wood including cut timber, this common fungus usually grows as a sessile bracket. On the undersides of branches, however, it more often forms centrally-attached circular fans.

Seen from above, this is just another small white bracket-like fungus, but beneath the cap are radial gill-like folds, each of which is centrally split. The splits close over the fertile surfaces as the fruitbody shrivels during prolonged dry weather, rehydrating when moistened by rain; then the splits reopen, the spore-producing surfaces are exposed to the air, and spores are released. Split Gills can survive several such cycles.

From the top, perhaps just a hairy polypore...

...but look underneath to see the split gills.

Fruitbody: white and hairy, sometimes tinged purple; the individual caps are typically 1 to 3cm across and 0.3 to 1cm thick; frequently fused into the edges of adjacent caps. More often than not many tiers of fruitbodies cover damaged areas of bark on a sickly tree's trunk or on dead or dying branches.
Gills: pinkish grey; radiating from the attachment point (whether lateral or central); splitting lengthways and curling back to protect the fertile surface (hymenium) during dry weather.
Spore print: white.

These inedible fungi are long lived, and the fruitbodies can be seen throughout the year.

Sparassis crispa (Sparassidaceae) – Wood Cauliflower

Here is a parasite that seems to know when it is on to a good thing. The Wood Cauliflower is a weak pathogen of conifers, and particularly pines. It limits its brown-rot damage to a tree's root system such that its host can live for many years while producing useful timber and still providing food for its fungal vampire. The tiered fruitbodies are annual, fairly short-lived, and most often seen in Britain and Ireland between early July and late October. Although these unusual fungi do not look much like cauliflowers, they look even less like anything else. Young fruitbodies are much the same colour as young cauliflowers, although invariably they hug the ground rather than standing up on stalks.

Fruitbody: off-white, soon turning cream; later browning at the edges and then turning brown all over and rotting away; to 40cm across and 30cm tall; arising from a stout base branching at or just below ground level; branches terminate in contorted fronds; the flesh, which is edible, is firm and crisp and is easily broken.
Fertile surface: spores are produced on basidia, usually on the lower surface of the fronds but sometimes on both upper and lower surfaces, each of which is smooth and matt without tubes/pores.
Spore print: white or very pale yellow.

Meripilus giganteus (Meripilaceae) - Giant Polypore

This huge polypore appears at the bases of living broad-leaved trees - notably Beech – and produces fruitbodies annually in summer and early autumn, sometimes for a decade or more. When eventually the tree dies, the fungus continues fruiting for another year or two.

Fruitbody: individual caps can be up to half a metre across and typically 1 to 4cm thick. As the caps are often produced in clusters or in rosettes when growing from roots away from the tree, the compound fruitbody can extend to a metre or more across. Short-lived, soon turning black and collapsing.
Tubes: white; 4 to 6mm deep.
Pores: white; round; 3 to 5 per mm. When bruised, the pores turn brown and then black.
Spore print: white.

Young caps of Giant Polypore _Meripilus giganteus_ have yellow, rounded edges, whereas the edges of older ones become paler, sharper, more wavy and much less spongy.

Cooked very slowly, young caps of the Giant Polypore are reportedly edible. Soaking the caps in milk for a few hours is a recommended way of reducing their bitter taste (a feature of many of the polypores). However, as it has been known to cause stomach upsets in some people this is one of the bracket fungi that you might decide not to have for lunch.

Grifola frondosa (Meripilaceae) - Hen of the Woods

Hen of the Woods is a weak parasite found mainly at the bases of oak trees. This edible fungus causes white rot.

Fruitbody: tan to olive or cream in undulating concentric zones; individual fronds 4 to 10cm across and 5 to 10mm thick in circular tiers from a branching stem, forming a rosette 20 to 50cm across.
Tubes: white; 2 to 4 mm deep.
Pores: pale cream; between 3 and 4 per mm; decurrent to the stem.
Spore print: white.

Hen of the Woods at the base of an oak tree

Hericium erinaceus (Hericiaceae) - Bearded Tooth

Unmistakably a 'hedgehog', albeit in squirrel habitat, this beautiful toothed bracket occurs on living and dead hardwood trees, notably Beech. At one time included in the order Cantharellales along with *Hydnum* species, these wood-rotting tooth fungi are now recognised as belonging to the Russulales. In the wild, Bearded Tooth is quite a rare find in Britain and Ireland but more common in mainland Europe.

Fruitbody: off-white; 10 to 15cm dia.
Fertile surface: spines to 6cm long.
Spore print: white.

The prized edible Bearded Tooth fungus is now produced on sawdust logs in cultivation.

Hericium cirrhatum (Hericiaceae) - Tiered Tooth

A very rare sight in Britain and Ireland, this tooth fungus forms bracket-like tiers on the trunks and, less frequently, fallen branches of deciduous trees. I have only ever found it on Beech. Like the Bearded Tooth fungus, the Tiered Tooth is edible, but rarity makes its collection for food inexcusable, and please note that it is strictly illegal to pick *Hericium* fruitbodies in the UK.

Fruitbody: creamy-white; in irregular tiers; 5 to 15cm across.
Fertile surface: white, flexible spines 10 to 15mm long.
Spore print: white.

Gilled mushrooms on standing trees

Only a tiny minority of common cap-and-stem mushrooms are parasitic on living trees. Many more consume dead wood on standing trees; but, because it not easy to determine which part of the timber a fungus is feeding on, in this section I have simply included a selection of the mushrooms most commonly seen on living trees.

Armillaria mellea (Physalacriaceae) - Honey Fungus

Honey Fungus attacks living trees, but it hangs around after the crime to feed on the corpses, including stumps and fallen trunks if they are not taken away for their timber value.

One of the most deadly and widely distributed parasites of trees and occasionally of other plants, too, Honey Fungus forms its fruitbodies only after the timber in which it grows has been killed. It is usually the appearance of fruitbodies that betrays the presence of this parasite, whose vegetative mycelium then spreads as a saprophyte in the dead tissues of the tree and forms bootlace-like strands, called rhizomorphs, that travel through soil, feeding on leaf litter and other rotting plant tissue until they encounter a new potential host. Honey Fungus is now classified as several distinct species most of which have stem rings and scaly caps. All are associated with woodland habitats. The macroscopic differences between the various species are small and are not detailed here.

Cap: yellowish-brown, sometimes with an olive tint; to 12cm across; convex, flattening later; often with minute light-brown scales, a slightly depressed centre and a wavy margin.
Gills: white, turning brownish-yellow; crowded; adnate or very slightly decurrent.
Stem: off-white, turning brown; to 15cm long, with a persistent white or pale yellow ring; covered in brown scales, particularly below the ring.

Armillaria tabescens, the Ringless Honey Fungus, is a smaller and darker mushroom, and as the common name implies the stem lacks a ring. *Armillaria gallica*, the Bulbous Honey Fungus, is distinguished by a club-shaped stem base; it has only an ephemeral stem ring.

Honey Fungi lifting skirts to flaunt their rings

Ringless Honey Fungus *Armillaria tabescens*

Flammulina velutipes (Tricholomataceae) - Velvet Shank

One of the few species that fruit most prolifically in the depths of winter, often with snow on their caps and surviving sub-zero temperatures, Velvet Shank is a popular edible mushroom. (The stems are tough, and so most mushroom gatherers retain only the caps.)

Cap: reddish brown; initially convex or bell-shaped, becoming almost flat when fully mature; smooth, matt and finely velvety; to 8cm across.
Gills: initially white, gradually turning reddish ochre; crowded; adnexed.
Stem: fawn at the top, progressively a darker brown towards the base; 4 to 10cm long and 4 to 8mm diameter; tough; cylindrical and curved near attachment to substrate; velvety, especially nearer to the base.
Spore print: white.

Most often seen growing in tufts on hardwood trees, including Beech and elms, but occasionally on conifers too, this attractive mushroom also occurs on wood chip mulch. This implies that it is saprophytic; however, many apparently healthy trees have tufts of Velvet Shank fungi emerging from areas of damaged bark.

Cultivated forms of Velvet Shank have been available in Japan for at least 300 years and are known as Enokitake or simply Enoki. Initially they were grown on wood, but nowadays they are cultivated in controlled environments inside plastic bottles; as a result, the stems are very long and the mushrooms are white rather than brown. Supermarkets in Britain, Ireland and throughout mainland Europe now stock Enoki mushrooms, sometimes fresh but often also in jars and cans.

Mucidula (formerly _Oudemansiella_) _mucida_ (Marasmiaceae) – Porcelain Fungus
When sunlight shines down through a Beech canopy via the caps of these neat little fungi the sight is quite magical. Often high up on trunks or large branches, tufts of Porcelain Fungus curve upwards like pure white umbrellas. On breezy days they sometimes get dislodged, falling to earth rather faster than a parachute but in a similar manner.

Cap: translucent white or ivory with ochre tints in the centre; slimy; convex, gradually flattening but often retaining a broad umbo; to 8cm across.
Gills: white; adnate; distant.
Stem: white with a brownish base; persistent ring, white on its upper surface and brownish below; fine striations above the ring and slightly scaly below; to 10cm long and 3 to 10mm dia.; cylindrical, thickening abruptly at the base.
Spore print: white.

Pleurotus dryinus (Pleurotaceae) – Veiled Oyster
Among the oyster mushrooms (so called because the shape of the cap is similar to that of an oyster shell) are some outstandingly photogenic fungi, and the Veiled Oyster is certainly one of the finest. The fruitbodies can be found on living or dead hardwood trees, notably Beech trees and oaks, and very occasionally on conifers.

Veiled Oysters displaying felt-like cap surfaces

Cap: white or cream; convex and usually bracket-like with either radial or eccentric stem; convex, gradually flattening but often retaining a broad umbo; felt-like, often breaking into large scale-like patches; to 15cm across.
Gills: white; decurrent.
Stem: white or cream; up to 3cm long and 1 to 2cm dia.; tapering towards base; with a short-lived white or cream ring.
Spore print: white or cream.

Fragments of the partial veil can often be seen hanging from the inrolled cap margins of young specimens of the Veiled Oyster. It is the partial veil (rather than a universal veil of the kind that leaves a volva at the stem base of *Amanita* and *Volvariella* species) from which this edible mushroom gets its common name. The frosted appearance of the cap distinguishes this oyster mushroom from the other common members of the *Pleurotus* genus.

The Veiled Oyster's ring zone is ephemeral.

Pleurotus ostreatus (Pleurotaceae) - Oyster Mushroom

So variable in size, shape and colour are the many kinds of oyster mushrooms that identification is tricky or impossible without resorting to microscopic analysis. The process is not helped by the fruiting habit of many *Pleurotus* species: they seem to delight in emerging beyond reach, sometimes high up in the crowns of trees. For the most part these fungi are saprophytic on deciduous trees, and only very rarely are they found on conifers.

Cap: white, cream, blue-grey or brown; usually bracket-like with either radial or eccentric stem; convex gradually becoming centrally depressed with a wavy margin; 5 to 15cm across.
Gills: white, turning pale ochre with age; crowded; decurrent.
Stem: white or cream; woolly at base; no ring; 1 to 3cm long and 1 to 2cm dia.; tapering towards base.
Spore print: white or cream.

The genus name *Pleurotus* is Latin for 'sideways' and refers to the lateral attachment of the stem; *ostreatus* is a reference to oysters, and in shape the fruitbodies do sometimes resemble oyster shells. Many people assert that oyster mushrooms actually taste like their bivalve namesakes; certainly the texture is similar to the that of cooked oysters.

Pleurotus cornucopiae (Pleurotaceae) – Branched Oyster Mushroom

The branching nature of these funnel-shaped oysters helps distinguish them from other members of the *Pleurotus* genus. Often several caps share a common stem.

Cap: cream or light ochre; covered in a fine white bloom when young, becoming smooth with age; convex, becoming centrally depressed and then funnel-shaped with a wavy margin that sometimes splits when old; attached to the substrate via an eccentric stem or occasionally appearing to be stemless; groups of caps often overlapping in tiers up the trunk of an infected tree.
Gills: white, maturing to pale buff; branching; deeply decurrent, becoming shallow grooves that often extend right down to the substrate.
Stem: white or cream; to 5cm long and 1 to 2.5cm dia.; no ring.
Spore print: white or cream.

Branching Oysters were a common sight at the height of Dutch elm disease. While they continue to show a partiality for elms, they are now most often seen on dying or dead Beech trees.

Pholiota squarrosa (Strophariaceae) - Shaggy Scalycap

An opportunistic parasite, Shaggy Scalycap attacks a wide range of broadleaf host trees but is only rarely seen on conifers. This fungus can also live as a saprobe, deriving nutrients from decomposing wood of the 'recently deceased' and so can occasionally be found also on stumps after trees have been felled and the saleable timber removed.

Cap: straw yellow; covered in upturned rusty-brown scales; convex initially, flattening at maturity but retaining a slightly inrolled margin; usually 5 to 8 cm but exceptionally 12cm across.
Gills: pale yellow, turning cinnamon and later rusty brown when mature; adnate; crowded.
Stem: upper stem concolorous with cap, but darker brown near base; covered in scales, as cap; 5 to 12cm long and 1 to 1.5cm dia; persistent cream-coloured ragged ring near top of stem.
Spore print: rust-brown.

Gymnopilus junonius (Strophariaceae) – Spectacular Rustgill

Sometimes seen on living trees, but often on stumps of recently-felled hardwoods, this rustgill is unusual in having a persistent ring.

Cap: Convex, flattening with a broad umbo and incurved margin; 7 to 15cm across; gold or orange with brown fibrils or small scales.
Gills: yellow, turning rust-brown when mature; adnate or slightly decurrent; crowded.
Stem: concolorous with cap, but paler above ascending ring; swollen near base; 7 to 15cm long and 2 to 4cm dia; persistent brown ring.
Spore print: rust-brown.

Gymnopus fusipes (Marasmiaceae) - Spindleshank

The distinctive stem of this mushroom is often buried and visible only after excavation. Spindleshank occurs in tufts on basal roots of hardwood trees, notable Beech and oaks.

Cap: Convex, flattening with an irregular incurved margin; 3 to 7cm across; brown, often with dark brown blotches.
Gills: white, tinged tan-brown, developing rusty spots; adnexed or free; distant.
Stem: white near apex, tan towards base; spindle-shaped; 7 to 15cm long and 0.8 to 1.5cm dia; no ring.
Spore print: white or cream.

Ascomycetes on Living Trees

To conclude this section, here are some tree-rotting fungi from the phylum Ascomycota. (Many other ascomycetes with much smaller fruitbodies not easily spotted from a distance are known to parasitise trees or to decompose the wood of dead standing trees.)

Daldinia concentrica (Xylariaceae) – King Alfred's Cakes

This ascomycete fruits as dark brown (initially) balls on the trunks and large branches of Ash trees and very occasionally other hardwood trees. The fruitbodies quickly turn black and become very hard – so hard that removing them from their host often requires a substantial thump with a rock. (A sharp knife makes the job a lot easier and safer!)

Fruitbody: dark brown and later black; 2 to 7cm in diameter; roughly hemispherical, often with a slightly undulating matt surface.
Fertile surface: perithecia, visible with a strong magnifying lens, are typically 0.4mm in diameter and are distributed all over the surface that is open to the air.
Spore print: black.

Like other members of the Ascomycota that grow on wood, King Alfred's Cakes cause a soft rot.

Nectria cinnabarina (Hypocreaceae) – Coral Spot

Coral Spot, another member of the pyrenomycetes group within the Ascomycota, is a weak pathogen of broadleaf trees. It is hardly ever seen on conifers. Beech is the host most often infected, but this parasite is also fairly common on Sycamore, Horse Chestnut and Hornbeam. Particularly susceptible are trees that have already been weakened by other stressing factors such as drought, another fungal infestation or physical damage. The effect of Coral Spot infection is that (usually small) twigs and branches die back, and then dense clusters of soft, pinhead-sized pink fungal blobs break through the thin bark. Later the blobs harden and turn dark reddish-brown, and by this time the infected timber is so weak that it usually snaps off during windy weather.

Fruitbody: pink blobs, turning reddish brown when mature; 1 to 4mm diameter and becoming hard.
Fertile surface: the rough surface comprises tiny perithecia each with an apical hole via which spores are discharged.
Spore print: white or cream.

Coral Spot can be seen throughout the year but is most noticeable on trees when they are devoid of leaves during autumn and winter.

Coral Spot fruitbodies densely packed together on a twig, have made exit wounds through the bark.

***Bulgaria inquinans* (Bulgariaceae) – Black Bulgar**
This leathery wood-rotting fungus can be seen throughout the winter months, nearly always on oak trunks and branches. Even on living trees it is saprophytic on dead wood.

Black Bulgars on an oak trunk

Fruitbody: black or dark brown; top is flat at first, becoming saucer shaped; upper (fertile) surface shiny; infertile sides felty and a lighter brown; flesh is dark ochre-brown, soft and rubbery in wet weather becoming tough and more elastic when dry; individual fruit bodies 0.5 to 4cm across and typically 1cm tall.
Spore print: Very dark brown, almost black.

Jelly-like Rust Fungi

Rusts can have very complex life cycles compared with other fungi in the Basidiomycota. Although some rusts complete their life cycle on a single host, there are many more that alternate between two hosts; they are then said to be heteroecious, with the primary host being infected by aeciospores (special kinds of vegetative spores) and the alternate host being infected with basidiospores. Some rusts go through as many as four or five spore-producing stages with different kinds of spores produced at each stage. Most rust fungi do not produce large fruitbodies and so they are generally outside the scope of this book; however, rusts of the genus *Gymnosporangium* can be easily confused with some of the jelly fungi, and so here is an example of the kind of thing to look out for…

***Gymnosporangium clavariiforme* (Pucciniaceae) – A Juniper Rust Fungus**
On Juniper (family Cupressaceae), which is the primary host, a *Gymnosporangium* fungus forms a ball of horns that expand in wet weather and take on a jelly-like consistency. Spores are released and carried on the wind until they infect and induce galls on a tree in the family Rosaceae. Later the fungus produces yellow depressions on the leaves of its secondary host. It also infects the fruit, causing it to sprout small white tubes, which in due course release spores that must infect a Juniper in order to complete the lifecycle.

Fruitbody: rust-coloured horns; rubbery; each typically 1cm across and up to 3cm long; clustered around stem, usually in the form of a ball.
Spore print: white.

Note: Junipers do not seem to be damaged by this fungus, but its alternate host, Hawthorn in this instance, is more seriously affected. Other *Gymnosporangium* species use fruit trees such as apples (*Malus* spp.) and pears (*Pyrus* spp.) as secondary hosts and can destroy entire crops.

Ganoderma applanatum **on a Beech tree. Guess what colour the spores are!**

Chapter 6 - The Rest of the Rotters

Saprophytic fungi of the forest floor

Without the work of the woodland waste disposal team there would soon be no room for new trees in a forest. Fallen trunks and branches, dead stumps, leaves and twigs don't litter the forest floor forever (although some trunks take as long to rot away as they did to grow). In time various agents of decay turn all dead matter back into basic compounds that trees and other plants can feed upon. Bacteria, beetles, bugs and other small animals all make important contributions, but central and crucial to the complex recycling process are the multiplicity of forest floor saprophytic fungi.

Stumped? The colourful wood-rotting fungus tucking in to supper on the base of this dead oak tree is Tufted Bracket *Fuscoporia torulosa*. Microscopic analysis (see Chapter 10) is often necessary in order to separate with confidence the many lookalikes in this and several other bracket fungi genera.

Like people, some fungi are very good at getting stuck in to new challenges but then seem to lose interest after a while. (What they leave behind, however, has usually been softened up sufficiently for beetles and other bugs to be able to get their teeth into it.) Quite different kinds of fungi operate as 'completer-finishers'. Vulture-like, they take over a tough old carcass and pick at it until there is virtually nothing left.

The species diversity of woodland recycling fungi is truly amazing. Unfortunately, this genetic diversity is not matched by a corresponding physical diversity: many species have a huge number of lookalikes, and I have yet to meet anyone who finds identifying forest-floor fungi easy. A few species are so visually unique and consistent that once you have seen one you have seen them all; then identification is solely a matter of pattern recognition, a feat of memory (or, to be more precise, of recall... keeping track of so many names is no mean feat!)

Clues to Identifying Forest-floor Fungi

Because fungi have food fads, the substrate on which you find a fruitbody is a vital clue in the detective process of identification. Certain species are found only on newly felled trunks, fallen branches or stumps; others feed on rotten wood buried in the litter of the forest floor, while many groups are more or less confined to small twigs, to dead leaves or to humus-rich woodland soil. In this introduction to the recycling rotters of the forest floor these basic habitat types are valuable clues in the early stages of our detective work.

Unlike many of the mycorrhizal mushrooms, few of the forest-floor rotters are addicted to the wood of just one tree or even one genus of trees, which suggests that identifying the tree species from which rotten wood originated (often a very difficult thing to do in the field or forest) is rarely going to help much with a tricky identification. The two categories of broadleaf and conifer do provide useful clues, however, as many wood-rotting fungi feed exclusively (or in some cases almost always so) on either one category or the other. It's also worth noting the stage of decomposition – in particular whether it has fallen recently or has become buried within the litter of the forest floor.

Here are some substrate types that are worth noting:

- Conifer stumps and fallen trunks
- Broadleaf stumps and fallen trunks
- Fallen conifer twigs
- Fallen conifer needles
- Fallen hardwood twigs
- Fallen hardwood leaves
- Buried conifer timber (softwood)
- Buried broadleaf timber (hardwood)
- Woodland soil rich in rotted conifer litter
- Woodland soil rich in rotted hardwood litter

This fallen conifer trunk has been split asunder by the emerging fruitbodies of Common Rustgill *Gymnopus penetrans*, opening up opportunities for the many small lignicolous species to finish of the corpse.

In the introduction to each of the groups of fungi described in this chapter, the substrate type or types on which they most commonly occur is stated.

It's not always possible to determine by visual inspection whether soil is acidic or alkaline, but because many fungi have a preference for one extreme or the other a bit of detective work can turn up additional clues. For example it is a good idea to make a note of any plant species that you can recognise in the vicinity of an unidentified fungus, since knowing their habitat or soil preferences can speed the process of elimination.

Agaricaceae

This well-known family of gilled fungi includes the button mushrooms and chestnut mushrooms that dominate supermarket shelves in Britain and Ireland – indeed across most of the Western World. In northern Europe several large edible mushrooms and a lot more small and inedible ones (plus quite a few poisonous *Lepiota* species) belong to this family; however, perhaps the biggest surprise to many people is that puffballs (*Lycoperdon*) and some of the inkcaps (*Coprinus*) are now recognised as belonging to the Agaricaceae.

The True Mushrooms

Field Mushrooms *Agaricus campestris*, Horse Mushrooms *Agaricus arvensis*, and so many other members of the genus *Agaricus* are found only or mainly in grassy habitats that there is an understandable tendency to think of the whole genus as a grassland group. For the most part that is true, but there are some notable exceptions including a few of the finest of large edible fungi. Woodland *Agaricus* fungi are litter rotters and they all grow on humus-rich soil. Free pink gills that turn brown at maturity plus (albeit in some cases short lived) white stem rings are characteristics common to nearly every member of the genus, but because size and cap colour are such unreliable characteristics accurate identification often demands careful attention to detail and a sensitive nose.

Agaricus augustus (Agaricaceae) - Prince

Unfortunately far from common, this is one of the very finest of edible fungi (indeed, it truly deserves the title Prince of Mushrooms!); it usually appears in small groups in open woodland or beneath parkland trees, particularly conifers. The Prince is exceptional among woodland mushrooms in being instantly recognisable from a distance; however, if you are ever in any doubt its bitter-almond odour provides additional assurance.

Cap: 10 to 22cm across; initially hemispherical, becoming broadly convex; cream surface covered in large reddish-brown scales, increasingly dense towards the centre.
Gills: free; pale pink, turning dark purple-brown with age.
Stem: 10 to 20cm long and 2 to 4cm dia.; large pendulous white ring; white surface smooth above ring, and with small woolly scales below.
Spores: purple-brown.
Odour: strong, of bitter almonds.

Agaricus impudicus (Agaricaceae) – Tufted Wood Mushroom

There are several largish *Agaricus* mushrooms that appear solely or mainly in woodland habitats, and separating them with certainty can be quite a challenge. Many of these are superficially similar to *Agaricus augustus*, but beware: some are known to be poisonous, and even among the edible ones there are none that compare in terms of flavour with The Prince. *Agaricus impudicus* is one of the edible wood mushrooms, but it is far from remarkable for its flavour. This attractive species is widespread but only an occasional find in many parts of Britain and Ireland. Although it occurs most often in groups beneath conifers, you may also find it occasionally in deciduous woods.

Cap: 5 to 10cm across; initially convex, often becoming flat topped as it expands; large scales usually in various shades of dark brown on a pale brown background; whitish flesh not changing colour significantly when cut or bruised.
Gills: free; crowded; greyish pink, turning brown with age.
Stem: 6 to 10cm long and 0.8 to 1.2 cm dia., with a slightly bulbous base; white pendulous ring; surface smooth and white, turning brown with age.
Spores: chocolate brown.

***Agaricus sylvicola* (Agaricaceae) – Wood Mushroom**

Very much like a Horse Mushroom *Agaricus arvensis* but with a thinner cap that expands until almost perfectly flat, the Wood Mushroom is a good edible species and quite common in southern parts of Britain and Ireland. This slender, pallid mushroom is easy to spot, but as if anxious not to be overlooked it also gives off a hard-to-miss aniseed scent. The Wood Mushroom and can be used as a substitute in recipes calling for Field Mushrooms *Agaricus campestris* or for Horse Mushrooms; no one is likely to notice any difference. The cap surface bruises yellow, but when cut the stem base does not turn the garish chrome yellow associated with its poisonous lookalike the Yellow Stainer *Agaricus xanthodermus* which, although mainly a woodland-edge species, is sometimes found inside woods. An odour test also helps avoid collecting Yellow Stainers (which give off an unpleasant ink-like odour) in mistake for Wood Mushrooms. When collecting young Wood Mushrooms, which have pallid gills, be alert to the risk of confusion with the Destroying Angel or pale forms of the Deathcap.

Cap: 8 to 18cm across; initially convex, becoming flat but usually retaining a shallow umbo; dull satin surface, initially white then turning cream and eventually ochre; bruises slightly yellow (most noticeably at margin).
Gills: free; crowded; initially white or pale grey, turning purple and then dark brown.
Stem: to 15cm long and 1 to 2cm dia.; slightly bulbous base; prominent skirt-like white ring sometimes with a faint cogwheel pattern on the underside; surface smooth and pale grey tinged with pink above the ring, and slightly cottony (floccose) below.
Odour: aniseed, sometimes only faint when young but usually quite strong in mature specimens.
Spores: chocolate brown.

Wood Mushrooms rarely appear as singletons, and more often they occur in small groups. Occasionally these stately fungi form long arcs or even complete fairy rings.

Agaricus xanthodermus (Agaricaceae) – Yellow Stainer

It is so easy to mistake this poisonous mushroom, commonly found on woodland edges and under trees in parkland, for one of the edible woodland *Agaricus* species. The cap and particularly the stem base stain bright chrome yellow when cut (pictured right).

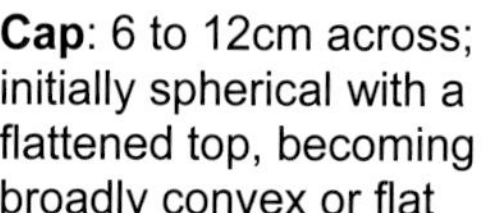

Cap: 6 to 12cm across; initially spherical with a flattened top, becoming broadly convex or flat with an incurved margin; white, developing small grey-brown scales; flesh quickly turning yellow when cut or bruised.
Gills: free; pale pink, turning dark purple-brown with age.
Stem: 6 to 12cm long and 1 to 2cm dia.; bulbous base turns chrome yellow when cut; white ring; surface smooth and white.
Spores: purple-brown.
Odour: inky.

Phaeolepiota aurea (Agaricaceae) – Golden Bootleg

One of the most striking of mushrooms, Golden Bootleg is an uncommon species in most parts of Britain and Ireland; however, if you are in the right place at the right time this huge and flamboyant mushroom is almost impossible to miss. The right place is shady woodland edges where the soil is rich in humus – often among nettles, which themselves are a sign of humus-rich soil. Rarely alone, these inedible mushrooms usually form scattered groups. There is only one known species in this genus, and so *Phaeolepiota* is termed a monotypic genus.

Cap:10 to 25cm across when fully expanded; initially a flattened hemisphere, becoming broadly convex with an umbo; veil tatters hang from rim, other chunks form collar-like sheathing ring on stem; surface dry and granular; golden brown to light orange-brown.
Gills: adnate or free; crowded, white at first, turning ochre as spores mature.
Stem: 8 to 15cm long and 2 to 5cm dia.; tapering slightly towards apex; pale and smooth above stem ring, fibrillose and concolorous with cap below; persistent ring, pale on upper surface, as cap below.
Spores: yellowish brown.

***Echinoderma echinaceum* (Agaricaceae) – No Common Name**

A rare find, this lovely mushroom favours mixed woodland on calcareous soil. The pointed scales on the cap, the fragmentary stem ring, and intermediate gills of varying sizes all help to differentiate between *Echinoderma echinaceum* and the many other similar smallish pale-capped dapperlings.

Cap: 1 to 3cm across, conical then convex or bell-shaped and finally expanded; cream or ochre background covered in pyramidal brown scales in concentric rings.
Gills: free; crowded; intermediate gills of varying lengths; pinkish cream, turning browner with age.
Stem: 2 to 4cm long and 4 to 4mm dia.; pinkish, lower part covered in brown scales, darkening towards base; ring fragmentary.
Spores: white or pale buff.
Odour: **mild, pleasant.**

Dapperlings

Until recently known as parasols, the many woodland *Lepiota* fungi include some seriously poisonous species and none distinctive enough to be considered safe to eat. Fortunately the dapperlings are generally much smaller than any of the edible *Macrolepiota* parasols, so that with care it is easy to avoid that confusion. Included in this group are some very attractive little fungi, three of which are pictured and described here.

***Lepiota cristata* (Agaricaceae) – Stinking Dapperling**

This species is also referred to as the Stinking Parasol, a common name that is fully justified by its unpleasant smell, which is perhaps not a cause for regret because this poisonous mushroom is very variable in appearance and pale specimens just might, on visual characteristics alone, be mistaken for edible mushrooms from the genus *Agaricus*. (Gill colour, visible on expanded caps, is another helpful discriminator.) Expect to find scattered groups of this very common dapperling in all kinds of deciduous and mixed woodland.

Cap: up to 4cm across; initially hemispherical, becoming convex and sometimes almost flat with a broad umbo; initially creamy white with a tawny centre surrounded by concentric rings of reddish-brown scales, more dispersed towards the rim; veil fragments sometimes hang down from the rim.
Gills: free; crowded; initially white or cream turning buff with age.
Stem: 2 to 5cm long and 2 to 5mm dia.; base sometimes swollen; surface smooth or only slightly scaly and coloured as cap background, darkening towards base; white ring is fragile and often ephemeral.
Spores: white or very pale buff.
Odour: strong and unpleasant.

Lepiota felina (Agaricaceae) – Cat Dapperling

No dapperling is more dapper than this dark-scaled little mushroom of dense coniferous forests. Leopard-like in its spots, and with an almost black central eye stark against a white background, the cap is not difficult to find. Often in small groups, these attractive mushrooms are fairly common in the kinds of acid areas where most large conifer plantations are sited. It looks good, and doesn't even smell bad, but like the other small dapperlings *Lepiota felina* is of doubtful edibility and may even be poisonous.

Cap: 1.5 to 3cm across; initially hemispherical, becoming convex and sometimes almost flat with a slight umbo; white with a dark brown or black centre surrounded by concentric rings of relatively large (compared with other dapperlings of similar cap size) dark-brown scales.
Gills: free; crowded; initially white or cream turning buff with age.
Stem: 2.5 to 4cm long and 2 to 4mm dia.; base slightly swollen; creamy white; the persistent ring is creamy white on top and brown beneath.
Spores: white or very pale buff.

Lepiota ignivolvata (Agaricaceae) – No Common Name

Although very variable in stature and in colour, this is quite the easiest of dapperlings to identify, and the diagnostic feature to look out for is an orange band on the edge of oblique rings on the stem. Although far from common, *Lepiota ignivolvata* occurs in deciduous and coniferous woodland.

Cap: 4 to 9cm across; initially hemispherical, becoming convex and then almost flat with a broad umbo; cream or ochre background with a smooth mid-brown centre surrounded by concentric rings of small brown scales.
Gills: free; crowded; white or cream turning buff with age.
Stem: 5 to 12cm long and 0.3 to 0.6cm dia.; base slightly swollen; creamy white, turning brown with age or when bruised; one or more oblique floccose rings, creamy white with orange indented edges.
Spores: white or very pale buff.

Puffballs: Gill-less Cousins of the Humble Button Mushroom!

DNA analysis has supported suspicions that the various puffballs, earthballs, stinkhorns and earthstars have little in common but for the fact that they all produce spores internally rather than on gills, pores or spines. The puffballs are now recognised as close relatives of the true mushrooms (*Agaricus* spp.) and are placed in the family Agaricaceae.

Lycoperdon perlatum (Agaricaceae) – Common Puffball

The type species of the *Lycoperdon* genus, this puffball is one of the most common of woodland fungi, turning up on most forays from July through to the first heavy frosts. The Common Puffball is edible when young and white throughout, but once the spore mass begins turning yellow the fungi are unsuitable for eating.

Fruitbody: rounded fertile top with a thick sterile stem; surface covered in tiny pyramidal warts or 'pearls' of different sizes; warts initially pale cream, turning ochre before falling off to leave an olive-brown surface; darker area at apex where a pore develops, through which spores are released when either raindrops hit the mature puffball or a breeze blows across the pore hole; empty cases can remain intact for several weeks after all spores have been discharged; the apical hole is sometimes enlarged (pictured left) by small creatures making temporary homes there; 3 to 6cm across head, 2 to 4cm across variable-length stem, 4 to 9cm tall. **Spores**: olive-brown.

Note: Unusually, the fruitbodies shown above are branched. More often Common Puffballs occur either singly, in scattered groups or in small tufts.

Lycoperdon echinatum (Agaricaceae) – Spiny Puffball

An uncommon woodland puffball, *Lycoperdon echinatum* is covered in spines arranged in groups of three or four that meet or cross over at their tips.

Fruitbody: pear shaped, the whole surface covered in spines (inset picture) 4 to 5mm long; initially pale creamy brown, turning mid brown (at which stage reminiscent of a curled-up hedgehog); spines fall off at maturity and an apical pore opens, through which spores are released when either raindrops hit the mature puffball or a breeze blows across the pore hole. 2 to 5cm across, and 3 to 6cm tall. **Spores**: olive-brown.

Note: The specific epithet comes from the Greek word *echinos* meaning 'hedgehog' or 'sea-urchin'. (There is a difference!)

Lycoperdon pyriforme (Agaricaceae) – Stump Puffball

Swarms of these pear-shaped fruitbodies are a common sight on dead stumps. When they appear to be growing on soil they are an indicator of buried trunks or branches.

Fruitbody: pear shaped; surface initially covered in tiny warts that soon fall off; surface gradually turning brown (pictured below, left) and opening at top; interior initially white, turning olive green and eventually becoming brown as the spores mature; 4 to 5cm across and 4 to 6cm tall.
Spores: olive-brown.

Note: although edible, stump puffballs are not highly regarded because they do not taste nearly as good as the best edible puffballs - the Giant Puffball in particular.

Lycoperdon utriforme (Agaricaceae) – Mosaic Puffball

An uncommon find in many areas, the Mosaic Puffball fruits most often in scattered groups in unimproved grassland and occasionally on woodland edges. The similarly-sized but irregularly-shaped flakes, looking rather like crazy paving, distinguish the Mosaic Puffball from its many similar relatives (at least 13 *Lycoperdon* species occur in the UK); the scales do not persist to maturity, however.

Fruitbody: surface background pale pinkish when young, covered in pale woolly patches that fall away as fruitbody matures; typically subspherical or sometimes slightly pear shaped, 6 to 15cm across and up to 15cm tall. Rather than opening neatly like the Common Puffball, at maturity the top of the fruitbody tears irregularly to release the spores, and the fruitbody disintegrates from the top to leave a short infertile base that may persist for several months. Gleba white and firm at first, becoming yellow-brown and then olive brown and powdery.
Spores: olive brown.

Note: Most puffballs are edible when young and fresh, and Mosaic Puffballs are highly rated by some chefs.

Lycoperdon nigrescens (Agaricaceae) – Dusky Puffball

Very similar to the Common Puffball, but darker skinned and with small dark warts that persist longer than those of other frequently-encountered puffballs, the Dusky Puffball is a frequent find in acid coniferous woodland. This ubiquitous mushroom also occurs on heathland and in sand dunes, either singly or in small groups.

Fruitbody: pear shaped, surface background initially pale brown turning mid brown, covered in dark-brown spines 1 to 2mm long; spines fall off at maturity leaving a mottled, smooth surface; an apical pore opens, through which spores are released when either raindrops hit the mature puffball or a breeze blows across the pore hole; 2 to 4cm across, and 3 to 5cm tall.
Spores: brown.
Odour: an unpleasant gassy smell when flesh is cut.

Note: The most commonly encountered synonym for this species is *Lycoperdon foetidum* - a clue to its unpleasant odour!

Lycoperdon excipuliforme (Agaricaceae) – Pestle Puffball

Very much in evidence all through the year – in woodlands and hedgerows the dead stems of the previous season's fruitbodies persisting well in to the following summer – these tall truncheon-like puffballs are common with broadleaf trees and with conifers. In some spruce plantations they are one of the most common finds on forays.

Fruitbody: pale brown rather than white, but in other respects looking rather like a Common Puffball with a greatly elongated stem; covered in tiny warts that fall off at maturity, when the top splits open raggedly; spores are released when either raindrops hit the mature puffball or a breeze blows across the open top; head 5 to 10cm across, stem 3 to 5cm across, overall 6 to 20cm tall.
Spores: brown.

Note: The infertile stem shrivels and its spongy flesh dries out and becomes very light in weight; once dislodged from the forest floor, dead stems blow about in the slightest of breezes, gradually turning dark brown.

Woodland Inkcaps

Until 2001 all inkcaps were placed in the genus *Coprinus*, as they all produced black (or nearly black) spores and most decayed by deliquescing (dissolving into an inky fluid). DNA analysis has shown convincingly that this classification is not based upon a close ancestral relationship, and so the whole genus has been revised. The original genus type species *Coprinus comatus*, now recognised as a close relative of *Agaricus* species such as the Field Mushroom *Agaricus campestris* has been moved to the family Agaricaceae. Most of the larger litter-rotting inkcaps are now in the genus *Coprinopsis*, with stump rotters and a few others becoming *Coprinellus;* these two genera belong to the family Psathyrellaceae.

Coprinus comatus (Agaricaceae) – Shaggy Inkcap

This is the only common inkcap that remains in what is now the very small genus *Coprinus*; it had to be so, because the Shaggy Inkcap was, and therefore remains, the type species for the genus *Coprinus*. The term *Coprinus* means living on dung, which many former members of this genus do; however, *Coprinus comatus* is not really a dung fungus but rather an ubiquitous mushroom of humus-rich soil. I am including it here in the woodland rotters because it so often occurs in open woodland, beside forest footpaths, under hedgerows or in field margins on woodland edges. You are also likely to come across these readily-identifiable fungi on grassy roadside verges and other disturbed land.

Cap: Initially egg-shaped and opening into a long bell, caps are at first pure white, developing a pale brown area at the top; surface soon breaking up into large recurved scales. In dry weather the pale flaking scales stand out from cap surface. 5 to 15cm tall and 4 to 6cm dia.; caps darken and then deliquesce from the rim (pictured below), eventually leaving just the stem with a small black disc perched on top.
Gills: adnexed to free; narrow and crowded; initially white, turning pink and then black before deliquescing (liquefying) from the outer edge.
Stem: white, quite brittle and hollow; 1 to 1.5cm dia.; stem ring becomes stained with black spores, becoming movable and sometimes falling to base of stem.
Spores: black.

Note: Shaggy Inkcaps rarely fruit singly, and groups of between two and twenty are very common. Occasionally these stately mushrooms fruit in meandering lines through disturbed areas of conifer forests. When young and white throughout they are edible, but they do not keep – even in a refrigerator – and so should be cooked and eaten right after being picked. (They are therefore an ideal breakfast mushroom!)

Coprinopsis – a *Coprinus*-like Genus

This genus has existed since 1881, but in 2001 following much heated debate about the findings of genetic research it received an influx of species from the *Coprinus* genus. Among the immigrants were several common and conspicuous woodland species including the Common Inkcap, formerly *Coprinus atramentarius* (now *Coprinopsis atramentaria* – note the changed ending in the specific epithet), and the Magpie Inkcap, which was formerly *Coprinus picaceus* and has been renamed *Coprinopsis picacea* – again note that the species name has a new ending. All of the *Coprinopsis* fungi now belong to the family Psathyrellaceae, along with the genera *Psathyrella, Coprinellus, Lacrymaria* and *Parasola*.

Coprinopsis picacea (Psathyrellaceae) – Magpie Inkcap

It is always a delight to come across a Magpie Inkcap. So often are they solitary or so well spaced that those of us who like to photograph our finds have little prospect of capturing a photogenic group (a 'parliament' of magpies) that we can crow about to others!

The wonderful patterning of white or silvery grey on a shiny dark-brown background makes this one of the most beautiful mushrooms to photograph for reproduction as a monochrome print. Like all inkcaps the fruitbodies are short lived, and so a patient observer could have an educational day watching a cap expand from an elongated egg to conical and then bell-like as the cottony universal veil remnant breaks into separate patches to reveal the glossy dark background. As with other large inkcaps, the gills of the Magpie Inkcap deliquesce, a process which aids spore dispersal particularly in wet weather.

Generally as solitary specimens or well spaced in small groups, Magpie Inkcaps occur most often in deciduous woodland, particularly under Beech trees and less frequently under oaks. They are rare finds in Britain and Ireland, where they are mainly restricted to alkaline areas. Occasionally I find them also in damp, well-shaded grassland where deciduous hardwood debris has collected at the edge of a floodplain.

Cap: 3 to 7cm across and 7 to 12cm tall; initially egg-shaped, becoming bell shaped, the margins turning outwards before blackening and deliquescing from the rim; very dark grey-brown glossy background covered with silvery-white fibrils that separate into patches as the cap expands.
Gills: adnate or free; crowded; white, turning reddish and then black before deliquescing.
Stem: 10 to 20cm long and 0.7 to 1.5cm dia.; base often slightly bulbous; white with a floccose surface; no ring.
Spores: black.

Coprinopsis lagopus (Psathyrellaceae) – Hare'sfoot Inkcap

Mature Hare'sfoot Inkcaps look so unlike the immature form that it is hard to believe that the transition between the two does not involve some kind of metamorphosis, as when a caterpillar becomes a butterfly. The furry white coating that initially covers caps and stems disappears as the caps change from egg-shaped to convex and flat, the rim finally turning upwards and shrinking in diameter to produce an inrolled margin that creates a shallow, translucent bowl. Seen in bright sunlight the intricate beauty of these delicate little inkcaps is quite stunning. Increasingly common on the relatively new urban habitat of woodchip mulch, in the wild this mushroom grows on humus-rich soil and leaf litter, most commonly beside woodland tracks and rides under deciduous trees.

Cap: 1 to 3cm across and initially to 4cm tall; egg-shaped, becoming conical and then flat with a striate margin, the edges turning upwards when old; grey-brown, covered in ephemeral white scales; short lived, deliquescing from the rim within a few hours of becoming fully expanded.
Gills: adnexed or free; crowded; white, turning slightly reddish and then black before deliquescing, together with the cap, starting at the rim.
Stem: 4 to 10cm long and 3 to 6mm dia.; white with ephemeral white scales; no ring.
Spores: black.

Note: Mature Hare'sfoot Inkcaps bear only a passing resemblance to their immature fruitbodies (left).

Coprinopsis atramentaria (Psathyrellaceae) – Common Inkcap

Teetotalers may wish to try these for lunch, but anyone who is partial to the occasional tipple needs to be aware that eating Common Inkcaps before or after drinking alcohol can result in illness. Even alcohol taken a couple of days before or after a meal of these mushrooms can cause disturbing symptoms such as sweating, light headedness, rapid heartbeat and sometimes nausea and vomiting.

Not everyone is seriously affected, and it may be that the amount of toxin (coprine) in different specimens of this chunky inkcap varies; nevertheless, as there are so many safe mushrooms it makes no sense to tempt Fate over something as mediocre as this very dubious source of free food. (Some things in life are grossly overpriced even when they are free.)

After the Shaggy Inkcap *Coprinus comatus*, *Coprinopsis atramentaria* is probably the best known (although not the most commonly encountered) of the inkcaps. If you are searching for additional information it is worth noting that all but the latest of field guides will have this mushroom listed as *Coprinus atramentarius*, and not all mycological websites have yet been updated either. Common Inkcaps can be found on decayed wood of deciduous broadleaf trees, either in forests or (surprisingly often) where discarded timber has become buried beside hedgerows, on grassy roadside verges or on waste land.

Cap: 4 to 7cm across and 4 to 9cm tall; initially egg-shaped, becoming conical, bell shaped or convex when old; various shades of grey-buff, sometimes rather leaden and matt but more often shiny; smooth but with small brown scales near the centre; with radial furrows or grooves, some of which split at maturity as the cap edges turn outwards.
Gills: adnexed or free; crowded; white, turning reddish and then black before deliquescing (pictured, right) from the rim.
Stem: 10 to 20cm long and 0.7 to 1.5cm dia.; base slightly bulbous; white with a floccose surface; no ring.
Spores: black.

Coprinellus, last refuge of small woodland inkcaps?

There are more small mushrooms than large ones, and this is certainly true of inkcaps. The genus *Coprinellus* contains several dozen species, most of which are rare finds; however, it is unusual for a woodland fungus foray not to turn up a few of these little rotters, and in the section that follows three of the most common ones are pictured and described.

Coprinellus micaceus (Psathyrellaceae) - Glistening Inkcap

The specific epithet is a reference to mica-like scales on the caps of young fruitbodies; with age the scales fall away (if they are not washed off by rain) to reveal a brown mushroom with a grooved margin quite similar to several other inkcaps. You will need to find some young specimens, therefore, if you want to be reasonably confident about identifying this very common inkcap. It grows mainly on decayed stumps and buried wood of deciduous broadleaf trees and is only very occasionally found in conifer forests.

Cap: 2 to 3.5cm across and initially 2 to 4cm tall; egg-shaped, becoming conical; mica scales disappearing to reveal a striate margin; mid-brown background, paler near the margin; turning black when old but taking several days to deliquesce.
Gills: adnexed or free; crowded; white, turning black before deliquescing slowly from the rim.
Stem: 4 to 10cm long and 4 to 7mm dia.; covered initially in fine scales; white with an ochre base; no ring.
Spores: black.

Coprinellus disseminatus (Psathyrellaceae) – Fairy Inkcap

Also referred to as the Trooping Inkcap, this little mushroom provides one of Nature's most amazing spectacles. You may think that the Terracotta Army is something special, but save your superlatives until you come across your first battalion of Fairy Inkcaps swarming over a rotten hardwood stump in a sunlit woodland clearing.

Cap: 0.5 to 1.3cm across and initially 0.8 to 1.5cm tall; oval becoming convex and finally bell-shaped with a deeply furrowed margin; creamy buff and covered in fine scales, with an ochre central 'eye', losing scales and turning black without deliquescing.
Gills: adnate or adnexed; crowded; white, turning black from the rim.
Stem: 2 to 4cm long and 1.5 to 2.5mm dia.; covered initially in fine powdery scales; white with a buff base; no ring.
Spores: black.

Coprinellus impatiens (Psathyrellaceae) – No Common Name

Similar to the Fairy Inkcap, but larger and with distinctive 'piano key' grooves almost to the cap centre, this rather uncommon (in Britain and Ireland) mushroom occurs in small groups on deciduous broadleaf litter; it is most often seen under Beeches on chalky soil. (The mature specimens pictured here were beneath a spreading Beech tree.)

Cap: 2 to 4cm across, initially oval becoming convex and finally bell-shaped; deeply furrowed; light ochre with a light orange central 'eye'; turning grey and eventually black but not deliquescing.
Gills: adnexed or free; creamy-beige, turning grey. (Mature gills are pictured inset.)
Stem: 4 to 9cm long and 0.2 to 0.4cm dia.; white; silky smooth; no ring.
Spores: very dark brown.

Lacrymaria lacrymabunda **(Psathyrellaceae) – Weeping Widow**
Not uncommon in churchyards but more often seen under trees in grassy parkland and occasionally inside deciduous woods, the Weeping Widow seems to be particularly fond of areas of disturbed soil with high humus content. The common name is a reference to the droplets of water exuded by the gills in wet weather; often these droplets cling to the rim of the cap, rather like teardrops – hence the common name.

Cap: 4 to 10cm across, convex becoming broadly umbonate; surface finely woolly; margin initially fringed with veil fragments; ochre-yellow to light brown or tan.
Gills: adnate or adnexed; crowded; initially yellowish-brown turning purple-brown and then black at maturity with pale edges.
Stem: 5 to 9cm long and 0.5 to 1cm dia.; creamy white above ring zone, brown and fibrous below; ring very short-lived.
Spores: black.
Taste: bitter (edible but not highly rated).

The Brittlestems

Psathyrella is a small genus of wood-rotting fungi generally referred to as brittlestems, and they can be found in forests and woods as well as beside hedgerows and in other grassy places where twigs and branches have fallen and decayed. Unlike the inkcaps, the brittlestems do not deliquesce. The generic name comes from 'psathyr', meaning fragile or brittle, and the suffix '-ella' simply indicates that they are diminutive. For most *Psathyrella* species the common name brittlestem is certainly no understatement of the fragility of these usually small and often gregarious mushrooms.

Psathyrella candolleana **(Psathyrellaceae) – Pale Brittlestem**
One of the most common fungi of deciduous broadleaf woods and forests, the Pale Brittlestem could just as well be called the Pale Brittlemushroom, because the cap and gills are just as easily broken as is the stem. This mushroom is also referred to as the Common Crumblecap. It is a wood rotter; however, if on a lawn, in parkland or in a riverside meadow you come across a small pale mushroom with greyish gills and no stem ring do not rule out the Pale Brittlestem as an option. Whenever decayed hardwood twigs or branches are discarded in grassland and become overgrown with rank vegetation - for example if your Golden Retriever ignores a 'fetch' command and behaves more like a Golden Gatherer, stashing away his hoard of sticks - these fragile fungi are likely to fruit there.

Cap: 3 to 6cm across, convex and later bell shaped or almost flat; surface silky smooth; hygrophanous, light ochre when moist, drying almost white; a bloom of fine velar fragments often clings to cap surface until washed off by rain, and veil fragments hang in tatters from the rim; very fragile.
Gills: adnate or adnexed; crowded; greyish with toothed white edges; turning purple-brown at maturity.
Stem: 5 to 8cm long and 0.4 to 1cm dia.; white and powdery at the apex, smooth towards base; no ring; very brittle.
Spores: purple-brown.

Note: the specific epithet honours Augustin Pyramus de Candolle (1778-1841), who was Professor of Botany in Geneva.

***Psathyrella multipedata* (Psathyrellaceae) – Clustered Brittlestem**

Several of the brittlestems fruit in clusters, but none in such dense posy-like bunches as *Psathyrella multipedata*. Although *multipedata* means having many feet, groups of the many legs within a cluster of these mushrooms share a single foot as they join together to form a common base.

Look out for impressive tufted groups of Clustered Brittlestems on soil in open woodland as well as on lawns and roadside verges where there is buried rotten timber.

Cap: 1.5 to 3cm across, conical or convex and later bell shaped but never entirely flat; surface silky smooth; hygrophanous, reddish or clay brown when moist, drying pale ochre but often retaining a brownish centre.
Gills: adnate or adnexed; light grey-brown with white edges, turning dark purple-brown.
Stem: 4 to 10cm long and 3 to 6mm dia.; white at the apex, browner towards base; no ring; several stems fused together at base to form clusters.
Spores: dark purple-brown.

Note: Colour is almost useless as an identifying feature. Depending on age, location and weather the caps of Clustered Brittlestems can be almost white, ochre, beige, brown, tan or purple-grey.

Psathyrella piluliformis (Psathyrellaceae) – Common Stump Brittlestem

One of the many brown mushrooms found on tree stumps, this species has a passion for deciduous hardwood and fruits in large and sometimes spectacular groups. Superficially similar to several other stump rotters, many of which are also hygrophanous (turning different colours in dry weather and in wet weather), the Common Stump Brittlestem is distinguished not only by the brittle nature of its stem but also by the dark brown colour of its mature gills. Lookalikes such as *Galerina marginata* and *Kuenheromyces mutabilis* have gills that are much redder at maturity.

Cap: 3 to 5cm across; initially bell-shaped (pictured on the right) broadly convex at maturity (pictured above), the margin of often retaining hanging tatters of the partial veil; hygrophanous, reddish brown when moist, drying out light tan or ochre from the centre.
Gills: adnate or adnexed; crowded; initially beige, turning dark purple-brown as the spores mature.
Stem: 4 to 7cm long and 3 to 6mm dia.; white at apex, progressively more red-brown towards the base; partial veil tears as cap expands, leaving no obvious ring.
Spores: dark purple-brown.

Parasola conopilus (Psathyrellaceae) – Conical Brittlestem

When moist, a group of fresh Conical Brittlestems can make a wonderful display, grouped as they invariably are on compacted layers of twigs or buried wood of deciduous broadleaf trees. Once the caps have dried they lose their lustre and become matt and much paler.

Cap: 2 to 3.5cm across, conical or sometimes bell-shaped; shiny red-brown when moist becoming matt grey-beige or ochre after drying out; margin finely striate.
Gills: adnate or adnexed; crowded; edges serrated; greyish brown with white edges, turning very dark brown (almost black) as they age.
Stem: appearing to be unusually long for the size of cap: 7 to 14cm long and 2 to 4mm in dia.; straight and vertical, or very nearly so; white; mostly silky smooth but more powdery near apex and slightly downy towards base; no ring.
Spores: very dark brown (almost black).

Sorting out the Strophs

Whereas botanists have what they colloquially refer to as the 'Scrophs' – the huge family Scrophulariaceae (foxgloves, figworts etc) - those of us interested in fungi have an equally confusing group, the 'Strophs' or Strophariaceae. The genus *Stropharia* (sometimes referred to as the roundheads, even though some of them do not at any stage in development have round heads!) is a group of brown-spored agarics most of which have membranous stem rings. (The scientific name comes from the Greek *strophos* meaning a belt.) Also in the family Strophariaceae are four other genera represented in many kinds of woodland: *Leratiomyces, Hypholoma, Pholiota* and *Psilocybe*. There has been much shuffling of species within this complex grouping, and as DNA analysis produces new finds we can expect further revisions, introductions and almost certainly evictions.

Leratiomyces ceres (Strophariaceae) – Redlead Roundhead

Once a rare find in Britain and Ireland, this attractive little mushroom has become much more common as more parks and gardens are mulched with woodchip. In sandy pine forests, particularly in sheltered coastal areas, Redlead Roundheads can occasionally be found growing in grassy areas rich in pine needle litter. This is an inedible species.

Cap: orange-red; convex, becoming flatter; pale veil fragments often cling to cap margins; 1.5 to 6cm across.
Gills: cream to olive becoming purplish-brown with paler edges; adnate.
Stem: 3 to 9cm tall and 3 to 8mm dia.; white, flushed red towards base; covered in fibrous scales when young; no ring.
Spores: purplish-brown.

Note: the synonym *Stropharia aurantiaca* is still preferred by some authorities.

Stropharia hornemannii (Strophariaceae) - Conifer Roundhead

One of the most beautiful and elusive of pinewood mushrooms, but in Britain known only from Scotland's Caledonian Forest, the Conifer Roundhead grows on rotting pine stumps and pine branches buried in moss and needle litter. The specific epithet is in honour of the Danish botanist Jens Wilken Hornemann (1770–1841).

Cap: 7 to15cm across, domed with an inrolled margin, becoming broadly umbonate; usually violet brown, sometimes with yellow tints, but occasional specimens are creamy white; surface sticky when wet, drying silky smooth.
Gills: adnate; grey turning purplish brown.
Stem: 7 to 12cm tall and 1 to 2cm dia.; smooth and white above ring zone; below ring covered in small white scales that become larger and more pronounced with age.
Spores: purplish-brown.

Stropharia caerulea **(Strophariaceae) – Blue Roundhead**

Blue mushrooms are few and far between, but this striking species is a wonderfully bold blue-green colour when young. Unfortunately the colour soon fades. Some people refer to this wonderful woodland-edge fungus as the Verdigris Mushroom, a name traditionally associated with *Stropharia aeruginosa*, which differs by retaining its cap scales to maturity but is best distinguished by the white edges to its mature gills.

Cap: 3 to 8cm across; convex, becoming flatter and sometimes retaining a shallow umbo; slimy; blue-green flecked with white scales when young, developing yellow-brown patches and losing scales with age.
Gills: adnate or sinuate (inset picture); initially white, turning clay brown.
Stem: 5 to 10cm tall and 0.5 to 1cm dia.; blue-green; smooth above persistent ring, covered in pointed white scales below.
Spores: purple-brown.

Pholiota flammans **(Strophariaceae) – Flaming Scalycap**

Quite rare and certainly a special find, the Flaming Scalycap must count as one of Nature's masterpieces. Monochrome orange all over, and with its cap and lower stem covered in upturned fleecy scales, it is quite as shaggy as *Pholiota squarrosa* that grows on the bases of living trees; however, the Flaming Scalycap is found only on dead wood, and nearly always rotting conifer stumps. Only occasionally growing in tufts, these fabulous forest fungi more often fruit singly. Like other *Pholiota* species this mushroom tastes very bitter and is inedible.

Cap: 3 to 7cm across; bright yellow when young, maturing orange-yellow with upturned fleecy scales covering the entire cap surface; slimy beneath the scales; convex, becoming broadly convex but not flattening entirely.
Gills: adnate; luminous orange-yellow.
Stem: 4 to 8cm tall and 0.8 to 1.5cm dia.; orange; smooth above ring zone; covered in fibrous scales below.
Spores: brown.

Note: The Flaming Scalycap is a short-lived mushroom. If you find one in good condition when you haven't a camera with you, don't leave it too long before returning or you will surely be disappointed.

Pholiota gummosa (Strophariaceae) – Sticky Scalycap

Some of the *Pholiota* fungi – for example *Pholiota squarrosa*, the Shaggy Scalycap - grow on the lower trunk areas of living trees, and so they are described in the previous chapter; others occur on rotting stumps or on buried rotten wood, and the Sticky Scalycap is one of the latter. It is an inedible mushroom.

Cap: 2 to 5cm across; pale cream or beige to light ochre with olive tints; convex, becoming flatter and sometimes retaining a small umbo; covered in large dark ochre scales spaced well apart.
Gills: adnate; cream becoming rusty brown.
Stem: 3 to 8cm tall and 0.5 to 1cm dia.; cream or pale beige, flushed brown towards base; covered in fibrous scales below ring zone.
Spores: brown.

Hypholoma fasciculare (Strophariaceae) – Sulphur Tuft

Clambering over stumps and fallen trunks in great swathes of bright yellow caps, Sulphur Tufts present a truly spectacular sight. Often, however, you arrive a few days after the main performance and blackening, collapsing corpses litter the scene, distracting attention from more deserving dishy debutantes. (Dishy in appearance they may be, but Sulphur Tuft fungi are definitely not suitable for dishing up for dinner; the bitter-tasting caps can cause severe stomach pains and sickness.) These wood-rotting fungi are not at all fussy feeders, taking a fancy to most conifers as well as to broadleaf trees.

Cap: 3 to 8cm across, convex, flattening out at maturity but often retaining a shallow umbo; margins of young caps retaining hanging tatters of the partial veil; matt yellow, often tan towards centre.
Gills: adnate; crowded; yellow-green turning olive then dark brown as spores mature.
Stem: 4 to 10cm long and 0.5 to 1cm dia.; sulphur yellow at first, darkening towards the base at maturity; ring zone becomes apparent when stained by falling spores.
Spores: purple-brown.

Note: The specific epithet is derived from the Latin *fascicularis*, meaning 'in bundles'.

Hypholoma capnoides (Strophariaceae) – Conifer Tuft

Slightly smaller on average than Sulphur Tuft and usually appearing in smaller tufts, as its common name implies the Conifer Tuft occurs on decayed softwood stumps and, less frequently, on old fallen trunks. This inedible mushroom is often confused with Sulphur Tuft. Apart from a difference in gill colour – Conifer Tuft gills do not turn green or olive - one other feature will help you to separate these two otherwise very similar fungi: mature caps of the Conifer Tuft (left) retain a slightly inrolled margin rather than flattening out entirely.

Cap: 3 to 6cm across, convex, not fully flattening out at maturity but remaining umbonate with a slightly incurved margin; margin of young caps retaining hanging tatters of the partial veil; dull matt ochre, tawny towards the centre; margin finely striate.
Gills: adnate; crowded; pale ochre or white at first, turning grey or lilac as the spores mature.
Stem: 4 to 7cm long and 4 to 9mm dia.; ochre with a tawny flush near the base; ring zone becomes stained brown by falling spores.
Spores: dark brown.

Note: Often the ring zone is not discernable until stained by spores.

Hypholoma marginatum (Strophariaceae) – Snakeskin Brownie

The cap colour of this uncommon mushroom is very variable and therefore not a helpful identification feature; however, that is hardly a problem because the snakeskin patterning on the stem is so distinctive. This inedible species can be found, often in great numbers, in all kinds of woodland, where it springs up through the leaf litter in autumn.

Cap: 1.4 to 4cm across, bell-shaped becoming broadly convex, not fully flattening out at maturity and retaining a slightly incurved margin; smooth; dull tan to dark tan with a paler buff margin (for which feature the specific epithet was selected).
Gills: adnate; crowded; pale ochre or yellowish at first, turning olivaceous brown as the spores mature.
Stem: 4 to 7cm long and 2 to 5mm dia.; brown; covered in silvery white silky fibres in a snakeskin pattern.
Spores: dark brown.

***Hypholoma lateritium* (Strophariaceae) – Brick tuft**

If it were not for the striking brick-red colour and large size of the caps, these rather uncommon wood-rotting fungi might easily be passed by, for they are in other respects similar to Sulphur Tufts and several other common tuft-forming woodland species. Brick Tufts (Syn. *Hypholoma sublateritium*) are very partial to well-rotted hardwoods, and there's nothing they seem to like better than an old oak stump.

Cap: 4 to 9cm across, convex, flattening out at maturity but retaining a shallow umbo; inrolled margin of young caps covered with woolly remnants of the partial veil; brick red in centre, paler towards margin.
Gills: (inset picture) adnate; crowded; cream turning olive then purplish brown as spores mature.
Stem: 5 to 10cm long and 0.6 to 1.5cm dia.; fibrous; light ochre at apex, darkening progressively to a reddish-brown base; faint ring zone usually discernable.
Spores: purple-brown.

***Kuehneromyces mutabilis* (Strophariaceae) – Sheathed Woodtuft**

Although also referred to as the Brown Stew fungus, this is not a mushroom you should try to make a meal of: a deadly lookalike lurks in the same habitat at the same time of year, and only very close and careful examination will separate nourishment from punishment. For details of the dastardly doppelganger see *Galerina marginata*, commonly known as the Funeral Bell. One of the 'deprecated synonyms' (superseded scientific names) of *Kuehromyces mutabilis* is *Galerina mutabilis*, which in effect placed both species in the same genus.

The Sheathed Woodtuft is found mainly on decayed wood from deciduous broadleaf trees but also sometimes on conifer stumps. That further increases the chance of misidentification, because the Funeral Bell also occurs on dead conifer stumps.

Cap: 3 to 6cm across, convex, flattening at maturity but often retaining a broad umbo; hygrophanous, matt yellow-brown when moist, drying out light ochre from the centre, producing a two-tone effect.
Gills: adnate or slightly decurrent; crowded; light ochre at first, maturing reddish-brown.
Stem: 4 to 8cm long and 3 to 5mm dia.; cream and fibrous above ring zone, brown and very scaly below; ring short lived.
Spores: reddish brown.

Galerina marginata **(Strophariaceae) – Funeral Bell**
The English name of this common wood-rotting mushroom is fully justified; it is extremely poisonous, containing the same deadly amatoxins found in the Deathcap *Amanita phalloides* and Destroying Angel *Amanita virosa*.

Included in the list of synonyms for this species is *Galerina autumnalis*; the two (that is *G. marginata* and *G. autumnalis*) were formerly classed as separate species but DNA analysis has shown them to be genetically indistinguishable.

Most often found on dead conifer wood, the Funeral Bell also appears occasionally on old elm logs and on stumps or rotted trunks of hardwood trees, including Silver Birch.

Cap: up to 5cm across, hemispherical then convex; greasy; hygrophanous, rufous brown in the centre, fading to honey yellow towards the edge; margin sometimes faintly striate when dry.
Gills: adnate or slightly decurrent; crowded; light ochre with white cottony edges, turning rusty brown at maturity.
Stem: 3 to 7cm long and 3 to 7mm dia.; dark ochre brown and powdery above fragile pale ring; lighter brown and covered in longitudinal white fibrils below ring.
Spores: rusty-brown.

Note: This fungus really is *deadly* poisonous. In 1998 a young German woman ate a meal of *Galerina marginata* and shortly after was hospitalised. Six days after the meal, having failed to respond to all treatment for the resulting blood coagulation disorder, she received a liver transplant; without it she would almost certainly have died.

Cyclocybe cylindracea **(Strophariaceae) – Poplar Fieldcap**
Most other fieldcaps seem to know where the fields are, but the Poplar Fieldcap (syn. *Agrocybe cylindracea*) is a bit of a rebel and fruits on dead poplar stumps. Again, refusing to be tied by its common name, this rather infrequent find can sometimes be seen on willow in damp woods and coppices. (Fieldcaps are a rather motley bunch; those that are most often seen in grassland habitats are described in Chapter 8, while those favouring marginal or man-made substrates are featured in Chapter 9.)

Cap: 4 to10cm across, hemispherical becoming broadly convex or flat and with a wavy margin; in dry weather the surface often cracks; pale buff, flushed mid brown in centre and darkening with age.
Gills: adnate or slightly decurrent; initially cream, turning grey-brown and later mid brown as spores mature.
Stem: 5 to 10cm long and 1 to 1.5cm dia.; creamy white, turning brown with age; persistent, pendent ring.
Spores: tobacco-brown.

Gymnopilus penetrans (Strophariaceae) – Common Rustgill

Most of the rustgills seen in pine forests and other coniferous plantations are Common Rustgills, and they seem to like one another's company: find one and you are likely to spot dozens more nearby. They grow on rotting stumps, fallen branches and the forest floor where conifer debris has become buried beneath needle litter. Sawdust or wood chippings provide an equally acceptable fare for these fiery fungi.

Cap: 4 to 8cm across; becoming flatter and sometimes developing a shallow central depression; silky smooth or occasionally felty but not breaking up into scales; various shades of fiery orange-brown, lighter at rim.
Gills: adnate; crowded; initially yellow, soon turning reddish-brown with rusty-brown spots.
Stem: 4 to 7cm long and 0.6 to 1.2cm in dia.; yellowish, becoming flushed orange-brown; with fine longitudinal fibres; no ring.
Spores: rust-brown.

Gymnopilus sapineus (Strophariaceae) – Scaly Rustgill

Growing on dead conifer wood buried in the forest floor, this beautiful mushroom is fairly common but easily confused with other members of its genus, all of which have orange caps. The easiest of the rustgills to identify is *Gymnopilus junonius*, the Spectacular Rustgill, which often grows on the trunks of ailing trees and so is included with other 'hangers on' in Chapter 5; it is the only *Gymnopilus* with a persistent stem ring.

Cap: 4 to 9cm across; becoming almost flat but retaining a broad central umbo; felted when young, breaking up into scales; orange-brown with reddish-brown scales.
Gills: adnate; crowded; initially yellow, soon turning orange and later reddish-brown.
Stem: 4 to 7cm long and 0.6 to 1.5cm in dia., tapering towards the base; smooth, occasionally with fine longitudinal fibres; yellowish flushed with cap colour; no ring.
Spores: rust-brown.

Gymnopilus decipiens (Strophariaceae) – No Common Name

This small and uncommon rustgill is found mainly on burnt wood and forest fire sites.

Cap: 1 to 3cm across; convex, flattening; scaly or fibrillose; orange.
Gills: adnate; fairly distant; yellow, turning reddish-brown, often with rusty-brown spots.
Stem: 1 to 2cm long and 3 to 5mm in dia.; light brown, lower half covered in white fibres.
Spores: rust-brown.

Oysterlings

Within the order Cortinariales sits a group of oyster-like fungi that produce brown spores rather than the very pale spores associated with the true oyster mushrooms (*Pleurotus* species, which, because they often occur on dead parts of living trees, I have included in the 'hangers-on' section of Chapter 5).

Known as oysterlings, fungi of the genus *Crepidotus* have small, fan-shaped sessile caps, and they grow on rotten wood. The oysterlings are the only members of the family Crepidotaceae that are commonly encountered on woodland fungus forays in Britain and Ireland. The prefix *Crepid-* means slipper, and that is why oysterlings used to be referred to as the slipper mushrooms.

Crepidotus mollis (Crepidotaceae) – Peeling Oysterling

Distinguished by its large (for an oysterling) size and jelly-like cap cuticle that can be peeled, *Crepidotus mollis* is a common find on fallen timber and stumps in broadleaf woodland. Beech, Ash and poplars are its most common food sources, but before the demise of so many of Europe's elm trees most fallen elms were eventually colonised by the Peeling Oysterling – also sometimes referred to as the Soft Slipper Mushroom.

Cap: 2 to 7cm across; convex oyster-shaped fan becomes nearly flat at maturity; margin initially incurved, flattening and becoming faintly striate and sometimes wavy; slightly downy at point of attachment; rubbery; hygrophanous, greyish-brown, drying out almost white.
Gills: (inset) radiating from attachment point; crowded; grey-brown, darkening.
Stem: absent or very rudimentary.
Spores: mid brown.

Crepidotus variabilis (Crepidotaceae) – Variable Oysterling

Much more common and widespread than the Peeling Oysterling, this smaller and often paler relative is equally addicted to the rotten timber of hardwood trees. Often twigs are covered by overlapping caps either attached laterally to the sides of a twig or suspended beneath the twig with attachment points on the upper (infertile) surfaces of the caps.

Cap: 0.5 to 3cm across, convex kidney-shaped fan flattening at maturity, usually with an irregular wavy margin; upper surface white and dry with some fine fibrils; sometimes laterally attached but often attached by its 'back' to the substrate.
Gills: (inset picture) crowded; pale grey-brown, radiating from point of attachment.
Stem: absent or rudimentary.
Spores: mid brown.

Note: Several other small white oysterlings are separable by microscopic characters.

Crepidotus epibryus (Crepidotaceae) – Grass Oysterling

Even smaller than the Variable Oysterling, this pretty little mushroom is widespread and very common in woodlands, particularly where bracken encroaches. Growing on deciduous hardwood twigs and occasionally on dead leaves, this is also a very common find on the dead stems of bracken and other herbaceous plants in woodlands.

Cap: 0.4 to 1.5cm across, convex kidney-shaped fan flattening somewhat but retaining an inrolled margin; upper surface white or pale buff and finely felted; laterally attached or attached by its 'back' to the substrate.
Gills: crowded; white becoming pinkish brown, radiating from point of attachment.
Stem: absent or rudimentary.
Spores: pale ochre.

Lentinellus cochleatus (Lentinellaceae) – Aniseed Cockleshell

Shaped like a cornet with a notch taken out of one side, *Lentinellus cochleatus* is an occasional fungus that appears on or beside hardwood stumps in autumn. There is a form of this mushroom with a mild aniseed odour and flavour, but you may also come across Aniseed Cockleshells where the odour and taste are virtually undetectable.

One of the defining features of the genus *Lentinellus* is the gill form: the edges of the gills are ragged or serrated. Although they may look rather like oyster mushrooms, in fact these fungi are more closely related to brittlegills than to other gilled agarics, and so the genus *Lentinellus* is included in the Russulales.

Cap: 3 to 7cm across; fawn to reddish-brown; shell-shaped, or sometimes funnel-shaped with a split down one side and the stem offset from the centre.
Gills: decurrent; crowded and very narrow with toothed edges; almost white, becoming pink and sometimes with inter-vein brown marks.
Stem: 1 to 4cm long and 0.8 to 1.5cm dia.; eccentric; colour as cap; sometimes rooting.
Spores: white.
Odour: faintly or sometimes quite strongly of aniseed.

Aniseed Cockleshell *Lentinellus cochleatus* is the type species of its genus.

Funnels

Among the huge family Tricholomataceae is a group of pale-spored mushrooms whose caps, while initially convex, expand and usually develop central depressions. Because their gills are decurrent, to varying degrees, the overall impression is of a funnel-shaped goblet, and this is reflected in both their common names and their scientific names. (*Clitocybe* means funnel head.)

Most of the funnels are notable not for their colours, which with few exceptions are rather dull, but for the splendid groups or troops which they so often form. One or two have very distinctive odours of either aniseed or of meal (flour dough), and all have rather fibrous stems that cannot easily be detached from the cap flesh. Here are pictures and details of some of the more common and distinctive members of the group:

Clitocybe nebularis (Tricholomataceae) – Clouded Funnel

This large and very common woodland mushroom, the type species for its genus, is difficult to miss. Not only is it singularly conspicuous but it also tends to occur in great numbers, often forming partial or complete fairy rings. Clouded Funnels occur in both coniferous and broadleaf woodland.

Despite being one of the 'funnels', sometimes the caps of this large mushroom remain slightly convex even when fully expanded. This trait may have contributed to some of the controversy over its rightful position in the classification system. Initially described in 1789 by August Batsch and named *Agaricus nebularis*, it was moved to the *Clitocybe* genus by Paul Kummer in 1871 and recorded as *Clitocybe nebularis*. Since then it has spent time in the genus *Lepista*, and later *Gymnopus*, but it is now safely back home in the *Clitocybe*… for the time being, at least.

Cap: 5 to 20cm across, convex, often depressed at maturity, sometimes with a small umbo and a wavy margin; pale grey to light beige-grey with irregular cloudy brown-grey areas towards centre.
Gills: decurrent; crowded; cream or pale greyish yellow.
Stem: 5 to 10cm long and 1.5 to 2.5cm dia.; base often slightly swollen; pale grey or buff-grey; fibrous; no ring.
Spores: cream.
Odour: fruity (some say like turnips!), becoming rancid when old and decaying.

Once regarded as good to eat, this abundant mushroom is now known to be poisonous.

Infundibulicybe geotropa (Tricholomataceae) – Trooping Funnel
Another fairly common and very large funnel, and one that for its form and fruiting habit is very much deserving of both parts of its common name, this woodland mushroom sometimes appears in spectacular fairy rings in grass or leaf litter, particularly beneath Beech trees and oaks. Trooping Funnels are also fairly common in conifer forests.

Cap: 5 to 20cm across, initially convex but soon flattening and developing a deeply depressed centre, usually retaining a small shallow umbo; margin incurved even when mature; surface dry and finely downy or felty; creamy white to pinkish beige.
Gills: deeply decurrent; crowded; creamy white or pale beige.
Stem: 5 to 15cm long and 2 to 3cm dia,; base downy and bulbous; cream or pinkish beige; no ring.
Spores: white.
Odour: sweet, usually only faint.

Infundibulicybe gibba (Tricholomataceae) – Common Funnel
A pale funnel distinguished by its almond odour from several species of similar size and colouring, the Common Funnel fruits in scattered groups in most kinds of hardwood and mixed woodland, and less often in conifer forests. It is, as the English name suggests, a frequent find. (The synonym *Clitocybe gibba* also refers to the funnelled form of the caps.)

Cap: 3 to 8cm across, convex, flattening and developing a shallow umbonate depression, usually with an undulating margin; creamy white or ochre usually with a pinkish tinge.
Gills: decurrent; crowded; creamy white, usually with a pinkish tinge.
Stem: 3 to 8cm long and 0.5 to 1cm dia., often with a slightly swollen base; colour as cap but slightly paler and covered in fine whitish fibrils; no ring.
Spores: white.

Clitocybe odora (Tricholomataceae) – Aniseed Funnel
Young fruitbodies of this fairly common woodland mushroom are unmistakable: if the strong aniseed odour is inconclusive the startling colour will surely clinch it. Stumbling across a blue fungus is almost a surreal experience, and all parts of this mushroom – cap, gills and stem – start off blue, usually with a greenish tinge. You do get an early warning, however, because the aniseed odour is detectable downwind for at least fifty metres. In fact, because they are most often tucked away beneath low-growing woodland shrubs, smell is by far the most reliable sense to use when you are searching for these edible fungi.

Cap: 3 to 8cm across, convex, flattening; margin often wavy; blue or blue-green when young and moist, fading to greyish green or buff (right) when old and dry.
Gills: adnate or only slightly decurrent; crowded; white tinged with blue or blue-green, becoming paler with age.
Stem: 3 to 6cm long and 0.5 to 1cm dia.; downy at base; white flushed with blue, fading to pale buff; no ring.
Spores: white.
Odour: strong, of aniseed.

Clitocybe phyllophila **(Tricholomataceae) – Frosty Funnel**
An infrequent find in both coniferous and deciduous broadleaf woodland, these pretty funnels are translucent when viewed from beneath in sunlight. The frosted nature of the cap surface is best seen on young specimens during dry weather.

Cap: 4 to 10cm across; convex, flattening with a wavy margin, usually developing a shallow central depression and retaining a small umbo; smooth and silky when dry; white with a fine bloom, developing buff or ochre spots mostly near the centre.
Gills: decurrent; crowded; white, turning cream with age.
Stem: 4 to 8cm long and 0.7 to 1.5cm dia.; smooth; white; downy at base; no ring.
Spores: pale ochraceous clay.

Note: This very poisonous funnel contains the toxin muscarine.

Lepista irina **- (Tricholomataceae) – Flowery Blewit**
An uncommon woodland species, the Flowery Blewit owes its common name to a distinctive flowery (not floury!) odour. This blewit is found with deciduous trees; it is most common in Beech woodland in southern England and is increasingly rare further north.

Cap: 5 to 10cm across; hemispherical then broadly convex with an undulating margin; smooth; pale beige, becoming pinkish brown towards the centre when moist, drying paler.
Gills: adnate or sinuate; narrow; crowded; cream, turning buff-pink when mature.
Stem: 4 to 9cm long and 0.5 to 1.0cm dia.; fibrillose; sometimes slightly swollen at base; pinkish brown; no ring.
Spores: creamy-white, in contrast with the Wood Blewit and Field Blewit, both of which have pale pink spores.
Odour: perfumed (like flowers).

Paralepista flaccida - (Tricholomataceae) – Tawny Funnel

Although the common name states that this mushroom is a 'funnel' (like the various *Clitocybe* species), in fact it is in many ways more like a 'blewit; however, its spores are white or cream whereas the Wood Blewit (below) and the Field Blewit produce pale pink spores. Caps frequently have a spout-like low point, making for a jug-like appearance; this, together with warty spores and the much thinner cap flesh, help in distinguishing the Tawny Funnel from the superficially similar Common Funnel. Found in all kinds of woodlands, the Tawny Funnel turns up on nearly every autumn forest fungus foray.

Cap: 4 to 9cm across, convex and later funnel shaped with a wavy inrolled margin; smooth and matt; tawny or orange-brown.
Gills: deeply decurrent; crowded; white at first, becoming pale tawny when mature.
Stem: 3 to 5cm long and 0.5 to 1cm dia.; slightly fibrillose; downy at base; tawny but paler than cap; no ring.
Spores: creamy white.
Odour: pleasantly sweet.

Lepista nuda - (Tricholomataceae) – Wood Blewit

Easily mistaken for one of the many violet or purple *Cortinarius* species – for example *Cortinarius violaceus*) - this edible mushroom often fruits into the New Year in mild winters. Wood Blewits are very common in both broadleaf and coniferous woodland. Although generally regarded as edible when thoroughly cooked, even then these attractive looking fungi have been known to cause allergic reactions in some people. This mushroom contains the sugar trehalose (also known as mycose), a disaccharide which most but not all people find edible.

All blewits are prone to maggot infestation, and so if you intend gathering them for food the stems and caps should be cut through to check for occupants.

Cap: very variable, 5 to 14cm across; initially convex, flattening out or developing a central depression at maturity; often with a wavy margin; bluish lilac at first, turning brown (left) from the centre with age.
Gills: sinuate; crowded; bluish lilac fading to buff with age.
Stem: up to 10cm long and 1.5 to 2.5cm dia.; base slightly bulbous; fibrillose; bluish lilac, ageing pale buff; no ring.
Spores: white.
Odour: fragrant, like perfumed aniseed!

Lepista sordida **- (Tricholomataceae) – Sordid Blewit**

A somewhat smaller and less robust mushroom than the Wood Blewit, and with deeper violet colours and a thinner cap margin when mature, *Lepista sordida* is not easily separated from *Lepista nuda*. To make matters worse it occurs in some of the same habitats.

Cap: 3 to 8cm across; initially convex, flattening out or developing a central depression at maturity, usually with a slight umbo and a wavy margin; deep lilac, turning brown from the centre in dry weather.
Gills: sinuate; crowded; greyish lilac fading to buff with age.
Stem: 4 to 6cm long and 5 to 8mm dia.; fibrillose; lilac; downy and white at base; no ring.
Spores: white.

Note: This thin-capped blewit is commonly found under hedgerows and in the headlands of fields at woodland edges. I have even found it under rhododendron bushes – not usually productive foray sites!

Pseudoclitocybe cyathiformis **(Tricholomataceae) – Goblet**

Aptly named, both in its English name and its scientific epithet, the shape of this common woodland mushroom is distinctly reminiscent of a goblet. In broadleaf and deciduous woodland you can often find these robust, sombre fungi well in to the colder months of winter. Most often these mushrooms spring up from the litter-rich humus of the forest floor, but occasionally they emerge from well-rotted wood.

Cap: 4 to 8cm across; convex with a central depression and often a small umbo, becoming deeply funnel shaped with age; margin remaining inrolled; purplish-brown when moist, turning paler in dry weather.
Gills: adnate or decurrent; usually forked (differentiating it from true *Clitocybe* species); crowded; dark greyish-beige, fading to light brown with age.
Stem: 4 to 10cm long and 3.5 to 6mm dia.; base slightly clavate; fibrillose; reddish brown to purplish-brown, downy and white at base; no ring.
Spores: white.

Note: The caps are edible but their flavour is reported to be nothing special.

Melanoleuca polioleuca **(Tricholomataceae) – Common Cavalier**
With a dark cap covering pallid gills, this is a tricky species to identify from macroscopic features alone. This is something it shares with most other members of this genus, which can be separated with difficulty only after detailed microscopic study. The Common Cavalier occurs in deciduous broadleaf woodland and with conifers, notably pines.

Cap: 4 to 8cm across; convex developing a central depression and often a small umbo; smooth; slightly greasy; dark grey-brown when moist, turning paler in dry weather.
Gills: sinuate; white, turning creamy-grey with age.
Stem: 3 to 8cm long and 0.5 to 1cm dia.; base slightly bulbous; white, covered in grey-brown fibrils, densest towards base; no ring.
Spores: very pale cream.

Leucocybe connata **(*Insertae sedis,* Agaricales) – White Domecap**
A common sight in the disturbed soil beside woodland footpaths, the White Domecap fruits either singly or in small clusters.

Cap: 3 to 8cm across; convex, expanding but not flattening completely; often developing a wavy margin; white; smooth and dry.
Gills: adnate or slightly decurrent; crowded; white.
Stem: 3 to 6cm long and 0.8 to 1.5cm dia.; usually slightly swollen at base; white; no ring.

Note:Related *Lyophyllum* fungi are known to contain toxins and are classed as inedible. The White Domecap could be confused with the deadly poisonous Destroying Angel.

Lyophyllum decastes **(Lyophyllaceae) – Clustered Domecap**
Varying greatly in size and cap colour, these clump-forming mushrooms are very common in deciduous woodland and under trees in parks. They seem to thrive on soil disturbance.

Cap: 4 to 10cm across; convex, usually irregular, margins often scalloped; cap peels easily; smooth, shiny; shades of grey-brown.
Gills: adnate; fairly crowded; very pale grey, becoming slightly ochraceous with age.
Stem: 4 to 8cm long and 0.8 to 1.8cm dia.; tough; longitudinally fibrillose; usually curved, as several stems meet at base; base usually swollen or slightly clavate; off-white to grey-brown; no ring.
Spores: white.

The Genus Tricholomopsis

Closely related to the *Tricholoma* mushrooms, this small genus (some 30 species are known worldwide, most being apparently restricted to America and Australia) contains only two species that are regularly reported in Britain and Ireland. The suffix *-opsis* occurs quite a few times in fungi genera and simply means 'looks like'. So, the genus name *Tricholomopsis* means 'looks like a *Tricholoma*'. Usually when a genus ends in *–opsis* the species within it were formerly included in the genus without the extension. (Incidentally, the suffix *–oides* means 'resembles'... I'll have to leave you to work out the difference!)

Tricholomopsis decora (Tricholomataceae) – Prunes and Custard

Quite a rare find in southern Britain and Ireland, although more common in Scotland, this beautiful but inedible mushroom grows on conifer stumps, fallen trunks and branches and, as in the picture below, untreated pine fence posts that are past their use-by date.

Cap: golden yellow, covered with fine grey-brown scales concentrated towards the centre of the cap; convex, becoming broadly umbonate or almost flat at maturity, often with a shallow central depression; margin slightly wavy when fully expanded; 4 to 10cm dia.
Gills: yellow; sinuate; crowded.
Stem: yellow background covered in fine brown scales; 5 to 10cm tall and 0.6 to 1.6cm in dia.; no ring.
Spores: creamy white or very pale yellow.

Note: This mushroom occurs on pinewood edges and in open conifer and mixed woodland, sometimes as solitary specimens but more often in small, localised groups.

Tricholomopsis rutilans (Tricholomataceae) – Plums and custard

Against a background of mossy pine stumps, these large, colourful mushrooms make a spectacular sight, especially when, as is often the case, they occur in large numbers. Unfortunately, despite their attractive appearance and encouraging common name these are bitter and inedible mushrooms. This is the type species for the genus *Tricholomopsis*.

Cap: egg-yolk yellow, covered with radial streaks of tiny purple scales; flesh thin; pale yellow; convex, becoming broadly umbonate or almost flat at maturity; 4 to 12cm dia.
Gills: egg-yolk-yellow; adnate or weakly sinuate; broad and crowded.
Stem: covered in purple-red scales on a white background, paler towards apex; stem flesh pale yellow; 4 to 10cm tall and 1 to 2cm in dia.; no ring.
Spores: creamy white.
Odour: of rotten pinewood.

Hymenopellis radicata (Tricholomataceae) – Rooting Shank

One of the early-fruiting wood rotters, *Hymenopellis radicata* (syn. *Xerula radicata*) usually has as much stem below the surface as above.

Cap: pale grey-brown to mid brown; 4 to 10cm across; convex or bell-shaped, becoming flatter and umbonate; sticky when moist, drying silky with radial wrinkles.
Gills: adnate with a decurrent tooth; distant; pale cream with browner edges.
Stem: 10 to 20cm long and 0.5 to 1cm dia., base rooting in buried wood; finely grooved; white at apex, browner near base; no ring.
Spores: pale cream.

Rooting Shank *Hymenopellis radicata*. The stems are sometimes twisted and nearly always finely furrowed, but an even more obvious distinguishing feature is the radial wrinkling (right) of the cap surface.

Macrocystidia cucumis (Marasmiaceae) – Cucumber Cap

Distinguished by its dark brown velvety cap and very dark stem, this relatively uncommon inedible wood-rotting mushroom has an unusual odour described variously as like cucumber (from which comes its scientific name as well as its common name) or like fish.

Cap: pale grey-brown to mid brown; 1 to 5cm across; convex or bell-shaped, developing an umbo but not flattening completely; surface smooth and velvety; hygrophanous, reddish-brown to dark brown, paler at the margin when moist; drying to pale brown or ochre.
Gills: adnexed; white at first becoming reddish ochre at maturity.
Stem: 3 to 6cm long and 2 to 4mm dia.; velvety; light ochre at apex, brown below shading to black at base; no ring.
Spores: pinkish brown.
Odour: cucumber; or, as one of my friends suggests, salmon and cucumber sandwiches!

Turmoil among the Toughshanks

Until recently a group of forest-floor fungi known as the toughshanks were thought to be close relatives, and they were all lumped together in the genus *Collybia* within the family Tricholomataceae. DNA analysis has shown that the physical similarities are not mirrored by genetic proximity, and all but the tiny members of the group they have been moved into two other genera, *Rhodocollybia* and *Gymnopus*. What they still have in common are tough, fibrous stems and a taste for rotten wood and leaf litter.

Rhodocollybia butyracea (Marasmiaceae) – Butter Cap

The synonym *Collybia butyracea* currently appears in most field guides, but this very common woodland mushroom is now formally listed in the genus *Rhodocollybia*. If you search for information using common names, try Greasy Toughshank, under which this species was listed for many decades. But if you search for these fungi in the wild you should have little difficulty in finding them in either deciduous broadleaf woods or conifer plantations. The cap colour is very variable, though.

Cap: 3 to 6cm across; convex, flattening often with a small central umbo; margin striate and often wavy; greasy; hygrophanous, purplish brown with a paler margin, drying much paler brown or buff.
Gills: adnexed or free; crowded; very light beige.
Stem: 4 to 8cm long and 0.5 to 1cm dia.; tough and fibrous; surface silky; swollen towards base; pale reddish brown, darker towards base; base downy, white; no ring.
Spores: white or very pale pink.

Rhodocollybia maculata (Marasmiaceae) – Spotted Toughshank

The synonym *Collybia maculata* currently appears in most field guides, but this fairly common woodland mushroom is now formally listed in the genus *Rhodocollybia*. Fruiting most often in small groups or clusters, this very attractive wood-rotting fungus is not a fussy feeder: it occurs under conifers (particularly under pines) and less often under deciduous hardwood trees; it is such a delight to come across a group in prime condition.

Cap: 5 to 12cm across; broadly convex, flattening with a wavy margin that often turns upwards to create an irregular saucer shape; creamy or pinkish white, developing tan spots or blotches.
Gills: adnexed; crowded; white, developing rust-like reddish-brown spots with age.
Stem: 5 to 10cm long and 0.8 to 1.2cm dia.; white, developing rust-like reddish-brown spots; no ring.
Spores: creamy white or pale pink.

Note: Despite their attractive appearance, these mushrooms are bitter and inedible.

Gymnopus confluens (Marasmiaceae) – Clustered Toughshank

The densely packed clusters and upright straight stems of this little woodland mushroom immediately distinguish it from other, larger toughshanks. Particularly under deciduous hardwood trees but also occasionally in conifer forests, crowds of these pale caps jostle with one another and often form impressive fairy rings. Although they may appear to be sprouting from the forest floor or in grass at woodland edges, there is often buried rotten wood (their staple diet) just below the surface.

Cap: 3 to 5cm across; convex becoming bell shaped, sometimes flattening with an umbo; hygrophorous, flesh pink, becoming wrinkled and almost white when dry.
Gills: adnexed; narrow; crowded; cream or pale buff.
Stem: 4 to 8cm long and 3 to 5mm dia.; laterally compressed; velvety; pinkish buff, paler towards apex, white and downy at base; no ring.
Spores: white.

Gymnopus dryophilus (Marasmiaceae) – Russet Toughshank

The synonym *Collybia dryophila* currently appears in many field guides, but following a recent review the BMS checklist currently records this very common woodland mushroom in the genus *Gymnopus*. Russet Toughshanks occur in both deciduous broadleaf woods and conifer plantations, but most commonly under oak trees.

Cap: 2 to 5cm across; convex, flattening often with a wavy margin; pale buff to light tan, paler at the margin.
Gills: adnexed or free; very light beige or pale buff.
Stem: 2 to 5cm long and 2 to 5mm dia.; tough and fibrous; surface silky; swollen towards base; tan, darker towards base; base covered in pale bristly hairs; no ring.
Spores: white.

Several other 'toughshanks' frequently turn up during woodland fungus forays. One of these, *Gymnopus fusipes* (syn. *Collybia fusipes*) is commonly known as Spindleshank. Rather than settling for dead wood, this rogue member of the clan is a weak parasite on the roots of oaks and Beech trees. Spindleshank has therefore been included and described in the previous chapter under the heading of parasitic woodland fungi.

Marasmius and *Marasmiellus* – the Parachutes

Apart from the Fairy Ring Champignon *Marasmius oreades*, nearly all of the other common species in this genus (more than 500 Marasmius species are currently known and described) are woodland fungi, and they are small. The question 'Can I eat them?' hardly arises - at least not from creatures anything like the size of people. If you thought that the *Clitocybe* mushrooms were a challenge then you shouldn't be in too much of a hurry to become a *Marasmius* maestro. Most are little and either brown (LBMs) or white (LWMs) and they all produce white or very pale spores.

The name *Marasmius* itself comes from the Greek word *marasmos*, meaning 'drying out', and is a reference to the ability of (most of) the mushrooms in this genus to survive desiccation, reviving after being soaked in water. An endearing feature of these rather neat little fungi is their tendency for gregariousness: find one and invariably you will find tens, hundreds or even thousands, so finding a nice group for that front-cover photograph should be easy... if only they weren't quite so tiny and tucked away in such terribly dark places.

Marasmius is elevated to family status by some authors, who place this genus together with several other white-spored mushrooms in the Marasmiaceae; others retain them within the larger family Tricholomataceae.

Marasmius rotula (Marasmiaceae) – Collared Parachute

This widespread and very common little mushroom is the type species of the genus *Marasmius*. Its widely-spaced gills are attached to a collar encircling the stem – hence the common name. The reason for the specific epithet becomes obvious when you turn over a cap and see that the inner collar, the gills and the outer rim of the cap look so much like the hub, spokes and rim of a wheel – 'rot' (as in *rotula*) is a reference to wheel, as it is also in 'rotate'.

Marasmius rotula is one of the most attractive of the many parachute mushrooms and quite the most distinctive. Its preferred habitat is dead deciduous hardwood roots and fallen trunks, branches and twigs – in hedgerows as well as in woodlands. Only occasionally is the Collared Parachute found on conifer wood.

Cap: white or pale cream; convex initially, flattening at maturity; radially wrinkled at margin; 0.5 to 1.5cm across.
Gills: pinkish-white turning ochre when old; adnate; narrow; distant.
Stem: upper stem concolorous with cap, but darker brown towards base; shiny; 4 to 7cm long and less than 1mm dia; no ring.
Spores: white.

Note: As hundreds of *Marasmius* species have been described, and many of them are small and white, that collar is very helpful!

***Gymnopus androsaceus* (Marasmiaceae) – Horsehair Parachute**

There is little obvious difference between this tiny mushroom and the Collared Parachute, until you glance beneath the cap and see that the gills are attached directly to the stem and not to a collar. Other distinguishing features are the remarkably long stem in comparison with the size of the cap, and fine horsehair-like threads of densely interwoven mycelium extending outwards from the stem base in search of new substrate material to colonise. They may be small, but these little mushrooms certainly know how to swarm.

Cap: convex initially, flattening with a depressed centre at maturity; radially grooved and wrinkled; 0.4 to 1cm across. pinkish buff, usually paler towards the margin;
Gills: adnate; distant; pinkish-buff, turning ochre when old.
Stem: very thin, tough and wiry; 2.5 to 5cm long and less than 1mm dia.; black; no ring.
Spores: white.

***Marasmiellus ramealis* (Marasmiaceae) – Twig Parachute**

The closer you look at fungi the more you see; and the more you look closely at tree trunks and branches the more fungi you see. Some little mushrooms are so tiny that they are often overlooked or assumed to be some of the numerous blob-like ascomycetes of millimetric dimensions. Many of the tiniest cap-and-stem mushrooms fruit on dead twigs - even those attached to living trees, and so it's important to look up as well as down when wandering through woodlands in search of interesting new finds. *Marasmiellus ramealis* is a little white parachute-like mushroom that often grows at or above head height, first appearing in springtime and recurring throughout summer and autumn on twigs and small branches of conifers and deciduous broadleaf trees. (It is also a common sight on dead bramble stems.)

Cap: white or pale cream; convex initially, flattening at maturity; radially wrinkled at margin; 0.3 to 1.5cm across.
Gills: (inset picture) pinkish-white turning ochre when old; adnate; narrow; distant.
Stem: upper stem concolorous with cap, but darker brown near base; slightly scurfy; delicate; 0.5 to 2cm long and typically 1mm dia; no ring.
Spores: white.

Other little white mushrooms

LBMs (little brown mushrooms) do not have it all their own way in woodlands; there are scores of tiny white mushrooms, dwarf red mushrooms and small fawn mushrooms (let's call them all little boring mushrooms, LBMs). Few people can correctly identify more than half a dozen of them, so there really is no need to worry on that score. Enjoy!

Mycena – the Bonnets

Mycena is a very large genus (worldwide about 500 species have been described to date) containing small saprophytic cap-and-stem mushrooms with conical or bell-shaped caps. All have either white or very pale spores. Some authors now place these fungi in their own family, the Mycenaceae, while others continue to classify them as part of the family Tricholomataceae. Although a few of them are known to be edible and others are proven to contain toxins, the edibility of most of the bonnet fungi remains unknown; however, their small size (most species are less than 4cm in cap diameter) must surely be a major deterrent to all but the most determined or desperate of mushroom addicts.

Several of the *Mycena* fungi, including *Mycena polygramma* and *Mycena haematopus* are weakly bioluminescent - in the dark they glow green rather eerily. The light is clearly visible in a darkened room once your eyes are fully adapted to low light levels, but you really need to go to more exotic climes (notably the Amazon Jungle or Japan) to find bonnets with sufficient luminescence to be visible to the human eye in a woodland setting. Of course, to bugs and other creatures that might help with spore distribution such weak lights might be quite enough to act as an attractor at night time – or, on the other hand, to scare them away so that the fungi do not get eaten! (It is nonsense to ascribe to the fungus a 'purpose' for its bioluminescence, but we can guess at and maybe in time perhaps discover its effects on other organisms.

The name *Mycena* is similar to Mycenae, the ancient Greek city (some 90km south west of Athens) reputedly founded by Perseus, slayer of Medusa, one of the Gorgons. There may be links between the two words. Perseus is said to have eaten a hallucinogenic mushroom in the place that became Mycenae; however, in another version of the tale he chose the site for the city because when he was thirsty a mushroom sprang up there and supplied him with a stream of water. The Greek word for cap comes from the same stem. Oops!

Mycena haematopus (Mycenaceae) – Burgundydrop Bonnet

There are several *Mycena* species with pinkish caps, but what makes this one rather special is the dark red 'blood' that exudes from its cut flesh. The Burgundydrop Bonnet grows in fused tufts on dead hardwood stumps and trunks, and only very occasionally on conifer stumps.

Cap: 2 to 4cm across; conical, becoming bell shaped with a slight umbo; silky smooth; striate almost to centre when moist; usually pinkish-brown, sometimes reddish-brown, drying to pale greyish-pink.
Gills: adnate or adnexed; white turning pale pink, often darker at the edges.
Stem: 4 to 7cm long and 2 to 3mm in dia.; pinkish-brown; no ring. Blood-red liquid oozes from cuts (inset picture, right).
Spores: white.

Note: A similar but much smaller and more slender species, *Mycena sanguinolenta*, the Bleeding Bonnet, grows on forest-floor litter mainly under conifers.

Burgundydrop Bonnets clustered at the base of a dead Holm Oak, *Quercus ilex*.

Mycena inclinata (Mycenaceae) – Clustered Bonnet

Nearly always found on stumps, fallen branches or dead parts of standing oak trees, the Clustered Bonnet has (depending on your nose!) either a spicy or a rancid odour that helps distinguish it from the many similar bonnet mushrooms.

Cap: 2 to 3.5cm across; conical, becoming bell shaped and eventually broadly umbonate; smooth with striations almost to centre; margin scalloped or sharply toothed;various shades of grey or greyish-brown, becoming darker towards the centre.
Gills: adnate; white turning pinkish-grey.
Stem: 5 to 10cm long and 2 to 4mm in dia.; white at the apex, progressively darker red-brown towards the downy base; no ring.
Spores: white.

Mycena polygramma (Mycenaceae) – Grooved Bonnet
Cap colour is rarely of much help when you are struggling to identify a *Mycena*, as they vary so much with age, location, humidity and growing substrate. If you look closely at the stem (inset, below) of a Grooved Bonnet you will see that it has longitudinal striations, whereas other common bonnet mushrooms have smooth stems.

Cap: 2 to 3.5cm across; conical, becoming bell shaped and eventually umbonate; smooth with striations almost to centre; margin scalloped or sharply toothed; greyish brown, becoming darker brown towards centre.
Gills: adnate; white turning pinkish grey.
Stem: 5 to 10cm long and 0.2 to 0.4cm in dia.; white at apex, progressively darker red-brown towards the downy base; no ring.
Spores: white.

Note: Caps on the right of the picture are being attacked by the fungal parasite *Spinellus fusiger* – a common occurrence.

Mycena arcangeliana (Mycenaceae) – Angel's Bonnet

Most often found on stumps, fallen trunks and branches of Beech or Ash trees, but occasionally on other dead hardwoods, the Angel's Bonnet is distinguished by its odour of iodine, which is most noticeable in dried specimens.

Cap: 3 to 5cm across; conical, becoming bell shaped and eventually broadly umbonate; smooth with translucent striations; greyish brown tinged with yellow or olive when moist, drying pale grey.
Gills: adnexed; gill edges slightly toothed; crowded; white turning pinkish grey.
Stem: 4 to 8cm long and 2 to 4mm in dia.; white at the apex, the lower part grey tinged with olive; the base covered in white downy hairs; no ring.
Spores: white.
Odour: of iodine.

Mycena epipterygia (Mycenaceae) – Yellowleg Bonnet

Vivid yellow stems identify these slimy little bonnet mushrooms, which are very common in all kinds of woodland, particularly on acid soils. Although found mainly on forest-floor debris, the Yellowleg Bonnet occasionally grows on dead twigs of standing trees.

Cap: 0.8 to 1.8cm across; conical becoming convex then bell shaped, occasionally flattening out completely; margin striate and often slightly scalloped; creamy or olive-yellow, darker at centre.
Gills: adnate or slightly decurrent; white becoming yellowish at maturity.
Stem: 3 to 6cm long and 1 to 2mm dia.; greenish, watery towards base; no ring.
Spores: creamy white.

Note: The stems are often a deeper yellow when growing in well-shaded locations:

Mycena galericulata (Mycenaceae) – Common Bonnet

Larger than most of the other tuft-forming bonnet mushrooms found on stumps, the Common Bonnet shows a distinct preference for decayed stumps and fallen trunks of deciduous broadleaf trees. Only very occasionally is it found on conifer stumps.

Cap: 2.5 to 6cm across; conical, becoming bell shaped and eventually almost flattening with a shallow umbo; smooth with marginal striations; pallid greyish-brown fading to white at the margin.
Gills: adnate; white or light grey turning pinkish-grey with age.
Stem: 5 to 10cm long and 3 to 8mm in dia.; white at the apex, beige towards the finely woolly base; no ring.
Spores: creamy white.

Note: The Common Bonnet, the type species of the *Mycena* genus, often grows on wood buried below a layer of moss.

Mycena acicula (Mycenaceae) – Orange Bonnet

Despite the striking colour, these bonnet mushrooms are easy to overlook because they are so small. Rarely are the caps much more than 1cm across, and they tend to become obscured in the moss and leaf litter of the woodland floor. Look out for these pretty little mushrooms in damp deciduous broadleaf woods, often in deep shade.

Cap: 0.5 to 1.8cm across; conical, becoming bell shaped; smooth with marginal striations; mid to dark orange, but often a lighter shade of orange or yellow towards the rim.
Gills: adnexed to almost free; white or pale yellowish-orange with paler gill edges.
Stem: 3 to 5cm long and 1 to 2mm in dia.; yellow; smooth or slightly powdery, particularly towards the apex; no ring.
Spores: white.

Note: A similar species *Mycena adonis*, known as the Scarlet Bonnet, is also very small. An occasional find in both deciduous hardwood forests and in conifer plantations, the Scarlet Bonnet differs in having a reddish-orange or bright pink cap, and its stem is usually white. Both species tend to occur as singletons or in small scattered groups.

Mycena pura (Mycenaceae) – Lilac Bonnet

This fairly large but rather delicate bonnet mushroom has a very obvious radish-like odour, particularly when the gills are crushed; however, several other woodland fungi share this characteristic. Fairly common in all kinds of woodland, this is one of the many mushrooms that have a particular liking for Beech trees, and they in turn prefer alkaline soil.

Cap: 3 to 5cm across; bell shaped but often opening out almost flat or with an upturned rim, retaining a central umbo; smooth with marginal striations; in various shades of lilac, often tinged with grey; hygrophanous, drying paler from the centre.
Gills: adnate; white or grey tinged with lilac.
Stem: 5 to 10cm long and 4 to 9mm in dia.; yellowish white flushed with pale mauve; smooth; widening abruptly near base; no ring.
Spores: white.

Note: The Lilac Bonnet usually fruits singly or in very small groups.

Mycena rosea (Mycenaceae) – Rosy Bonnet

Larger and altogether more attractive than *Mycena pura*, the Rosy Bonnet is treated by some authors as merely a form of Lilac Bonnet. It does indeed occur with Beech and oaks in chalk-rich habitats similar to those favoured by its smaller and duller close relative, but it seems to be equally at home in acidic coniferous forests. While neither of these species is edible, the Rosy Bonnet has been implicated in poisonings.

Cap: 3 to 6cm across; bell shaped (generally more so than caps of *Mycena pura*); smooth with marginal striations; pink, often fading almost to white at the margin.
Gills: adnexed to adnate, may be sinuate and notched; pale pink.
Stem: 5 to 10cm long and 0.5 to 1cm in dia.; yellowish-white near the apex, flushed with pale pink in the lower half; smooth; widening abruptly near the base; no ring.
Spores: white.

Note: The Rosy Bonnet often fruits in moderate-sized groups, sometimes in lines or partial rings.

In dry weather old specimens are difficult to distinguish from *Mycena pura* because both the Rosy Bonnet and the Lilac Bonnet become almost pure white when their caps are very dry.

Rollrims Rationalised

Despite having gills, two common fungi in the genus *Paxillus* have long been thought to have a closer affinity to boletes than they do to other gilled fungi. *Paxillus involutus*, the Brown Rollrim (the type species of its genus) is an EM fungus, as also is *Paxillus rubicundulus*, and so they are covered in Chapter 4 with other ectomycorrhizal fungi. Recent DNA analysis supports this assumed ancestral relationship; however, it has also led to a reappraisal of other members of the former *Paxillus* genus, which have now been moved to the genus *Tapinella*. In northern Britain and in Scandinavia one of these, the Velvet Rollrim, is almost as common as the poisonous Brown Rollrim.

Tapinella atrotomentosa (Hygrophoropsidaceae) – Velvet Rollrim

Only an occasional find in southern Britain and Ireland, this large wood-rotting mushroom is a very common sight on pine stumps in the Caledonian Forest. The specific epithet is a reference to the unusual surface of the stem: *atro* means black and *tomentosa* means covered with short, dense, matted hairs – in short, velvety!

Cap: initially a rounded cap with an eccentric stem, expanding and developing an irregularly scalloped and wavy inrolled margin; surface finely felty; golden-brown to orange-brown with darker patches; 10 to 30cm across.
Gills: decurrent; crowded; creamy-yellow, turning brown.
Stem: 3 to 8cm long and 4 to 7cm dia.; velvety; grey, brown or black; no ring.
Spores: brown.

Hygrophoropsis aurantiaca (Hygrophoropsidaceae) - False Chanterelle

The fact that the various (and very delicious) chanterelles have ribs on the undersides of their caps and these imposters have true gills has not deterred countless impetuous mushroom pickers from cooking up bitter-tasting meals due to misidentification. False Chanterelles are, nevertheless, very attractive to look at. These woodland fungi are common sights on needle litter and occasionally on well-rotted timber in coniferous forests, and they can sometimes be found under birch trees in dry heathland.

Cap: initially convex, flattening and then often developing a shallow depression; usually retaining an incurved but slightly wavy margin; surface finely felty; various shades of golden-orange or yellow-orange, paler near the rim; 3 to 8cm across .
Gills: decurrent; crowded; forked; yellowish-orange with paler gill edges.
Stem: 2 to 4cm long and 4 to 8mm dia.; smooth; yellowish-orange, blackening when old; no ring.
Spores: white.

Pluteus – Close Cousins of *Amanita*

With their whitish free gills, *Pluteus* species have many physical features in common with the genus *Amanita*, but the latter are EM fungi and so they are included in Chapter 4 as Friends of the Forest. What is meant by this, of course, is that EM fungi are friends of living trees, helping them to scour the woodland soil for the nutrients that they need. But the wood rotters are friends of the trees, too. They break down dead wood, recycling it into simple chemicals that plants and living trees (with help from EM fungi) can make use of. Among these wood rotters are the 'shields', mushrooms of the *Pluteus* genus.

Apart from a few very colourful or conspicuously large species – this beauty is the Goldleaf Shield *Pluteus romellii* - most shield mushrooms (more than 100 species are known) are difficult to identify. Far too many of them are dull brown, with convex caps and featureless stems. Gill features aren't much help either: all are free, initially white but turning pink when mature, and they provide pink spore prints. It is only by examining microscopic characters that the many lookalike species can be separated.

Why not concentrate on a few of the distinctive shield fungi, beginning with a species that turns up on most woodland forays in summer and autumn?

Pluteus cervinus (Pluteaceae) – Deer Shield

The type species of its genus, this large and very common mushroom fruits on well-rotted hardwood and, just occasionally, on conifer stumps, piles of sawdust or woodchip.

Cap: 7 to 12cm across, bell shaped, becoming broadly umbonate; smooth and matt sometimes with fine radial fibrils, particularly in centre; various shades of fawn, mid brown or dark brown, paler towards rim.
Gills: free; crowded; white, turning pinkish-brown as the spores mature.
Stem: 6 to 12cm long and 0.8 to 1.5cm dia.; smooth; white background with sparse, dark-brown longitudinal fibrils; slightly swollen base; no ring.
Spores: pink.

In the past this mushroom was generally referred to as the Fawn Pluteus, and indeed it is not at all uncommon to find specimens with fawn caps. True, deer can have fawns, but no, that's not it. Deer also have antlers or horns, and so do these woodland fungi... but to see them you need a microscope. The horns in question are two or more tiny projections a few microns tall on the tips of the gill cystidia. The cystidia stand much taller than the spore-bearing basidia, and so it is not at all difficult to see the horns from which the Deer Shield gets its currently-accepted name.

Pluteus leoninus (Pluteaceae) – Lion Shield

The striking yellow cap of this medium-sized shield mushroom makes it easy to spot; its scarcity means that its appearance on fungus forays is all too infrequent.

Cap: 3 to 5 cm across, convex, developing a slight umbo but never fully flattening; smooth and finely velvety; margin only slightly striate (more visible when wet); golden-yellow with a slightly darker centre.
Gills: free; crowded; white, often with yellowish edges, turning pink as the spores mature.
Stem: 4 to 7 cm long and 3 to 6mm dia.; smooth or slightly fibrillose; white background flushed with yellow, darkest near the base; no ring.
Spores: pink.

Note: Long-dead moss-covered fallen trunks or stumps of deciduous hardwood trees are the staple diet of the Lion Shield.

Pluteus chrysophaeus (Pluteaceae) – Yellow Shield

This is another uncommon mushroom, found on rotten hardwood in damp, shady places.

Cap: 1.5 to 4 cm across, convex, becoming broadly umbonate; matt surface; margin faintly striate when moist; mustard-yellow with olivaceous tones near centre.
Gills: (inset picture) free; crowded; white, turning pink as spores mature.
Stem: 3 to 6 cm long and 2 to 4mm dia.; smooth; white or pale cream; longitudinally fibrillose; no ring.
Spores: pink.

Pluteus salicinus (Pluteaceae) – Willow Shield

The distinctive Willow Shield grows on dead deciduous hardwoods, including willow.

Cap: 3 to 7 cm across, convex, flattening and often becoming broadly umbonate; smooth surface; margin striate when moist; bluish-grey often with olivaceous tones near centre.
Gills: free; crowded; white, turning pink as the spores mature.
Stem: 3 to 6 cm long and 4 to 6mm dia.; smooth; white or pale cream; longitudinally fibrillose; no ring.
Spores: pink.

Woodland Pinkgills

Mention the genus *Entoloma* and those who know about mushrooms will say *'Ah, yes! Grassland fungi.'* In general they are right, too; but the pinkgills, as *Entoloma* fungi are commonly called, also include quite a few interesting woodland species. (Grassland pinkgills are discussed in Chapter 8.) Rather like the shields, among the pinkgills are rather too many dull brown jobs and they can be very difficult to separate; however, if you can 'catch them young' – by which I mean before their colours fade towards a uniform yucky brown - there are some very beautiful mushrooms in this group. Older field guides may refer to groups of fungi formerly known as *Leptonia* and *Nolanea*; these genera are now obsolete and their species have been subsumed into the genus *Entoloma*.

Most *Entoloma* species are saprophytic, although there is evidence that some spring-fruiting pinkgills can form mycorrhizal relationships with members of the Rosaceae. The family Entolomataceae includes not only the *Entoloma* fungi but also the genus *Clitopilus*, the type species of which is *Clitopilus prunulus*, commonly referred to as The Miller. (It smells farinaceous or mealy, like bread dough… get the connection?) This common edible mushroom, which occurs in grassy areas of deciduous woodland, also has pink gills.

Alboleptonia sericella **(Entolomataceae) – Cream Pinkgill**

This tiny white pinkgill is very common in grassy and mossy areas under broadleaf trees in parkland and in or on the edges of open deciduous woodland.

The Cream Pinkgill is often mistaken for one of the small white waxcaps such as *Hygrocybe virginea*, the Ivory Waxcap. The distinction becomes much clearer when the fruitbodies reach maturity, as the gills of the waxcaps remain white while those of the pinkgills turn pink.

Although mainly seen as singletons or in small groups, Cream Pinkgills (Syn. *Entoloma sericellum*) occasionally appear in arcs (pictured below) or in complete fairy rings.

Cap: 0.6 to 2cm across, conical becoming convex, flattening with an undulating and slightly incurved margin; white, becoming pale ochre from the centre with age; silky smooth.
Gills: sinuate; white, turning pink as the spores mature.
Stem: 2 to 3cm long and 2 to 3mm dia.; smooth; the base sometimes slightly swollen; white, becoming gradually yellow-ochre with age; no ring.
Spores: pink.

Note: The specific epithet *sericellum* refers to the silkiness of the cap surface, although this feature is unreliable as some specimens have very smooth caps.

Entoloma rhodopolium (Entolomataceae) – Wood Pinkgill

This very common pale pinkgill occurs in deciduous broadleaf woodland, usually in groups.

Cap: 3 to 5 cm across, convex, flattening and often becoming broadly umbonate, occasionally with a shallow depression; margin striate when dry, slightly incurved and wavy; beige, turning paler when dry.
Gills: adnate; white, turning pink as spores mature.
Stem: 4 to 9 cm long and 3 to 6mm dia.; smooth; white or pale beige, silky; no ring.
Spores: pink.

Entocybe nitida (Entolomataceae) – Pine Pinkgill

Blue species of *Entoloma* are very difficult to identify with certainty from macroscopic characters alone; however, this indigo-coloured woodland mushroom is an exception; the trick is to note the habitat. *Entoloma nitidum* grows in wet, mossy conifer forests on acidic soil, whereas other blue species grow in grassland or in light woodland on chalky soil.

Cap: 2 to 4 cm across, convex, flattening and sometimes becoming broadly umbonate; silky fibrillose surface; margin striate, slightly incurved and often becoming wavy; dark blue or greyish-blue, paler towards the rim.
Gills: adnate; white, turning pink as spores mature.
Stem: 3 to 6 cm long and 1 to 2mm dia.; smooth; greyish-blue; white and felty at base; longitudinally fibrillose; no ring.
Spores: pink.

Clitopilus prunulus (Entolomataceae) – Miller

With its smooth matt cap surface and mealy smell it ought to be difficult to confuse this common mushroom of forest tracksides and woodland-edges with any of the white poisonous species, but it does happen. The deeply decurrent gills are a helpful diagnostic feature, clearly differentiating The Miller from most poisonous white-capped fungi.

Cap: 5 to 10 cm across, irregularly convex, flattening, often with a shallow depression; smooth surface; margin often irregularly scalloped, wavy, incurved; white or pale cream, sometimes tinged with pink or grey.
Gills: deeply decurrent; crowded; white, turning pink as the spores mature.
Stem: 2 to 4 cm long and 1 to 2cm dia.; smooth; white or pale cream; finely fibrillose; no ring.
Spores: pink.
Odour: farinaceous (less so when cooked).

Crust Fungi

There is no formal definition of crust fungi, and they certainly do not represent any phylogenic group; rather this is a term describing their growing habits. So, for example, some crust fungi have smooth fertile surfaces; others have pores, producing their spores in shallow tubes. There are also crust fungi with tiny mazegill-like slots and others with hedgehog-like spines on their fertile outer surface.

Within the same genus as a crust fungus there may also be bracket fungi; indeed, some species can exist in bracket and in crust form. Within the same genus as some crust fungi there are mushroom-like relatives that produce fruitbodies with distinct caps and stems.

Often beginning as small pale spots on dead wood, crusts grow outwards across the surface of the substrate. Some (notably members of the family Stereaceae) later tend to turn their edges outwards to form shelf-like brackets, while many other groups (the *Peniophora*, for example) usually remain entirely resupinate.

Finding crust fungi is easy: turn over any fallen branch that has settled down into the litter of the forest floor and you will find one or more crust species growing on it. Many crusts persist throughout the year, so no fungus foray should ever be a complete blank.

Stereum hirsutum (Stereaceae) – Hairy Curtain Crust

The type species of its genus, Hairy Curtain Crust is one of the most common and conspicuous of the crust fungi found in deciduous hardwood forests, woods and hedgerows. (Very occasionally this crust fungus appear on conifers, and then nearly always on long-dead fallen trunks or large branches that have lost their bark, as in the example shown here.) This is also one of the most variable of fungi, both in terms of colour and more particularly in form: sometimes resupinate but more often to a variable extent bracket like. The hairy or velvety upper surface tends to become smoother as the fruitbody ages. Although this is a saprophytic fungus and mainly seen on fallen trunks and branches, it is not unusual to come across tiers of fruitbodies on dead trunks or branches of standing trees.

Fruitbody: form may be bracket or resupinate; brackets roughly semicircular, up to 6cm across and projecting 1 to 3cm from substrate; upper surface velvety and covered in fine pale-grey hairs near centre; ochre-orange colour bands interspersed with darker brown bands, turning greyish with age; pale margin is wavy; lower, fertile surface (pictured right) is smooth but lumpy, pale yellow-brown.
Spores: creamy white.

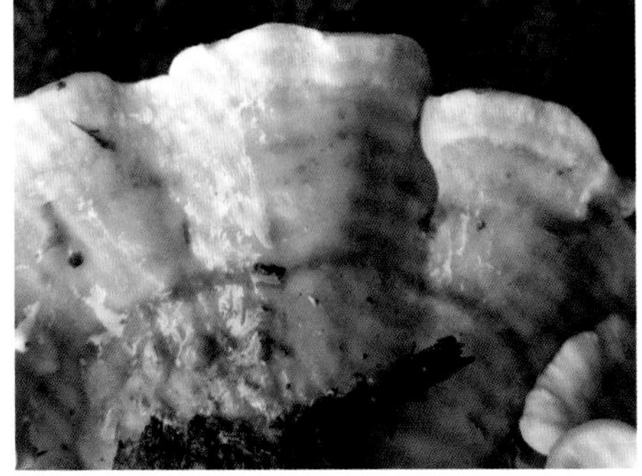

Note: All crust fungi are inedible.

Stereum rameale (Stereaceae) – No Common Name
This very variable crust forms lines and sometimes tiers on dead twigs and small branches.

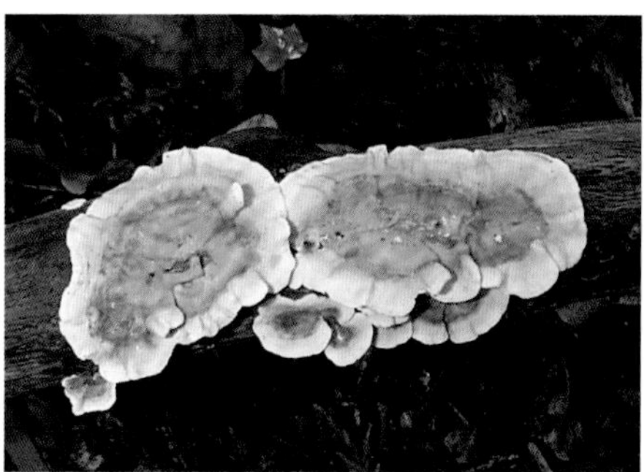

Fruitbody: patches typically 1 to 3cm across, often merging; edges may be detached and sometimes reflexed from substrate; fertile surface smooth, ochraceous in centre, paler towards wavy margin; upper (when in bracket form) infertile surface banded yellow-brown; downy but not hairy.
Spores: creamy white.

Note: This crust persists all through the year but releases spores only during autumn. It favours Beech and other hardwoods.

Steccherinum ochraceum (Stecherinaceae) – No Common Name
A wood-rotting crust fungus of deciduous hardwoods, this attractive fungus produces its spores on spines. It is uncommon in the UK but much more abundant in southern Europe.

Fruitbody: occasionally in bracket form but more often resupinate; roughly circular or oval when first forming, but expanding irregularly, often in peninsular form covering large areas; when shelf-like, extending horizontally to typically 1 to 2cm beyond edge of substrate; upper surface velvety almost white at edge but elsewhere ochre brown (often rather darker than the specimen shown here); fertile outer surface covered in short blunt spines; infertile surface white and velvety.
Spores: white.

Dichomitus campestris (Polyporaceae) – Hazel Porecrust
Look out for this rather rare resupinate polypore if you visit Scotland in the autumn, as it is very rarely found in the south of Britain or Ireland.

Fruitbody: in form occasionally a bracket but more often resupinate; roughly circular or oval, up to 6cm across and projecting 1 to 3cm from substrate; upper surface velvety and covered in fine pale-grey hairs near centre, ochre-orange bands interspersed with darker brown bands, turning greyish with age; pale margin is wavy; lower (fertile) surface is smooth (without pores) but lumpy, pale yellow-brown.
Spores: creamy white or creamy yellow.

Syn. *Trametes campestris.*

Xylodon radula **(Schizoporaceae) – Toothed Crust**

Neat round fruitbodies of this pale resupinate crust fungus grow and meet to form irregular patches, sometimes covering almost the entire surface of a fallen branch. Toothed Crust consumes dead deciduous hardwood, and is an occasional find in most parts of Britain and Ireland. This is one of the waxy crust fungi that can revive after desiccation.

Fruitbody: patches are rounded at first, ochraceous yellow with creamy-white margins, merging to cover large area; surface wholly or mainly resupinate; fertile surface covered in blunt teeth.
Spores: white.

Syn. *Basidioradulum radula, Hyphoderma radula; Radulum radula.*

Phlebia tremellosa **(Meruliaceae) – Jelly Rot**

Initially resupinate, this pale rubbery fungus can produce brackets on the upper surfaces of dead wood, but more often it is hidden beneath a dead branch and visible only when you turn the branch over; then the fruitbodies are almost invariably resupinate. Jelly Rot is an infrequent find, occurring nearly always on dead deciduous hardwood but just occasionally on well-rotted softwood.

Fruitbody: patches rounded at first, creamy-white, expanding and turning pale salmon pink in the centre but retaining white margins; individual fruitbodies often merging to cover large area; fertile surface wrinkled folds in the form of mazegill-like slots; infertile upper surface (when in bracket form) white or pale pink, covered in short stiff hairs.
Spores: white.

And sometimes you simply have to admit defeat...

There are hundreds of other crust fungi. It's a virtual certainty, therefore, that even when you have gone through all of your field guides, consulted websites and sought the help of experts, you won't always be able to make a definite identification. (It doesn't help, of course, that many of these can occur either in resupinate form or as reflexed brackets.) If you didn't collect a sample for detailed microscopic analysis, file the pictures under *'Look more closely next time…'* Right: I *think* this is Purplepore Bracket *Trichaptum abietinum*; it was growing on oak bark.

Bjerkandera adusta (Hapalopilaceae) – Smoky Bracket

A very variable small-pored fungus, the Smoky Bracket can occur either as a resupinate crust on the underside of a fallen branch, as a reflexed bracket on the side of dead hardwood (or very occasionally on conifer wood), or even as a rounded cap with a short stem when growing on the upper surface of dead wood. Despite its shape-shifting capability, this crust fungus is recognisable by its grey fertile surface.

Fruitbody: in crust, bracket or cap form; 2 to 6cm across; when resupinate or cap form, infertile surface felty, becoming smooth; rounded, concentrically ringed in ochre, grey-brown and mid brown. Fertile surface (left) covered in tiny grey pores, paler at margin.
Spores: straw yellow.

Coltricia perennis (Hymenochaetaceae) - Tiger's Eye

Although most polypores grow as either crusts or brackets, there are a few that form cup-like fruitbodies. One of these is Tiger's Eye, a very attractive cup-and-stem fungus that grows on humus-rich sandy soil on woodland edges and on heathland.

Cap: shallow, thin-fleshed cup, 3 to 10cm dia.; upper surface velvety, becoming smooth, concentrically zoned in shades of ochre, mid brown and red-brown, margin pale.
Pores:, grey-brown, angular; tubes decurrent, 3 to 4 per mm.
Stem: 2 to 4cm tall and 4 to 8mm dia., brown.
Spores: golden brown.

Polyporus brumalis (Polyporaceae) - Winter Polypore

Found mainly on dead hardwood, these tough brown cap-and-stem polypores can persist through winter into spring (as pictured here).

Cap: 3 to 8cm across, various shades of brown; flat then with the centre slightly depressed; margin wavy; flesh tough.
Pores: (inset) white, maturing tan; tubes slightly decurrent; oval, 2 to 3 per mm.
Stem: brown 3 to 7cm tall, 3 to 5mm dia.
Spores: white.

Polyporus tuberaster (Polyporaceae) - Tuberous Polypore

An uncommon find, the Tuberous Polypore grows on fallen branches of deciduous hardwood trees. Sometimes these funnel-shaped polypores grow from a sclerotium-like tuber (a hard mass of mycelium that stores food reserves, enabling the fruitbody to survive harsh environmental conditions).

Dryad's Saddle can form similar fruitbodies but with much larger cap scales.

Cap: 5 to 15cm across, covered in fine scales, various shades of yellowish-brown to orange-brown; flat or with centre slightly depressed at stem attachment point; margin inrolled and slightly wavy.
Pores: white, maturing cream or ochre; tubes decurrent; angular, 1 to 2 per mm.
Stem: 2 to 6cm tall; whitish; central when growing from top of substrate, eccentric or sometimes lateral when growing from side of substrate; 3 to 5cm dia.
Spores: white.

Albatrellus ovinus (Albatrellaceae) – Sheep Polypore

Seen from above these creamy white or grey-brown polypores, not known to be in Britain but common in some European countries, cold be mistaken for Wood Hedgehogs. Often, however, the caps are so distorted that they look like crumpled paper bags. A shepherd very with poor eyesight might possibly mistake them for sheep a long way off...

Cap: 7 to 18cm across, creamy white or pale grey; convex, soon flattening and becoming centrally depressed, distorted and lobed; margin wavy and usually remaining incurved; skin cracks when old or in very dry weather. Often several caps merge and become firmly conjoined.
Pores: white or creamy yellow; oval; tubes decurrent; 2 to 3 per mm.
Stem: creamy white or light grey; 3 to 7cm tall, 1 to 3cm dia.
Spores: white.

I have included the Sheep Polypore in with the Rest of the Rotters – the saprobic forest-floor fungi; however, some authorities believe that this edible mushroom may in fact be mycorrhizal with spruce trees. The group pictured here was growing under pines.

Albatrellus subrubescens (right) is often tinged slightly violet but otherwise it is very similar in physical appearance to the Sheep Polypore. The two can be distinguished by studying the spores. An in-the-field test should also throw up another discriminating feature: when bruised the surface of *Albatrellus subrubescens* flushes orange.

Jelly Fungi

The jelly fungi (heterobasidiomycetes) are a group of species from several orders within the Basidiomycota, most notably the Auriculariales, Dacrymycetales and Tremellales. All of these fungi share the feature that their fruitbodies are, or appear to be, of jelly-like consistency. (Actually, some of them are more rubbery than jelly-like.) Another remarkable characteristic shared by fungi in this group is the ability to survive desiccation and to return to their jelly-like form and full viability when wet weather returns. Although most of the common heterobasidiomycetes are edible (one or two of them are even considered good when eaten raw in salads), very few of these fungi have much in the way of taste, and so they are usually added to stews or used with other kinds of mushrooms to make soup.

Tremella mesenterica (Tremellaceae) – Yellow Brain

This common jelly fungus is most frequently found in winter on dead branches of hardwood trees, where it is a parasite of resupinate crust fungi of the genus *Peniophora*.

Fruitbody: orange-yellow; gelatinous; convoluted or lobed; greasy when damp, shrivelling and darkening in dry weather but reviving once wet again; up to 7cm across. A white form (inset picture) is less common.
Spores: white.

Note: The yellow specimens shown here were photographed during dry weather when the fruitbodies had begun shrivelling. Note the darker orange colour of the dried areas.

Exidia glandulosa (Exidiaceae) – Witches' Butter

In wet weather Witches' Butter certainly has a butter-like consistency, and its sombre appearance may account for the dark connotation. An alternative basis is the belief that witchcraft can be counteracted by throwing these fungi on to a blazing fire. This jelly fungus is found on all kinds of dead or dying hardwood trees and on fallen branches.

In wet weather *Exidia glandulosa* turns black and jelly like; however, during prolonged dry spells it shrinks to a series of cone-shaped olive-brown crusts. The individual fruit bodies often coalesce into large blobs typically 5cm to 15cm long.

Fruitbody: black and gelatinous when wet, becoming olive-brown and shrivelling to cone-shaped crusts during prolonged dry weather; individual fruitbodies 1 to 2cm across often coalesce to form compound blobs typically 5 to 15cm long.
Spores: white.

Note: *Exidia nigricans* (inset picture), which also appears on dead hardwoods, is very similar but with brain-like wrinkles and folds. Both of these sombre jelly-like fungi are common and widespread throughout Britain and Ireland.

Exidia thuretiana (Exidiaceae) – White Brain
A very common jelly fungus, White Brain appears on dead hardwood, particularly Beech. In dry weather the fruitbodies shrivel and become thin, translucent rubbery membranes that are almost invisible, and so you really need wet weather to find this species. *Exidia thuretiana* is found in most parts of Britain and Ireland.

Fruitbody: pure white and gelatinous when wet, drying to almost invisible; individual fruitbodies are cushion shaped, 0.2 to 1cm across, becoming contorted with age and fusing with neighbouring fruitbodies to form a large mass several cm across.
Spores: white.

Note: Crystal Brain *Exidia nucleata* is very similar and equally common, but within its very soft gelatinous fruitbodies hard white inclusions are clearly visible.

Neobulgaria pura (Helotiaceae) – Beech Jellydisc
Unlike *Bulgaria inquinans*, which sometimes fruits on dying branches of living trees, *Neobulgaria pura* is invariably found on fallen trunks and branches of broadleaf hardwood trees, and in particular Beech – hence the common name.

Fruitbody: pinkish-ochre, gelatinous fruitbodies initially shaped like spinning tops but eventually distorting as they push up against one another in groups; becoming more cup-like; 0.4 to 1.5cm across and up to 8mm tall. (A brain-like form, *Neobulgaria pura* var. *foliacea*, also occurs but is rare.)
Spores: white.

Note: This ascomycete is not one of the heterobasidiomycetes or true 'jelly fungi'.

Dacrymyces stillatus (Dacrymycetaceae) – Common Jellyspot
Gregarious or in large merging groups on dead broadleaf or conifer wood, including fence posts and rails, this common fungus has a preference for timber that is already fairly well rotted. The fruitbodies can appear at any time of the year during periods of wet weather.

Fruitbody: dull orange-yellow when moist and fresh, becoming more brown and translucent with age; cushion-shaped blobs, slightly flattened; 1 to 8mm across and up to 4mm tall.
Spores: white.

Auricularia auricula-judae (Auriculariaceae) – Jelly Ear

Mainly seen in winter and spring, the Jelly Ear Fungus is most commonly seen on dead elder trees and on fallen branches. This rubbery fungus is sometimes used in cookery.

Fruitbody: outer surface is tan-brown with a purple tinge and covered in a fine greyish velvety down; wrinkled inner surface is smooth; rubbery rather than gelatinous when moist, brittle when thoroughly dry; 1 to 10cm across and 0.3 to 1.5cm tall.
Spores: white.

Note: in China this or a closely related species is a popular edible delicacy.

Calocera viscosa (Dacrymycetaceae) – Yellow Stagshorn

Common on dead conifers, this jelly fungus is often mistaken for a coral fungus.

Fruitbody: bright orange or orange-yellow (in dry weather sometimes orange-red); greasy and viscid, with antler-like branches often forked near the tips; rubbery rather than gelatinous; 2 to 10cm tall
Spores: white.

Note: sometimes this fungus seems to be growing in leaf or needle litter, but invariably there is buried wood hidden just beneath the surface.

Calocera cornea (Dacrymycetaceae) – Small Stagshorn

This unbranching jelly fungus can be seen on trunks and twigs of deciduous broadleaf trees. It looks rather like a club fungus; however, microscopic examination reveals that it has distinctive Y-shaped basidia, which are diagnostic characteristics of members of the order Dacrymycetales

Fruitbody: bright yellow (in dry weather becoming more orange); greasy and viscid, with curved, blunt-pointed horns that are only very rarely forked; clustered in non-merging groups; 2 to 10mm tall and typically 1mm dia.
Spores: white or very pale yellow.

Pseudohydnum gelatinosum (Dacrymycetaceae) – Jelly Tooth

Tooth-like projections on the underside are normally associated with *Hydnum* species; however, the Jelly Tooth is not a member of the family Hydnaceae (hedgehog fungi). This wood-rotting fungus is found mainly on well-rotted conifer trunks and branches.

Fruitbody: pallid grey or light brown upper surface; irregularly fan-shaped, sometimes with a laterally-attached rudimentary stem; gelatinous; upper (infertile) surface slightly rough or finely downy; individual fruitbodies 2 to 4cm tall and 3 to 5cm across; sometimes clustered in rosette form.
Fertile surface: pale grey-brown blunt spines (inset picture) 2 to 5mm long on underside of fruitbody.
Spores: white.

Ascocoryne sarcoides (Helotiaceae) – Purple Jellydisc

Most commonly found on the trunks and branches of dead Beech trees, this colourful ascomycetous wood-rotting fungus can form large and conspicuous clusters.

Fruitbody: various shades of pinkish purple; spherical at first, either sessile or with a very short stem, later becoming centrally depressed and then irregularly cushion shaped; forming brain-like compound groups; gelatinous; individual fruitbodies 0.5 to 1.5cm across; clusters often 5 to 10cm across.
Spores: white.

Note: *Ascocoryne cylichnium* is similar but has more obviously cup-shaped fruitbodies (and larger spores).

Bisporella citrina (Helotiaceae) – Lemon Disco

This colourful wood-rotting fungus is commonly found on dead oaks and other hardwoods.

Fruitbody: lemon or bright yellow, paler at margin; flat-topped or saucer-shaped disc with a very short, tapered stem; normally in swarms; gelatinous; individual fruitbodies 1 to 3mm across and 1 to 2mm tall.
Spores: white.

Note: What makes this tiny ascomycetous fungus easy to find are its bright colour and its gregarious nature. A common find, the Lemon Disco occurs throughout Europe (right up into the Arctic Circle) and in the USA.

***Leotia lubrica* (Leotiaceae) – Jellybaby**
Sticky or even slimy when damp, gelatinous and becoming more rubbery with age, these strange little ascomycetous fungi are saprophytes of conifer and deciduous hardwood litter. Occasionally they spring from well-rotted fallen trunks and branches, but damp mossy forest floors are usually the best places to look for these kinds of fungi. Despite its common name this kind of jellybaby is inedible.

Cap: 0.3 to 2cm across, the irregularly lobed fertile head is roughly convex, flattening but retaining an inrolled margin; yellow with olive tints; sticky or slimy; the flesh is gelatinous or rubbery.
Gills: despite its cap-and-stem form, this is not a gilled mushroom.
Stem: 2 to 5cm long and 2 to 5mm dia.; yellow-orange background finely granular with minute greenish scales, sometimes also with longitudinal grooves; no ring.
Spores: white.

Fairies in the Forest

Fairy clubs such as *Clavaria fragilis* are generally thought of as grassland fungi, and indeed many of them are; however, fairies can live wherever they choose, and some choose to live in forests – but we have known this since we were tiny tots.

Of course, you can expect to come across some of the grassland fairy clubs in woodland edges and grassy verges beside woodland tracks and rides, but there are also club-shaped fungi that grow on decaying sticks and on branches buried in damp leaf litter. Here is one that turns up very frequently on woodland fungus forays:

***Clavulinopsis laeticolor* (Clavariaceae) – Handsome Club**
One of several very similar yellow or orange club fungi, this club can be found on leaf litter in damp deciduous woodland or occasionally in hedgerows. Although the Handsome Club is most often found in woodlands, it also occurs in unimproved grassland habitats.

Fruitbody: 2 to 5cm tall and 1.5 to 3mm dia.; usually clustered but not often fused at base; rarely branched; straight or only slightly curved; sometimes flattened in cross-section; tip either obtuse, spatulate, or very occasionally pointed; tapering toward the base; surface smooth, yellow-orange to orange, paler near base.
Spores: white.

Note: Identification of yellow or orange fairy clubs from macroscopic characteristics alone is not generally feasible; microscopic characteristics have to be examined to confirm the identity of many of these superficially very similar club fungi.

Clavariadelphus pistillaris (Gomphaceae) – Giant Club

Sticking up from the forest floor like ancient standing stones, and often with the weathered appearance to match, these massive fairy clubs might more appropriately be described as goblin clubs or troll truncheons. These are the archetypal weapons depicted in the hands of Neanderthal men as they drag their womenfolk, always by the hair, into their cold dark caves. The world may have moved on (a little) but *Clavariadelphus pistillaris* seems to remain stuck in the past.

This untufted fairy club, type species of the genus *Clavariadelphus*, is easy to spot when young and yellow, but with age the fruitbodies take on the dull coloration of the decaying leaf litter around them and so, despite their large size, can be missed.

Fruitbody: Occasionally somewhat laterally flattened and longitudinally wrinkled or grooved, these large simple (not forking) truncheon-shaped clubs taper slightly towards the base and have rounded tips. At first yellow (far left), the Giant Clubs turn various shades of pink, mauve, violet and brown with age (near left) or when bruised.

The individual clubs are typically 8 to 30cm tall and 5 to 8cm across at their widest point when fully developed.

Firm when young, the white flesh of *Clavariadelphus pistillaris* turns violet-brown when cut; it becomes soft and spongy when fruitbodies reach full maturity.
Spores: white.

Typhula fistulosa (Typhulaceae) – Pipe Club

Unless you are crawling on hands and knees you are more likely to tread on than to notice the hordes of tiny thread-like club fungi on dead leaves and twigs on the forest floor. For example within the genera *Pterula* and *Typhula* lurk many species that rarely exceed 1cm in height. It's hard to miss a monster among midgets, however, and *Typhula fistulosa* really stands out from the crowd.

Fruitbody: Up to 40cm tall and looking like worms standing on tiptoe, these simple, unbranched clubs can occur either singly or in small tufts. Pipe Clubs are soft and so flexible that in open locations they can be seen waving in even the gentlest of breezes.

They appear to be growing from soil, but if you clear away the leaf litter you will find a buried twig from which the clubs emerge.
Spores: white.

Phallus impudicus (Phallaceae) - Stinkhorn

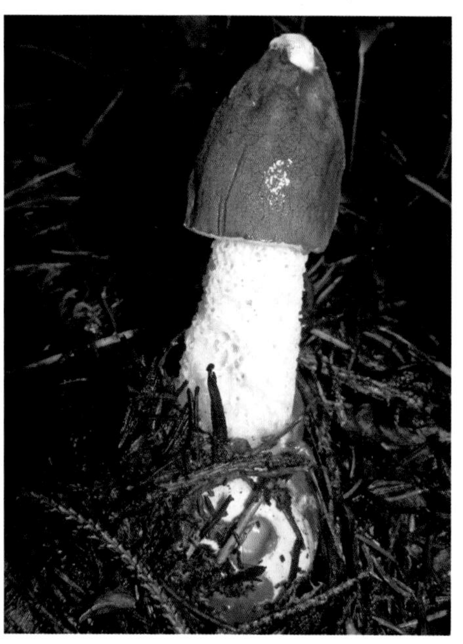

The Stinkhorn emerges from an 'egg' that develops beneath the leaf litter of the forest floor. (Eggs of the stinkhorn can be found at any time of year, but they lie dormant until the summer months.) The cap is initially covered with olive-green 'gleba', a smelly spore-laden coating that attracts insects which in turn distribute the spores.

It is fairly easy to find the 'eggs' of this species, because they are usually only partly buried in conifer needles or leaf letter and the white skin stands out clearly. The white cap beneath the gleba is all that most people ever see because insects quickly eat the spore-bearing gleba, at the same time getting some of it stuck to their legs so that spores are transported over large distances when the insects fly off in search of food elsewhere.

Early morning is the best time to look (or sniff) for this very smelly species.

Fruitbody: oval at the 'egg' stage, rupturing as the gleba-laden cap is pushed upwards on a spongy stem; volva and stem, are white; the cap is white, covered in dark-olive gleba that is soon eaten by flies to reveal an underlying white cone, wider than the stem, with a honeycomb surface; the egg is white, 3 to 5cm dia., and 4 to 7cm long; the stem is also white, 12 to 18cm tall, 1.5 to 3cm dia.
Spores: olive-brown.

Mutinus caninus (Phallaceae) - Dog Stinkhorn

A slender stinkhorn that in most areas is much less common than *Phallus impudicus*, the Dog Stinkhorn is also nowhere near as smelly – in fact I have never been able to locate these fungi other than by sight. Even so, they are quite able to attract all the insects they need, and so again this is one of those woodland fungi that are seen at their best in the mornings. Although in many parts of Britain and Ireland this stinkhorn is most often found in broadleaf woodland, it can also occur in conifer forests, particularly under spruces.

Fruitbody: oval at the 'egg' stage, rupturing as the gleba-laden cap is pushed upwards on a slender spongy stem; volva is white; stem, is pale orange; red cap is covered in dark-olive gleba that is soon eaten by flies to reveal an underlying spongy tip that is narrower than the stem; egg is white, 1.2 to 2cm dia., and 2 to 3.5cm long, often set in leaf litter at an angle of 30 to 45° from vertical; stem 7 to 10cm tall, 1 to 1.5cm dia.

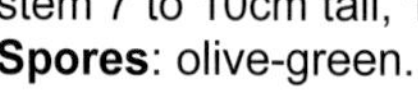

Spores: olive-green.

Aseroë rubra **(Phallaceae) – Starfish Fungus**

Aseroë rubra is arguably the most striking of all stinkhorn species found in Britain. It is, however, a non-native species, having been first imported to England from Australia (probably via the Netherlands in 1828, when it was first seen in Kew Gardens, in Surrey).

Fruitbody: Before rupturing, the pale brown ball or egg of *Aseroë rubra* is typically 3cm in diameter and often visible above the surface of the leaf litter or rotting woody debris upon which it feeds. The pink-tinged stem of the Starfish Fungus emerges from its egg, leaving the torn remains of the outer peridium (the rubbery 'shell' of the egg) as a bag-like volva surrounding the base of the stem. Usually eight, but sometimes as few as six or as many as ten or more initially conjoined but later bifurcated arms emerge from the volva of the egg of this stinkhorn; the arms, each typically 3.5cm long, are attached to the top of a whitish stem 5-9cm tall and about 3cm in diameter.

Spores: The upper surfaces of the sponge-like stem and the inner parts of the arms are coated with an olive-brown gleba that is laden with spores.

Colus hirudinosus **(Phallaceae) – No Common Name**

Colus hirudinosus (syn. *Clathrus hirudinosus*) is one of the neatest and arguably also the most beautiful of the cage-like stinkhorns found in temperate regions. (Most stinkhorns are tropical fungi.) To date this striking fungus has not been found in Britain and Ireland, but its presence in southern and central Europe suggests that it might well move in if, as expected, climate change accelerates.

Fruitbody: This stinkhorn has an elongated hollow fruitbody comprising a short, thick stalk that divides into several spongy, wrinkled columns which unite towards the top.

Spores: olive-brown.

Clathrus ruber (Phallaceae) – Red Cage

Another rare stinkhorn originally from the antipodes, the Red Cage is a startling sight but also a very smelly find. Spore-bearing gleba coats the inside of a sphere whose outer surface is in the form of a lattice (right). Attracted by the smell of the gleba, flies and other small insects enter via the holes. It can take many attempts for a fly to find an exit route, and failed attempts result in the insect picking up dabs of gleba on it head, wings, thorax or abdomen – a more effective process than merely relying on feet alone!

The Red Cage colonises damp woodside ditches full of rotting twigs and leaf litter; it is also partial to woodmulch on flowerbeds.

Fruitbody: oval with a rather bumpy surface at the 'egg' stage (left), rupturing as the gleba-laden cage expands; no stem; lattice walls spongy, bright red or orange; inner surface coated in dark-green gleba that is soon eaten by flies; volva, white or very pale pink; egg 2.5 to 4cm dia., and 3 to 4.5cm tall; cage 4 to 7cm across and 6 to 10cm tall.
Spores: olive-green.

Note: *Clathrus ruber,* native to central and southern Europe, was almost certainly introduced to Britain and Ireland.

Clathrus archeri (Clathraceae) - Devil's Fingers

From a white egg springs a short stem topped by four to six gleba-laden arms, arching outwards and giving the fruitbody the appearance of a squid. This exotic stinkhorn, only rarely seen in southern Britain, is a litter rotter in broadleaf woodland; however, it is also partial to woodchip mulch and so it is now seen increasingly in parks and gardens.

Fruitbody: oval at the 'egg' stage, rupturing as the gleba-laden arms push upwards and arch outwards; stem and arms bright red or deep pink, upper surface of arms coated in dark green gleba that is soon eaten by flies; volva pale ochre or pinkish white; eggs 2.5 to 4cm dia., and 3 to 4.5cm tall; stem 2.5 to 5cm tall and 2 to 3cm dia.; arms 4 to 7cm long.
Spores: olive-green.

Note: *Clathrus archeri* is native to Australia and New Zealand, and introduced elsewhere.

Earthstars

In the kingdom of fungi we come across an amazing range of forms, but the earthstars must be some of the weirdest of all. Some sit down on the ground, while others arch their limbs and raise themselves up like alien beings surveying their new surroundings. To much the same effect the stalkballs (also known as stilt puffballs) raise up their spore-filled peridia on long necks that seem far too slim to support their heads. Although not widely distributed, where they do occur both earthstars and stalkballs tend to congregate in great hordes, sometimes appearing to be jostling one another as they lean at crazy angles.

Geastrum triplex (Geastraceae) – Collared Earthstar

This large earthstar often fruits in huge fairy rings in coniferous and deciduous broadleaf woodland; it can also be found in woodchip-mulched gardens and parks.

Fruitbody: initially a part-buried ball with a prominent 'beak', the mature fruitbody eventually comprises an outer star, an inner saucer-like collar, and a central ball. Onion-shaped fruitbody splits open at maturity and 5 to 8 creamy-buff outer rays fold back, splitting to leave a fleshy collar as the remainder of each ray folds downwards and the tips curl part-way under the fruitbody; rays turn brown with age; outer dia. 5 to 12cm. Unstalked creamy buff spore sac, surface smooth, 2 to 4cm across; fibrous apical pore.
Spores: chocolate-brown.

Notes: The Collared Earthstar doesn't always form a saucer-like collar, but there are some other distinguishing features that can help with identification, not least of which is its exceptional size compared with other earthstars. Look also for a pale area around the fuzzy spore opening, as other large earthstars do not have this feature.

Myriostoma coliforme (Geastraceae) – Pepper Pot

The holes in earthstars through which spores are released are known as peristoles. The Collared Earthstar has a single, quite prominent peristole whereas the very rare *Myriostoma coliforme*, known as the Pepper Pot earthstar, has several peristoles. (The specific epithet *coliforme* means 'like a colander'). Although still found in several locations in Sweden, this species was thought to be extinct in Britain until it was rediscovered on a site in Suffolk in 2006.

Geastrum fimbriatum (Geastraceae) – Sessile Earthstar

Initially looking like a round stone lying partly buried in the soil, the outer skin splits into rays that fold back neatly beneath the inner spore sac, raising it up from the ground. Sessile Earthstars fruit in small groups and occasionally in fairy rings, usually on alkaline soil; they seem to have no particular preference for either hardwood trees or conifers.

Fruitbody: 5 to 9 creamy-white outer rays recurved beneath spore sac; outer dia. 2.5 to 5cm; unstalked papery grey spore sac finely downy, 1 to 2.2cm across; apical pore fibrous. **Spores**: chocolate-brown.

Geastrum floriforme (Geastraceae) – Daisy Earthstar

This is one of the hygroscopic earthstars; it spreads its rays during damp weather but folds them back to protect the spore sac during dry weather. It is found mainly under conifers.

Fruitbody: 5 to 10 brown outer rays, hygroscopic, curved over spore sac in dry weather, lying flat on substrate or curved slightly beneath spore sac when moist; outer dia. 2 to 5cm; unstalked papery spore sac 0.7 to 1.4cm across, subglobose (a vertically squashed sphere), grey-buff, finely downy, fading to nearly white; apical pore fibrous. **Spores**: chocolate-brown.

Geastrum fornicatum (Geastraceae) – Arched Earthstar

Instead of lying flat or folding beneath the spore sac, the rays of this rather uncommon earthstar stand on their tips, usually still attached to the remains of a basal cup. Found particularly under old yew trees in churchyards, the Arched Earthstar also occurs occasionally under other conifers and broadleaf deciduous trees.

Fruitbody: 5 to 8cm tall, with 4 or 5 rays, brown often tinged with blue or purple; standing upright on ray tips that usually remain attached to a basal cup; rays are 4 to 7.5cm long; short-stalked round or subglobose spore sac is 1.5 to 2.5cm across, grey-buff, surface rough; fibrous apical pore. **Spores**: chocolate-brown.

Note: Prior to the Space Age, this earthstar may well have been the inspiration for fanciful impressions of what futuristic spaceships might look like. Not far wrong!

Oddballs

No end of oddball fungi that feed on forest floors, and even the best of field guides can only provide an insight into a small selection. Before leaving the Basidiomycota here are just two of the many other strange fungi you might stumble across on woodland forays. Setting out in search of these elusive mushrooms is not something I would recommend to anyone valuing their sanity, but it's helpful to know that they exist; otherwise the shock of finding them unexpectedly might do as much harm as enbarking on a quest in search of them.

Crucibulum laeve **(Agaricaceae) – Common Bird's Nest**

The bird's nest fungi are so called because they bear a fanciful resemblance to a nest, from which spore-filled eggs (peridioles) are ejected when raindrops hit them. Look for these fungi on dead twigs and fallen branches. Those pictured here are growing on a piece of discarded plywood, but the Common Bird's Nest is found increasingly often on woodchip mulch in gardens and parks.

Fruitbody: brown or buff cup (peridium) 0.5 to 1cm tall and 0.5 to 1cm dia., initially covered by a thin buff membrane (called an epiphragm) that peels back to reveal 7 to 15 flattened spheres (peridioles) each containing spore-laden gleba. When raindrops hit them, the peridioles are ejected tiddly-wink style.
Spores: light yellow-brown.

Cyathus striatus **(Agaricaceae) – Fluted Bird's Nest**

A shaggy outer surface together with striate inner sides of its cups (not unlike the paper cups in which fairy cakes are baked) make this species easy to identify. In woodland, Fluted Bird's Nest fungi grow in clusters on half-buried dead twigs. These little fungi (image: Wikipedia) are also found on woodchip mulch.

Fruitbody: cup outer surface brown, fleecy or hairy; inner surface smooth, also brown but with vertical striations; cup (peridium) 1 to 1.5cm tall and 0.5 to 1cm dia., initially covered by a hairy off-white membrane that peels back to reveal 4 to 12 flattened spheres (peridioles) containing the spore mass. Like other bird's nest fungi, *Cyathus striatus* acts as a splash cup, ejecting its peridioles when raindrops hit the cup at the right angle.
Spores: light yellow-brown.

Cyathus olla **(Agaricaceae) - Field Bird's Nest**

This species is distinguished by its relatively large peridioles, 3 to 3.5mm across. Initially silvery, the eggs soon turn grey, giving the mature fruitbody a sombre appearance (far right) in stark contrast to the bright colours when the 'lids' are on the 'nests'. Although they occur on twigs and woodchip mulch, another good place to look for these tiny fungi is on dead marram grass stems in coastal sand dunes.

Flask Fungi of the Forest Floor

The only flask fungus commonly seen high up on living trees is King Alfred's Cakes, *Daldinia concentrica*, which was described in Chapter 5 along with other 'hangers on'. Flask fungi are much more often seen on the forest floor and on well-rotted stumps and fallen branches, and many of the larger and more conspicuous of them belong to the family Xylariaceae. Here are details of the two species that are very common in broadleaf deciduous woodland throughout Europe; their fruitbodies can be found all through the year, although spore release occurs only in autumn and winter.

Xylaria polymorpha (Xylariaceae) – Dead Man's Fingers

Often fruiting in bunches or in lines along buried wood, and looking very much like a set of blackened fingers clawing their way out of a grave, Dead Man's Fingers must deserve the title of 'most descriptive name for a fungus'. These sombre fruitbodies grow from buried hardwood, and most often from Beech.

Fruitbody: 3 to 8cm tall and 1 to 2.5cm across, club shaped; several clubs often fused near base and attached to substrate via a short stem; brittle; grey-brown, blackening with age; rough texture comprising tiny raised pores (called perithecia) via which spores are released; inner flesh (inset picture) white.
Spores: black.

Note: The specific epithet *polymorpha* means 'many forms', a reference to the very variable shape of these fruitbodies.

You may also come across a similar but smaller and slimmer relative, *Xylaria longipes* – Dead Moll's Fingers – with a more obvious stem; another hardwood rotter, this tuft-forming black club is most commonly found on dead branches of Sycamore.

Xylaria hypoxylon (Xylariaceae) – Candlesnuff Fungus

When a lighted candle is snuffed out by quickly pinching the wick between finger and thumb (don't try this at home, kids… it can go terribly wrong), the flattened partly-burnt wick looks something like a fruitbody of *Xylaria hypoxylon* (although the black part of an extinguished candle wick is at the top!). Candlesnuff Fungus grows on dead hardwood.

Fruitbody: 2 to 6cm tall, round or more often flattened clubs each 1 to 4mm across, sometimes branching; in the asexual state branches are white with flattened or pointed tips; in the mature sexual state, above an infertile lower stem-like structure the fertile upper part (stroma) is uniformly black with a rough texture comprising tiny raised pores (perithecia) via which spores are released; inner flesh white.
Spores: black.

Cup and Ear Fungi

Most of the large and colourful woodland ascomycete saprophytes are cup or ear fungi of the order Pezizales. Some distinctive cup fungi belong to the families Pyronemataceae, but there are also a lot of cups - mainly brownish - within the family Pezizaceae and they can be very tricky to separate without resorting to a microscope. The *Otidea* differ from other cups in having a slit down one side, and the two edges overlap. The army of smaller ascomycetes include some very beautiful species, but identifying them with certainty is beyond most amateurs. If they don't make you blind they may well drive you mad.

Sarcoscypha austriaca (Sarcoscyphaceae) – Scarlet Elfcup

Scarlet Elfcup, a winter species, is found mainly in woodland with plenty of moss-covered hardwood litter; banks of tree-shaded ditches can also be productive sites. It is most common in Western Britain and in Northern Ireland but rare in many other regions.

Fruitbody: circular or oval cup; 1 to 5cm across and 1 to 3cm tall; smooth scarlet inner surface; buff-orange outer surface; buried stem typically 1cm tall and 3mm dia.
Spores: white.

Peziza micropus (Pezizaceae) – No Common Name

This common *Peziza* (possibly synonymous with *Peziza varia*) appears on very rotten hardwood, often inside hollow dead stumps, particularly of Beech trees.

Fruitbody: shallow cup 1 to 5cm across; inner surface smooth, ochre; outer surface slightly paler and finely granular or floury; margin inrolled; short, narrow stem usually buried in substrate.
Spores: white.

Note: This cup fungus is inedible.

Aleuria aurantia (Pyronemataceae) - Orange Peel Fungus

Looking even more like orange peel than the real thing, these irregularly-shaped shallow cups grow on paths and disturbed forest tracks, but few people take notice of them.

Fruitbody: wavy-edged cup with a bright orange interior and paler finely-downy exterior; sessile; 1 to 9cm across.
Spores: white.

Note: Orange Peel Fungus is edible if thoroughly cooked, but it is not highly prized.

Scutellinia scutellata (Pyronemataceae) – Common Eyelash

This remarkable ascomycetous fungus is very tiny, and so despite being quite common it usually goes unnoticed. What makes all of the 'eyelash' fungi species (and in Britain and Ireland there are getting on for 50 within this genus and related genera) so special is the fringe of dark hairs around the edge of each cap; what makes them difficult is that the differences between species are mainly seen by examining microscopic characters.

Fruitbody: Up to 10mm across, but more commonly 3 to 5mm, the shallow cups of Common Eyelash are shiny on the upper (hymenial or spore-bearing) surface and matt on the underside. Individual cups, which become almost flat when fully mature, are initially round but often develop irregular margins as they push up against their neighbours. The outer surface is infertile; the ascospores are produced on the shiny inner surface of the cup, which is typically 2 to 4mm tall and attached to the substrate by mycelial threads.
Spores: white.

Scutellinia trechispora (Pyronemataceae) – No Common Name

An uncommon find in Britain and Ireland, *Scutellinia trechispora* is also reported from several European mainland countries.
Fruitbody: Typically 5-6mm across, the upper surface is an orange-red disc with a slightly raised margin fringed with rigid thick-walled multi-septate hairs. The outer surface, or excipulum, is reddish brown and is also covered with sharply pointed brown hairs.

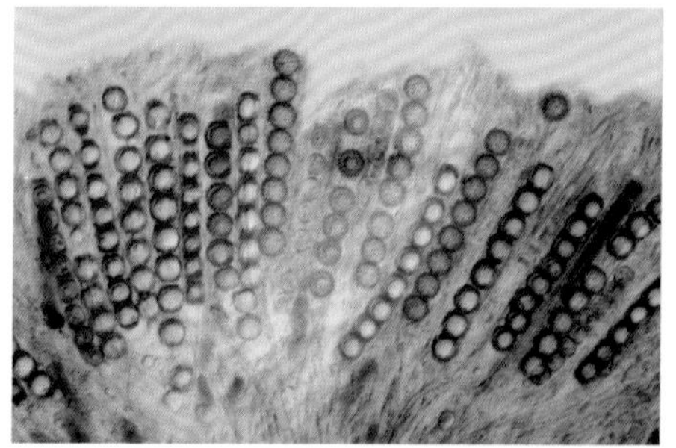

Here are some of the microscopic characters (identifying features) whose forms and dimensions help distinguish this 'asco' from the many other macroscopically similar ones. Other features of importance include the cell structure of the hairs and the way in which they are 'rooted' into the cup surface.

Asci: The cylindrical, thin-walled asci are 250 - 300µm x 19 - 25µm, and this is where the spores mature (eight spores per ascus).

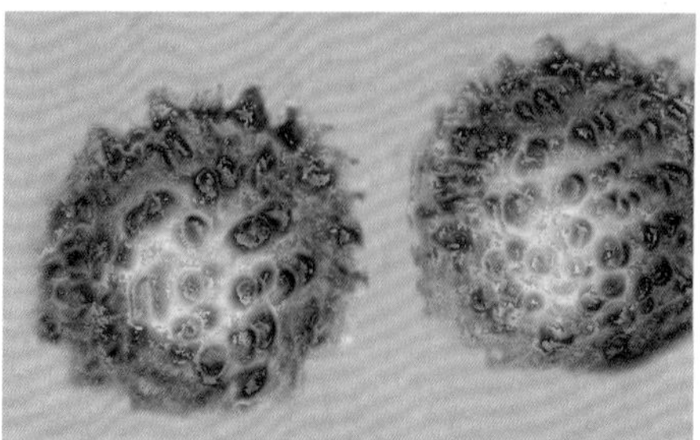

The club-shaped 'packing' between the asci are called paraphyses and are 2.5 - 4µm in diameter, expanded to 6-10µm at the apex.

Spores: Spherical, hyaline, 18 - 22µm in diameter, ornamented with conical warts most of which are truncated. Warts are 2 - 4µm tall and typically 2µm across. Spore print: white.

Tarzetta cupularis **(Pyronemataceae) – Toothed Cup**

Found on woodland tracks and occasionally on woodchip mulch, the Toothed Cup is a neat, inedible little fungus and rarely jostles its neighbours for growing space.

Fruitbody: fairly deep cup 0.6 to 2cm across often with a short buried stem; inner surface smooth, light ochre; outer surface also light ochre but downy; margin incurved; whitish stem up to 1cm long, 2 to 4mm dia.
Spores: white.

Otidea onotica (Pyronemataceae) – Hare's ear

An occasional find in deciduous broadleaf woodland, the Hare's Ear often fruits singly or in rather smaller groups than shown here.

Fruitbody: elongated cup with a split down the shorter side and edges overlapping rather than merely abutting; inner surface smooth, light brown; outer surface buff and scurfy; margin slightly incurved; 3 to 6cm tall and 1.5 to 4cm across; whitish stem up to 1cm long.
Spores: white.

Otidea bufonia **(Pyronemataceae) – Toad's Ear**

An infrequent species and easily overlooked in autumn, when it blends in with dead leaves on the woodland floor, Toad's Ear is most often found on forestry roads and paths.

Fruitbody: elongated cup with a split down the shorter side and edges overlapping rather than merely abutting; inner surface smooth, dark brown; outer surface mid brown and scurfy; 3 to 6cm tall and 1.5 to 4cm across; thick brown stem up to 1cm long.
Spores: white.

Fungi of Woodland Edges, Glades, Fire Breaks and Rides

Many fungi that are generally associated with grassland habitats can feature in the species lists of woodland forays, occasionally causing confusion when they turn up as unexpected finds deep inside a forest. More often they appear in shaded grassy clearings or among the vegetation beside paths, fire breaks and rides, where the warmth, extra light and shelter may stimulate fruiting over an extended season. Species seen only very occasionally in woodland habitats but which are more commonly encountered in open grassland habitats are described and illustrated in Chapter 8.

Chapter 7 – Grass, Grasses and Grasslands

Which types of turf are top for toadstools?

Mynydd Epynt, an undulating mountainous area in the Brecon Beacons National Park, is one of Britain's finest grassland fungi sites. As well as several kinds of fairy clubs, pinkgills and earth tongue fungi, some 33 waxcap species have been recorded at this SSSI/SAC. The grassland fungi assemblage is a designation feature for one of the sectors of this site.

Whether you get your exercise from mowing the lawn on Saturday afternoons or taking part in one of the many sporting activities that use grass as their playing surface, you will be well aware of the resilience of this wonderful natural resource and its ability to renew itself when damaged. And thank goodness for that, because our planet could not support anything like the vast throngs of people and other living creatures that it does if something catastrophic were to happen to the many kinds of grass whose benefits are so easily taken for granted. Another chastening thought is that every one of those grass species depends crucially upon fungi. It's a two-way trade, however, because a lot of valuable and beautiful fungi that can add so much to our lives are themselves totally dependent upon grass. What is less immediately obvious is how much else in our modern way of life is possible only because of various grasses and their grasslands ecologies and fungal communities.

Canes of the grass genus *Arundo* have long been used to make the vibrating reeds of clarinets, oboes and other woodwind instruments. Indeed, some panpipes are made entirely from reeds of this plant, as are the chanters and drone reeds in many bagpipes. My own first fishing rod was a garden cane, and I still treasure the heavy and difficult-to-cast split-cane flyfishing rod with which I caught my first wild trout on a dry fly. Old cane rods are now much sought after by collectors of antique fishing tackle, and their value continues to increase as car-door accidents (and fungal decay if they are stored while still damp!) reduce the pool of survivors. Old grassland is also valuable, as we shall see.

In many countries grasses of various kinds are used in building work - some in place of timber; others as scaffold poles. Esparto paper is made from *Lygeum spartum*, a species that looks rather like Pampas Grass *Cortaderia selloana* and is found in southern Spain and North Africa. Yet another industrial use for grass roots is in the removal of pollutants in water leaking from abandoned mines (of which there are several thousand in Britain and many more spread across mainland Europe). The reed grass *Phragmites australis* is commonly used in water treatment and land reclamation in many parts of the world.

A turf fire (fed with compressed peat formed from decayed grass and moss) warmed the kitchen of the house in Ireland where in my childhood summers I helped harvest hay from the garden. Nowadays grass is burned in some power stations; high-energy grasses including Asian Elephant-grass (*Miscanthus* species) and American Switchgrass *Panicum virgatum* are being seriously investigated as a source of biofuels to replace our dwindling supplies of the fossil fuels coal, oil and gas. Those ornamental grasses in the garden might soon become so valuable that they will need to be protected behind security fences!

For most of the world's human population just three kinds of grass, the cereal crops rice, wheat and maize, make up the majority of their diet. Grass is also the main food source for farm animals that are reared for milk products and as meat for human consumption. Of course, if you have a sweet tooth then you may well be aware that most of the world's sugar still comes not from sugar beet but from sugar cane (various *Saccharum* species), which belongs to the grass family. It could even be argued that most people are already at least half way to becoming vegetarians, as they eat only vegetables and herbivores (rather than dining on the meat of carnivores). All these mouths require a huge amount of the various grasses and therefore a vast amount of land – something like 20% of the earth's landmass by area. Unfortunately (for mycophiles, at least) very little of this grassland is rich in fungi that produce mushrooms or other large fruitbodies. The main reasons for this mycological paucity are the frequent cultivation and re-seeding of much agricultural land and the application of fertilisers which, while enriching the soil for crop production, produce an ecology that is toxic to most kinds of macro fungi.

A (Surprisingly) Brief History of Grass

Almost everywhere we go we see grass. In urban environments it creeps up through cracks in pavements, colonises old walls and gutters, and can even take root on flat roofs; and in the countryside grass invades every bit of bare ground, filling in the gaps between crops, springing up in woodland clearings, encroaching on the margins of lakes and streams. Apart from Antarctica, grass is so abundant and widespread on every continent that many people jump to the conclusion that grasses are an ancient form of plant life that has had all the time in the world to make itself at home. Not so!

Compared with most other families of flowering plants, grass is relatively new on the scene. When the early herbivorous dinosaurs dined, grass was not on the menu. Fossil records suggest that dinosaurs had to manage without grass until about 67 million years ago, and even then it was more of a treat than a staple diet. Grasses did not become abundant and widespread until at least twenty million years after the mass extinction of dinosaurs (and the majority of other large land animals) in a sudden, cataclysmic event some 65 million years ago, at the end of the Mesozoic era.

Many areas of unstable land would have been virtually barren when the dinosaurs disappeared, because at that time - the beginning of the Tertiary period – all the evidence points to many parts of the earth turning much colder and more arid, particularly within the large continental land masses. Many grasses are well adapted to dry ecosystems prone to fires, and grasslands (rather than forests) tend to occur in regions of lower rainfall. Grazing by animals is less of a problem for grasses than for most other plants, and this would also have contributed to the natural selection of grass as the dominant vegetation.

Grass has other strengths that equip it well in the battle for plant supremacy: its matted roots bind the topsoil and prevent it from being blown away on the wind or washed into rivers and carried out to the sea during heavy rain. Also, because many grasses are shallow rooting they get the first chance to soak up any moisture from dew or rain before it can sink down to the roots of trees and other deep-rooting plants. Grasses can even cope with freak weather conditions that kill off insect life; this is because, unlike the majority (around 90 per cent) of flowering plants, successful grass pollination relies only on the wind, which is much more dependable year on year than are insect populations.

A plant for all regions

At least one other characteristic of the grass family has contributed significantly to its dominance of the plant kingdom in nearly all non-forested regions apart from the driest of deserts. After the families Orchidaceae (the orchids), Asteraceae (daisies, sunflowers and the like), and Fabaceae (peas, beans, vetches and so on) the grass family, Poaceae, contains more species than any of the other plant families. Over time, grass has mutated to produce some 600 genera and 10,000 or more species. Some grasses are annuals, others are perennial; some are suited to high humidity, others thrive in arid places. The grass family really has a plant for all seasons and all regions.

The true grasses belong to the botanical family Poaceae, a relatively young family within the monocotyledons (or monocots, as they are most commonly called). Sedges (Cyperaceae) and rushes (Juncaceae) are close relatives within a larger grouping known as the Graminoids. Among older families in the monocot group are the Liliaceae and Iridaceae, which include the spring-flowering snowdrops, squills and irises that frequently occur in grasslands that are rich in autumn-fruiting fungi.

Spring squill *Scilla verna* on sheep-grazed cliff-top grassland beside Pembrokeshire Coast Path. Parasols *Macrolepiota procera* are also common sights on these grassy slopes from July right through to November.

It has been estimated that grasslands comprise about 20 per cent of the land-based vegetation cover of our planet, but this figure includes many plants that would defy the most powerful of lawnmowers. Not all grass is short. The common reed grass *Phragmites australis* can grow to a height of four metres, while bamboos (also true grass species) have been known to reach 40m. Grasses also turn up in a variety other habitats that are not normally considered to be grasslands, including wetlands such as fens, swamps, bogs and marshes); scrubland, woods and forests; and even bleak arctic tundra.

Although large fungi such as waxcaps and fairy clubs are known to feed upon and recycle the dead plant material in grassland, other less obvious fungi play a more active role in the wellbeing of grass. For example fescues (*Festuca* species), ryegrasses (*Lolium* spp.) and many other kinds of grass live in symbiosis with fungi of the genus *Neotyphodium*. These kinds of fungi, which are termed endophytic because they live inside the leaves and seeds of the grass, receive all the carbohydrate they need directly from their host. The relationship is not one of parasitism, however, because the fungi help the grass to grow more vigorously and they also increase the plant's resistance to extremes of heat and drought. Some kinds of endophytic fungi go a stage further, building defences within the grass, protecting themselves and their hosts against the ravages of grazing animals; this they do by manufacturing toxic alkaloids that attack the nervous systems of herbivorous insects and even ruminant mammals such as goats, sheep and cattle.

How grasses grow forth and multiply

Grazed or cut too short or too often, most plants would die, but many kinds of grass are able to thrive on such a regime. This is because grasses grow by elongating their stems rather than producing new material at their stem tips as do other plants. Roots and stems meet at ground level, at a junction called the crown. Provided the crown is not destroyed grass continues growing and producing new leaves (blades) whenever the temperature is a few degrees above freezing, the growth rate generally increasing with temperature provided the plant can get enough water and nutrients. AM fungi associated with the root system help in this process.

Left uncut, all kinds of grass eventually produce flowers and seeds, but many common grasses also have another way of propagating: they produce runners that are known as either stolons (if above the ground) or rhizomes (if below the ground). Stolons and rhizomes are simply horizontal stems at the ends of which new plants form. If they are not eaten by animals, old roots, crowns, stems, leaves and seed heads eventually die, and then different fungi play an essential role in breaking down this dead organic material into compounds that the new young grass plants can use. Most of the large fungi that we see fruiting in grasslands consume dead material derived, directly or indirectly, from grass and any other plants growing with it.

A stolon links these two crowns of Common Bent *Agrostis capillaris*. By this cloning process these kinds of grasses can grow to cover large areas even when mown frequently so that they cannot produce seed. Some grass species produce stolons more than a metre long and grow at a rate of several cm per day, enabling the grass to spread very quickly. Other kinds of grasses cannot propagate in this way, and although they can grow in steadily increasing bunches to extend their range they mainly depend upon seed for propagation into new territory.

Grass flowers are often in the form of a spike or a feathery plume, the precise structure being an important aid to grass species identification. Once pollinated, the flowers become seeds (or grain, in the case of cereal crops) and are distributed locally by the wind or more widely if of a kind that can get caught up in the coats of furry animals. Ants are also known to store grass seeds underground, where occasionally they germinate. In some countries there are ants that eat only the shucks, leaving the kernels of the grass seeds to grow.

An inflorescence (flower head) of Common Bent. In most grasses the nodes (those rounded swellings on the stems) are solid while the rest of the stems, known as culms, are hollow. The lower part of each blade sheathes the stem. The sheathes nearest to the crown are the first to die and fall to the ground, where grass-rotting fungi are waiting to consume them.

Getting to Grips with Grasslands

If you take an interest in the native reptiles of Britain you have just six species to learn about. With grasses as, coincidentally, with birds there are some 10,000 known species worldwide, and in each case around 600 have been found in Britain alone: that's a challenge! Don't be put off, though. Just being able to recognise a few grassland types via some of the common grasses and one or two of the flowering plants that grow with them can make a big difference when you go hunting for grassland fungi. That is because most grasses and many other wildflowers have particular habitat needs, and it's not usually individual species but rather communities of plant species that indicate the underlying geology, soil structure and chemistry and hence the fungi likely to fruit there.

In general, what determines whether a piece of grassland is good for fungi is not so much the grass species growing there as the underlying geology and soil type, and unfortunately these latter factors alone rarely determine which grasses are present, as most grasses are very versatile and cope in a wide range of situations. This means that the grasses alone are a poor guide to which kinds of fungi we can expect to find in a particular location. To solve this problem we need to look not only at the grasses but also some of the 'habitat indicator' plants growing with them – the grass-and-wildflower communities.

As with trees so also with grasses it is rarely necessary to identify them to species level, because grasses within the same genus are usually associated with broadly similar habitats. Some grass-and-wildflower communities are found in soil whose chemistry and associated biological features favour a great diversity and abundance of fungi, while others are relatively poor. (Of course, if you are looking for a particular fungus that is associated with a certain kind of grass, then being able to recognise that grass is a great help.) Oxides of nitrogen and sulphur make rainwater acidic. When rain falls on chalk or limestone the calcium carbonate neutralises the acids so that the soil remains on the alkaline side of neutral. Not so elsewhere, however, and acid rain causes acidification of the soil. In areas of high rainfall with no underlying chalk or limestone, the soil becomes acidic, and toxic metals such as aluminium dissolve into the soil. With few exceptions grasses do not serve as good indicators of soil acidity and hence the kinds of fungi likely to be found on a site; however, plants characteristic of acid grasslands are tolerant of aluminium, and so the wildflower communities on a site are good indicators of soil type.

Strangely attractive to this damselfly, the tall lowland catstail grass known as Timothy *Phleum pratense* grows to a height of 1.5m, often with other tall grasses. Timothy (named after American farmer Timothy Hanson who, in the 18th century, proved the high fodder value of this species on grasslands in Maryland) is a fairly common species of damp, shaded waysides and of enriched hay fields that are regularly spread with slurry or inorganic fertiliser; there creeping buttercups, thistles and clover are often the only other wildflowers in significant numbers. Dung fungi and small grass-rotting species such as the Yellow Fieldcap *Bolbitius titubans* are common throughout summer and autumn, but until the sward has been cut and grazed finding fungi in such fields is not easy.

In the grassland habitats pages that follow, some of the fungi most commonly encountered with particular kinds of grass and accompanying wildflowers are mentioned and illustrated. (A wider selection of commonly encountered grassland fungi is the subject of Chapter 8.)

Grassland Management

Other than in a few remote coastal sites and on high mountain tops, most grassland is manmade, either through planting for sand dune stabilisation, scrub clearance to allow grazing by farm animals, or ploughing and planting for fodder harvests such as silage and (less commonly nowadays) hay. In Britain, Ireland and much of mainland Western Europe, flower-rich hay meadows are increasingly rare, and unimproved grazed grassland is mainly restricted to steep upland slopes; nevertheless, these fragmentary habitats do exist and many are protected by legislation - for example in the UK as sites of special scientific interest (SSSIs) - most often for their plant communities and far less frequently for the fungi that live there. The European Union Habitats Directive has resulted in some of the best of these sites securing additional protection as Special Areas of Conservation (SACs). While the species and habitat features for which SACs are designated are rarely if ever chosen for their mycological value, many of these sites are of particular interest for their fungi. The chosen management regimes, while designed to safeguard other ecological features, are not usually damaging (and sometimes positively beneficial) to fungi. For this reason designated conservation sites can be good places for fungus forays, but note that a formal permit may well be required if you intend collecting samples for further investigation.

Like orchids and other habitat-sensitive plants, most terrestrial fungi need soil that is low in nutrients. This might seem to suggest that the kinds of places that are rich in spring wildflowers should be great places for fungi later in the year, but this is not necessarily so (at least for macro fungi). For one thing, the needs of flowers and fungi are not the same, and a practical problem is that the very presence of tall plants makes it harder to spot ground-hugging fungal fruitbodies. But perhaps the most significant factor is that grassland fungi, and in particular waxcaps, do not do well unless the sward is cut and taken off at the end of summer and then kept short throughout autumn and into early winter. Such a regime would not be incompatible with many spring-flowering wild orchids, for example.

Grassland fungi

What determines whether a site is good or poor for grassland fungi? The first question to ask is this: *What is the nature of the soil and its underlying geology?* If we are standing on a sand dune or an expanse of limestone pavement then the answer should be obvious, but what about other kinds of grassland where the substrate is not visible? How do we know whether we are in acid, neutral or alkaline grassland? Often the easiest way to find out is to determine whether the grasses and other plants growing there are lovers (or at least tolerant) of acid or alkaline conditions. For that we need to be able to recognise a few good indicator species, and many of us find wildflowers rather easier than grasses. It's also worth learning to identify a few common indicator grass species, especially when you are looking for fungi in autumn when most of the wildflowers finished blooming long ago.

Geology has a big influence on the kinds of fungi found in grassland, but it's not everything. The next question is: *How has the land been managed?* Even at the optimum time for fungi an otherwise ideal site can only achieve its potential if the long-term management regime has been favourable to grassland fungi. Artificial fertilizers or even large doses of organic fertiliser spell death for many sensitive grassland fungi. Land that has been ploughed and reseeded takes many decades to return to anything like its natural status and full mycological potential. Unless you can get advice from someone who has regularly visited a site - or better still from the person who has managed the land there for many decades - perhaps the only option is to visit the site and record its fungal diversity at times and in conditions that are generally favourable for fruitbody production. Let the mushrooms speak for themselves. Whenever known good sites are seen to be productive, try a few new locations too. Fungi can often tell us more (and certainly more quickly and easily) about the nature of the soil and how it has been managed than we can find out by any other means.

Lovely little Yellowleg Bonnet mushrooms *Mycena epipterygia* in damp grassland

There is one other important caveat. For reasons that are far from obvious, even in what seem like very similar circumstances grassland fungi sites vary considerably in productivity from year to year. For example at a location that provided more than 20 waxcap species in a single visit in the autumn of 2007, I found no more than 12 species in each of the two following seasons despite visiting the site many times. Some years are better than others. For this same reason, poor results on a single visit or even several visits in one season do not constitute sufficient reason to write off a potential site.

For all the reasons mentioned above (and simply the element of luck!) great new discoveries will inevitably be interspersed with disappointments, but there are things that you can do to reduce the failure rate. Once you know a bit about grasses and about soil structure you can at least avoid wasting time on the very worst kinds of locations. In summary, as far as fungal interest is concerned, the goodness of grassland is determined not merely by the grass itself but also by the habitat and its management history, and what we find on a particular day is also a matter of luck: it's all too easy to stand right beside (or on!) a rare mushroom and not notice it. The more hunting we do, the better we become at spotting what we are looking for.

The best way to find particular fungi is to visit habitats in which they are known to occur. What follows is a brief overview of some distinctly different grassland habitats with notes on the kinds of plants that betray the underlying soil and geology, and some of the fungi that commonly occur there. (The next chapter contains information on a range of common and some not-so-common grassland fungi, arranged in genera.)

As we move up from the coast through lowland, hills, moors and mountains the nature of the grassland changes, and so do the plant and fungal communities. Let's start at the shoreline...

Sand dune systems

Around our shores, rocky headlands with eroding coastal cliffs are in places interspersed with coves and beaches backed by one or more ranks of sand dunes. Mushrooms need moisture, of course, and one of the features of sand is that it drains and dries out very quickly. Intuitively, therefore, we might expect sand dune systems to be mycological deserts. It's not necessarily so: sand dune systems can be surprisingly rich in fungi, but the kinds of fungi vary depending on where you go within a dune system.

The embryonic dunes nearest to the sea comprise salt-laden shifting sand that is fast-draining, high in calcium (from pulverised sea shells) and very low in nutrients. These unstable young dunes are colonised (if at all) only by a few fleshy-leaved salt-tolerant wildflowers such as Sea Rocket *Cakile maritima* and Sea Stock *Matthiola sinuata*, and by one or two tough pioneer grasses, of which an easily-identified example is Lyme-grass *Leymus arenarius*.

Lyme-grass traps sand to create embryonic dunes near the shoreline.

Sand couch grass *Elytrigia juncea* is another pioneering species of embryo sand dunes.

Behind the unstable embryo dunes lies the first rank of semi-stable dunes, which are prone to blowouts in bad weather. Here the sand level can change rapidly as strong winds deposit dry sand that buries any grass growing there. Lyme-grass does not cope well, but another tall grass known as Marram *Ammophila arenaria* simply goes on extending its leaves from the base until the blades re-emerge from the sand. The roots of Marram can burrow down more than 10m below the surface, seeking the residual freshwater that, being lighter than salt water, floats above the saline water level. It is the roots of this amazingly tenacious plant that, over a period of hundreds or even thousands of years, gradually reclaim land from the sea. Some old dune systems extend inland for many miles.

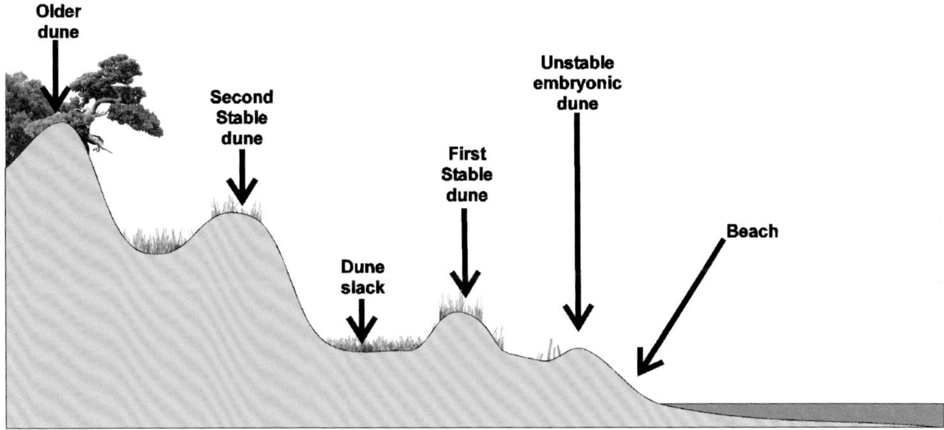

Fresh Young dunes would shift about continually were it not for the interaction of Marram roots with AM fungi (*Glomus* species in particular). The resulting endomycorrhizae bind tiny sand particles together, creating a 'soil' structure with granules of varying sizes that are better able to resist erosion by the wind. Planting bare dunes with Marram and other beach grasses was a widely used technique for restabilising dune systems that had lost their vegetation because of excessive trampling, fire or extreme storms.

Further inland from the high-tide line, in primary dunes that are somewhat protected from the wind by Marram, sand movement is not so great. Here we find salt-tolerant wildflowers such as Sea Holly *Eryngium maritimum* and Sea Bindweed *Calystegia soldanella*, and in places also Pyramidal Orchids *Anacamptis pyramidalis*. We are now in a habitat that can support a few large fungi. *Psathyrella ammophila* is one of the saprophytic fungi that feed on decaying Marram, for example. But, with no trees or shrubs as symbiotic partners, there is no real prospect of finding EM fungi on these young dunes.

You only have to move back from the littoral line a short distance to the low-lying 'slacks' behind the first and any subsequent ranks of stable dunes to find a wealth of mushrooms, and in particular Gasteromycete fungi - puffballs, earth balls, earthstars and the like - including *Tulostoma* species, the remarkable stalkballs (also known as stilt puffballs). Dune fungi are most plentiful during summer and autumn; however, in all but the harshest of winters it is unusual to walk through a sand dune system without coming across at least a few interesting mushrooms.

Between the ranks of stable dunes the low-lying flat areas, known as dune slacks, are often under water from autumn until late spring. Dune slacks near to the shore, where crushed sea shells raise the calcium level, are home to many chalk-loving plants such as Grass of Parnassus *Parnassia pallustris*, whose stately flowers spangle the herb-rich grassland in summertime. Bee Orchids *Ophrys apifera*, Common Twayblades *Listera ovata*, and the lovely Marsh Helleborine *Epipactis palustris* are typical of calcium-rich dune slacks.

In summer this North Wales dune slack is dominated by Marsh Helleborines and Grass of Parnassus. Later it will be home to several colourful autumn-fruiting fungi.

On the lower flanks of second and higher rank dunes and on shady edges of eroding footpaths a remarkable waxcap can sometimes be found in sheltered spots during late summer and autumn. Known as the Dune Waxcap *Hygrocybe conicoides*, this lovely orange-red mushroom is able to cope with the salt-laden air. Because the mycelium is unable to survive months of immersion, Dune Waxcaps are not usually found on the flat areas of dune slacks but rather beside them, on the lower flanks of dunes.

Dune Waxcaps *Hygrocybe conicoides*

Wood Blewitts *Lepista nuda* in a dune slack

Further back from the shoreline, in older dune slacks populated by Creeping Willow, *Salix repens*, short meadow grasses replace the tall Marram. There, several other kinds of waxcap fungi can usually be found along with Field Blewits *Lepista personata* and Wood Blewits *Lepista nuda* as well as a few *Cortinarius* and *Inocybe* species that form EM associations with the Creeping Willow.

Puffballs of various kinds are also common, as of course are dung fungi if the sward has been managed by grazing. Look out for colourful ascomycetes cup fungi on horse dung or on old pats of cow dung, where there is also the possibly of finding Fluted Bird's-nest *Cyathus striatus* growing on woody remnants within the dung.

On the flanks and tops of mature dunes well away from the shoreline, where over many years grass, wildflowers and patches of scrub vegetation have grown and decayed to create a humus-rich soil, several large mushrooms including the Parasol *Macrolepiota procera* and the Salty Mushroom *Agaricus bernardii* can appear from mid summer through to the first frosts (which tend to arrive somewhat later in coastal regions). More easily overlooked are the closely related but much smaller (and visually very different) Winter Stalkball *Tulostoma brumale*.

The Salty Mushroom *Agaricus bernardii*

Parasols *Macrolepiota procera*

Winter Stalkballs *Tulostoma brumale*

As you move further inland, the older dunes and dune slacks are progressively more acidic, as over time their calcium has dissolved and leached away. There, rank grasses such as cocksfoot together with acid-loving tall plants including brambles, bracken, gorse and heather tend to dominate, making it more difficult to spot any mushrooms that might be there; however, in springtime it's always worth a look beside any footpaths, as you might be lucky and find morels there.

Many dune systems are backed by stands of pines and an assortment of self-seeded trees including birch and hazel. In autumn these wooded dunes are rich in forest fungi, notably various *Russula* species, all of which form EM associations with the trees.

Left: Primrose Brittlegills *Russula sardonia* beneath Corsican Pines on a third-rank sand dune some 200m from the shoreline

Non-coastal Calcareous Grassland

Inland from the sea, semi-natural (the result of tree removal years ago and grazing by rabbits, sheep or cattle but without 'land improvement') calcareous grasslands, are characterised by shallow, rapidly-draining soils overlying chalk or limestone. This kind of land is home to many lime-loving plants and some interesting fungi that could not cope with the salt-laden winds of the coastal strip. Such places are rarely outstanding in terms of either fungal diversity or abundance, but they are worth visiting for the chance of seeing a few species that are hardly ever found anywhere else.

Lowland calcareous grassland (the term lowland being generally being taken to mean land at or below the altitude of field enclosures) has its own characteristic grass species including Common Bent *Agrostis capillaris*, Sheep's-fescue *Festuca ovina*, Sweet Vernal Grass *Anthoxanthum odoratum*, and Quaking Grass *Briza media*.

Quaking Grass

Seed heads of Greater Quaking Grass, *Briza maxima*

Within the *Briza* genus there are some 20 or more annual and perennial grasses native to northern temperate regions. They have very distinctive seed heads that make for easy recognition – at least to genus level which is what really matters.

In southern Britain, Ireland and much of Europe apart from Scandinavia the species most often seen in the wild is Common Quaking Grass *Briza media*. Even in the slightest of breezes the seed heads tremble on their stalks – hence the common name, of course.

Not surprisingly, under the Doctrine of Signatures where a plant was used to treat either a part of the body that it resembled or an illness whose symptoms it recalled, quaking grass was considered to be a remedy for all kinds of afflictions of the central nervous system.

This chalk-loving grass has many other local names including Totter Grass, Maiden Hair and Silver Spoons. A food plant of the Meadow Brown butterfly, it is largely restricted to unfertilised, flower-rich cliff-tops and meadows. Related species, popular as ornamental plants, sometimes escape from gardens and can be seen in nearby fields and hedgerows.

Flowering in Britain and Ireland between June and August, Common Quaking Grass (and indeed for that matter the very special habitat type known as calcareous grassland) is most common in lowland areas and rarely found above 400 metres. Quaking grasses also occurs on limestone outcrops in otherwise acid grassland areas, in old quarries, and on roadside verges where limestone chippings have been spread to improve the drainage. Creeping Bent *Agrostis stolonifera* is also fairly common on chalk downland, although it appears to have no particular preference for lime since it is also to be found on dry acid heaths. However, the distinctive seed heads of Quaking Grass are unmistakable and a very good indicator species for fast-draining soil with a high lime content.

Chalk Downs

Chalk and limestone are essentially just different forms of the same mineral, calcium carbonate, the only significant difference being in their hardness. Both chalk and limestone are water permeable, and so land overlying these substrates, commonly referred to as calcareous grassland, tends to dry out very quickly after rain, and particularly so on grassy south-facing slopes with no scrub cover, where exposure to sun and wind further accelerates the drying process.

Chalk downland (Hampshire) with Junipers

Wherever animal hooves strip away the turf and shallow topsoil, the white chalk shows through. Even without this evidence there are other clear indicators of soil with a high calcium content: lime-loving plants. Two of these, Chalk Milkwort and Wild Thyme, are much easier than Common Quaking Grass to spot from a distance – so why not let the flowers guide you in your search for good chalk grassland habitat?

Chalk Milkwort *Polygala calcarea*

Wild Thyme *Thymus polytrichus*

Chalk dries out so rapidly that many shallow-rooting perennials cannot survive on chalk hills. Plants that do well on chalk have deep root systems. For example Salad burnet *Sanguisorba minor* is rarely more than 15cm tall and yet its roots go down half a metre. The ground-hugging Common Rock-rose *Helianthemum nummularium* has a root system that can penetrate to a depth of 75cm, where the chalk holds moisture all through the year.

Unimproved chalk grassland is particularly good for orchids, and some 30 of Britain's 50 wild orchid species can be seen on the cliffs and wildflower-rich chalk meadows of southern England. For example the Early Spider Orchid *Ophrys sphegodes* and Late Spider Orchid *Ophrys fuciflora* occur in Britain only on coastal chalk grassland - the former most notably in Dorset and the latter nowhere other than in eastern Kent. Common Spotted-orchids *Dactylorhiza fuchsii* (pictured on the right) are probably nowhere a more common sight than in chalk grassland, and the presence of these large and conspicuous wildflowers is another good indicator of an alkaline soil. (Like Common Quaking Grass, these chalk-loving plants also occur in other calcium-rich alkaline habitats including limestone pavement.)

The lime-loving Common Spotted-orchid is often seen on chalk downland in springtime.

Fungi of chalk grasslands

Mushrooms need moisture, and chalk is therefore not an ideal mycological medium. In general, therefore chalk hills are not particularly good places for fungi; however, as with everything else in nature, some kinds of fungi have evolved to cope with and even thrive in dry chalk downland habitats, fruiting either in the early spring or in autumn and early winter.

St George's Mushrooms *Calocybe gambosa* are often the earliest of the large fungi to be seen fruiting, sometimes in fairy rings, on chalk downland. From late April and throughout May these chunky white mushrooms, which are not merely edible but very tasty indeed, stand out like stars in a green night sky on hillsides dotted with cowslips and primroses.

St George's Mushrooms

White Spindles

Later in the year, a rather less common fungus can be found in Quaking Grass habitats, but you really have to search for it. White Spindles *Clavaria fragilis* and several similar grassland fungi are commonly known as club fungi, or fairy clubs. Most club fungi are found in unimproved acid grassland, but *Clavaria fragilis* is a common sight on chalky soil.

The Meadow Waxcap *Cuphophyllus pratensis* (left) is one of the few waxcaps that seem to be as much at home on chalk as in acid grassland. With its large, orange or peach-coloured cap and strongly decurrent gills, this distinctive species is not at all difficult to spot. It is also one of the few waxcaps that can be reliably identified in the field from macroscopic features alone. So beautiful is this edible mushroom, until recently known as *Hygrocybe pratensis*, that surely it should be left for others to see rather than being picked for the pot.

Although the diversity of waxcaps on chalk hills is usually small, at least one species, the Limestone Waxcap *Hygrocybe calciphila*, occurs only on alkaline land. Some *Entoloma* species also show a marked preference for chalky grassland, which can also be good for (delicious) Parasols *Macrolepiota procera* and Field Mushrooms *Agaricus campestris*.

Limestone Landscapes

Chalk downland is largely confined to fairly steep slopes, as on level ground most of the (very productive) chalky soil has been ploughed and planted for arable crops or as leys - fields put down to grass for short periods as part of a crop-rotation system. (Leys are not good fungi sites.) Fortunately there are other lime-rich grasslands that cannot be ploughed so easily, and some of these are interesting places for fungi forays.

Soft (oolitic) limestone on steep-sided hills as well as the harder carboniferous limestone on level or sloping land cannot be ploughed, and so the grass and other plants that occur there survive as long as they can cope with the climate and with the intensity of grazing by any herbivores that feed there. Plants and fungi of these limestone grasslands must also be able to tolerate dry surface conditions, especially on south-facing slopes where the summer sun has maximum impact.

Spring Gentians *Gentiana verna* are characteristic of alpine limestone habitats; however, the lovely specimens shown here are found on Ireland's Burren limestone near sea level.

For plants the answer is to produce deep roots; for fungi a solution seems to be seeking shade from the sun and shelter from the drying winds, and so the north-facing slopes are usually more productive foray sites than south-facing slopes. In Britain there are outcrops of oolitic limestone from Dorset in the south of England to Yorkshire in the north – the attractive yellow Cotswold stone is an example.

The much harder (and older) carboniferous limestone is exposed spectacularly in The Burren, in south-west Ireland, and it can also be seen in many other parts of Britain and Ireland including Great Orme, in North Wales; Gait Barrows, in Cumbria; and numerous other locations throughout the English Pennines. Europe's largest expanse of exposed limestone is on the island of Öland, in Sweden.

Left: Limestone pavement on The Burren, with its characteristic clints (slabs) and grikes (narrow trenches eroded by water)

Fungi of dry limestone landscapes

On mainland Europe several EM fungi including *Rhizomarasmius epidryas* and *Lactarius dryadophilus* are associated with Mountain Avens *Dryas octopetala* in limestone grassland. In the UK the rare Date Waxcap *Hygrocybe spadicea* also occurs in this kind of habitat.

Mountain Avens is a good indicator of underlying limestone. Here outcrops of porous, lime-rich rock are visible in the background.

The Date Waxcap *Hygrocybe spadicea* is very rare in the UK. Look out for this elusive but very distinctive waxcap in limestone grassland.

Wildflower-rich Hay Meadows

While unlikely to be among the richest of grassland sites in terms of fungal diversity, a traditionally-managed herb-rich hay meadow can turn up a few nice surprises. Experts suggest that it is not the dominance of wildflowers over grasses but rather the suppression of mosses that is responsible for the fungal paucity commonly reported from wildflower meadows. Certainly the tall vegetation does not make it any easier to spot fungi. Spring and early summer is when the flowers are at their peak, but the best time to investigate high-grade wildflower sites of this kind is in the autumn, after the hay has been harvested.

It would be sacrilege to trample wonderful wildflower meadows in the vain hope of finding early-fruiting fungi.

Grass species are rarely dominant in the finest of wildflower meadows, but the mixture of plant species nearly always includes Sweet Vernal Grass *Anthoxanthum odoratum* (right). This is the grass that gives hay its characteristic scent; however, the substance responsible for the sweet smell (coumarin) has a bitter taste that makes it unpalatable to farm animals.

Sweet Vernal Grass grows in flower-rich hay meadows, but it is a versatile, drought-tolerant plant and can also cope in woods and even gardens on most kinds of soil.

Hay meadow fungi

Natural (or strictly that should be semi-natural!) herb-rich meadows are low in nutrients, and in the autumn they can produce some surprising fungi finds, including waxcaps. More commonly, hay meadows sprout a plethora of little brown mushrooms (LBMs), among which you will probably be able to identify to species level *Psilocybe semilanceata*, the psychoactive Liberty Cap or Magic Mushroom and at least to genera level some of the many little cone-caps (*Conocybe* spp.) of which *Conocybe rickeniana* is one of the most common. Unfortunately this LBM is inseparable from several others of the same genus without resorting to microscopic examination.

Meadow waxcap *Cuphophyllus pratensis* can spring up among the autumn regrowth in herb-rich grassland.

'Artificial' wildflower meadows, in which seed mixtures of traditional hay meadow species such as Corn Cockle, poppies and Cornflowers, are planted in 'cleaned' and ploughed nutrient-rich soil, are unable to sustain their floral supremacy. Within a couple of years the rich soil erupts in rank grasses and other vigorous vegetation, and the display soon fades away unless the field is re-sown.

Ryegrass Leys

Perennial Ryegrass *Lolium perenne* is generally regarded as native to Britain. In the past it was sown in most leys (regularly re-seeded fields), and is still common beside paths and farm tracks. As a source of fodder perennial ryegrass cannot compete with the visually similar Annual (Italian) Ryegrass *Lolium multiflorum* and cultivated hybrids. Fields of ryegrass are regularly 'improved' by applying organic and/or inorganic fertiliser and herbicide and by re-seeding.

It would be nice to show some of the wildflowers that thrive in these kinds of habitats, but there are so rarely any at all. It's almost as disappointing when your interest is fungi, but there is at least one interesting species that does well once hay or silage has been taken off a rye-grass field, and that is the Yellow Fieldcap, also known as the Egg-yolk Fungus.

Fresh fields and pastures new have little to offer to wildflower enthusiasts or to fungiphiles.

The Yellow Fieldcap *Bolbitius titubans*. These common little mushrooms are very variable in size, depending mainly on the amount of organic fertiliser on the land. When growing only on dead grass they are rarely more than 2cm across and rather spindly, however, where dung has been spread after a silage cut, the caps can be as much as 5cm in diameter when fully expanded. The young fruitbodies are bright yellow and distinctly egg shaped but they rapidly fade, becoming convex and then flat with very marked marginal striations.

Acid Grassland and Heath

Lowland acid grassland (of which very little now remains in an unimproved state in Britain and Ireland) occurs on nutrient-poor and generally free-draining soils over non-calcareous substrates (sandstone, igneous rocks and other lime-poor materials), or on soils formed from shallow deposits of sands or gravels. Upland acid grassland, on hills above the level of enclosures, is far more plentiful. From a plant and animal biodiversity viewpoint these are of limited value, but they are of particular interest to mycologists because of the diversity of grassland fungi that occur in these otherwise bleak habitats.

Wet acid grassland

Fungi cannot live without water, but too much water can be a problem too. If you want to find fruitbodies of large fungi, very wet acid grassland usually has little or nothing to offer. Plant indicators of this kind of land include Bog Asphodel, *Narthecium ossifragum*, and Sneezewort, *Achillea ptarmica*.

As the coverage by heathers, gorse and other acid-loving shrubs increases, the acid grassland grades into heath. A characteristic of wet acid heathland is Cross-leaved Heath *Erica tetralix*, while Common Heather *Calluna vulgaris*, and Bell Heather *Erica cinerea* are associated with drier areas. In many instances upland slopes are mosaics of wet and dry acid grassland and heath. Large fungi are rarely found in heathland, and so unless your interest is in microfungi and lichens it is generally best to concentrate on the more open areas.

Fortunately grasslands are rarely homogenous, and even in the boggiest of acid grassland there are usually dry areas (and quite often limestone outcrops surrounded by small areas of alkaline grassland); such micro habitats generally have plant and fungus communities quite different from those of the surrounding area.

A mosaic of wet and dry grassland at Cwm Idwal National Nature Reserve in North Wales. Carboniferous limestone outcrops on the slopes provide islands of alkaline soil in an otherwise acid landscape, and hence in this 'best of both worlds' habitat the diversity of plants and fungi is much greater than it would otherwise be.

Bog Asphodel is an easily-identified indicator of wet acid grassland. Its dead flower spikes remain yellow and persist through to winter.

Sneezewort favours damp acid soils. It is sometimes confused with Yarrow, more commonly seen in dry grassland.

Fungi of acid bogs

Among the mosses in acidic boggy areas you are likely to find mainly small *Galerina* and *Mycena* fungi. Identifying them to species level in the field is usually impossible, as with few exceptions they can be separated only by microscopic characteristics that are not visible to the naked eye.

The Bog Bell *Galerina paludosa* is typical of the many orange-brown members of this genus that spring up in the moss of wet acid heaths, marshes and bogs. With caps only 1 to 3cm across, most of these acid-loving inedible fungi are remarkable only by the consistent absence of any macroscopic distinguishing features. The Bog Bell is an exception: its ochre-coloured gills have white edges, and the stem is decorated with white patches of velar remains below the ring zone. Growing up through waterlogged moss, the stems are often very much longer than they appear to be.

Purple Moor Grass and Rush Pastures

Purple Moor Grass and rush pastures occur on poorly drained and usually acidic soils, often with a shallow layer of peat. These kinds of grasslands are most common in areas of high rainfall. The uneven nature of lowland wet pastures (known as rhos pastures) and of moorland dominated by Purple Moor-Grass, *Molinia caerulea* (below), and rush (*Juncus* spp.) provides plenty of shaded places for fungi; however, while a few interesting mushrooms occur in the drier parts, these areas are not generally high in either fungal diversity or abundance. The most productive places are banks bordering roads and ditches, where *Entoloma, Dermoloma* and *Hygrocybe* agarics as well as fairy clubs and earthtongues can sometimes be found. In the marshier parts it is unusual to find any large fungi.

Molinia is usually accompanied by many other grasses including bents (*Agrostis* spp.), fescues (*Festuca* spp.) and Sweet Vernal Grass *Anthoxanthum odoratum.* So easily recognisable is this tussocky grassland that other indicator plants are almost redundant; however, Tormentil *Potentilla erecta* and Devil's-bit Scabious *Succisa pratensis* are nearly always present, and if you are lucky you might also see the increasingly rare Marsh Fritillary butterfly *Euphydryas aurinia*.

Tormentil

Devil's-bit Scabious

Dry acid grassland

Dry acid grassland consists mainly of fine-leaved grasses such as Common Bent and various fescues, although there are invariably many other grasses present, including some that are more often seen in rhos pastures or even on chalk downland.

Heath Speedwell thrives in acid grassland. Here it is growing among Sheep's Fescue, a grass species particularly common on upland acid hillsides.

Good indicators of dry acid grassland include Heath Spotted-orchid *Dactylorhiza maculata*, Heath Speedwell *Veronica officinalis*, and Heath Bedstraw *Galium saxatile*. Harebells *Campanula rotundifolia* are commonly seen there too, but they occur also in alkaline areas.

Heath Spotted-orchids are good indicators of acid grassland; however, they do not survive heavy grazing pressure and so it is unusual to find these lovely wild orchids on sheep-grazed upland pastures.

Fungi of unimproved grazed grassland

Sheep-grazed pastures on free-draining soil are particularly good for fungi (as long as fertiliser has not been applied to the land during the past half century or more!), and so not surprisingly many of the very best waxcap sites are on steep upland hill slopes where the soil is shallow and farm machinery cannot operate either safely or effectively.

Despite its very variable cap colours, the Parrot Waxcap *Gliophorus psittacinus* (formerly *Hygrocybe psittacina*) is one of the most common of the waxcaps found in grassland.

Blackening Waxcaps *Hygrocybe conica* are among the earliest waxcaps to appear on upland sheep-grazed pastures.

Pinkgills (*Entoloma* species) are found on all kinds of unimproved grassland; most of the mushrooms in this genus are hard to identify.

CHEG scoring of fungi sites

There are many things that Science still has to reveal about grassland fungi and their relationships with the grasses and mosses with which they share habitats. Determining which grassland sites are of highest conservation value is far from straightforward, and many rating and ranking schemes have been proposed, mainly based upon species diversity rather than rarity. One such system, CHEG score, is based upon counts of the numbers of species recorded in each of four groups, the fairy clubs (***C**lavariaceae*), waxcaps (***H**ygrocybe*), pinkgills (***E**ntoloma*) and earthtongues (***G**eoglossaceae*).

The significance of the scores is not immediately obvious, as merely adding together the numbers of C, H E and G species is not really meaningful. For example an internationally important grassland fungus site might contain 33 *Hygrocybe* species but very few in the C, E or G groups; however another site with just 23 waxcaps might also be of exceptional conservation value if it contained a large number of pinkgills or was rich in fairy clubs and earthtongues. For simplicity, therefore, it is still common to select sites for further study based initially on the number of waxcap species found there – and even then several survey visits are necessary to have any realistic chance of seeing fruitbodies of most of the species that do occur there. (Note also that, like orchards, grasslands have good and bad years: a good site in a bad year can give a remarkably mediocre CHEG score.)

Fairy clubs belong to the family Clavariaceae. Spores are borne on the surfaces of the tips.

***Microglossum olivaceum*. Earthtongues are usually black, brown or olive green.**

There are many other grassland fungi, notably from the genera *Agaricus, Agrocybe, Conocybe, Dermoloma, Mycena, Panaeolus* and *Stropharia* as well as various puffballs, and a selection of these is included in Chapter 8, Grassland Fungi, with illustrations, descriptions and typical habitat information.

Greater Butterfly-orchid on a summer-grazed neutral grassland site.

Neutral grassland

Neutral grassland is an imprecise term, encompassing soils that can be either slightly alkaline or slightly acidic. Such sites are not characterised by plants found only on neutral soil but rather by the absence of wildflowers that require either strongly acidic or strongly alkaline soil. The main determinant of fungi species in neutral grassland is the water content, wet neutral grassland being generally poor for macro fungi just as, with few exceptions, most other very wet places are.

There are still a few lowland places where unimproved dry neutral grassland that is grazed in summer provides late-spring and early-summer displays of Greater Butterfly-orchids *Platanthera chlorantha* and Lesser Butterfly-orchids *Platanthera bifolia*. These permanent pastures can also be quite productive fungus sites later in the year, the species occurring there being generally similar to those commonly found on dry acid grassland.

Old Graveyards

Semi-natural grassland is not restricted to farming areas, and even in and around towns and cities there are grassy places that harbour an amazing diversity of fungi.

There are some 25,000 graveyards in the UK alone, and together they cover about 10,000 hectares. Many of these hallowed burial sites are also invaluable havens for plants and fungi. What makes graveyards different from most other grassland areas is the way they are managed, without the application of artificial fertilisers, without annual disturbance of the soil, and without periodic re-seeding with fast-growing grasses. In many old churchyards this stable management regime has been maintained down several centuries, safeguarding sensitive wildflower and fungi species that, if wiped out, could take decades to re-establish themselves even if there were other colonies nearby.

Ecologically diverse graveyards are invariably old, and they will have been managed in old-fashioned ways. Their biggest enemy is the modern obsession with a weed-free and moss-free appearance that many consider to be the epitome of a well-kept lawn. One application of a weed-and-feed chemical cocktail or a modern moss killer can destroy a rich ecology that centuries of traditional care have produced.

Waxcaps in a town-centre churchyard

Crust lichens flourishing on old gravestones

When managing a graveyard to favour wildflowers (and particularly annual species) it is important not to mow during spring and summer when flowers and seeds are being produced. Once the seeds have been dispersed, mowing and removing the clippings throughout the late summer and autumn months reduces the nutrient level in the soil and makes life tough for rank vegetation that would otherwise crowd out the delicate annuals.

A somewhat different regime is needed to favour autumn grassland fungi. The prospects of finding fungi are greatly dependent on the nutrient content of the soil. Regular mowing and removal of cut grass impoverishes the soil and reduces the vigour of the sward so that fungi are not buried in rank vegetation. Removal of grass cuttings is such an important factor that the very sight of a compost heap in the corner of a churchyard, with evidence of regular dumping of grass clippings, is enough to raise the spirits of any mycologist. Once the autumn rains start there is less opportunity and less need to cut the grass, and so grassland fungi can push up unmolested to flaunt their diverse forms and colours.

Gardens and Parks

Provided it is not mown too often, any lawn that is not treated with weed-and-feed chemicals is likely to sport a few fungi from time to time. Occasional mowing in spring and autumn followed by autumn 'neglect' is an ideal regime, particularly if the cut grass is removed rather being left to rot back and enrich the lawn.

Left: A mossy lawn (the kind most people would feel ashamed of) is great for fungi.

Traditionally managed old lawns and parkland generally contain a wealth of grass species, although the proportions vary from place to place, with creeping, drought-tolerant grasses dominating in exposed areas and species generally associated with wet pastures more prominent in shaded hollows. New lawns and parks are created either by laying cultivated turf or, for people with more time but less money, by seeding with a seed mixture of grass hybrids and cultivated varieties chosen to suit the location and intended use. Various hard-wearing rye-grasses are included in most lawn mixtures other than those where a 'perfect' appearance is considered more important than anything else (and certainly more important than mushrooms).Various meadow grasses (*Poa* spp.), bents (*Agrostis* spp.) and fescues (*Festuca* spp.) are common in old lawns and parkland.

If it is not mown, Smooth Meadow-grass *Poa pratensis* produces feathery branching clusters of pale flowers in June and July; it is a common grass of old lawns and parks. Rough Meadow-grass *Poa trivialis* (left) is very similar but a somewhat darker green and with rather rough sheaths; it shows a preference for damp, shady places.

One of the most common little brown mushrooms of garden lawns, but actually an LBM that is not too difficult to identify, *Panaeolina foenisecii* goes by the common names of Brown Mottlegill and Mower's Mushroom.

Brown Mottlegills or Mower's Mushrooms are often seen within a day or two of a lawn being mowed. Also springing up in hay meadows after the harvest has been gathered in, this common grassland species is sometimes referred to as the Haymaker Mushroom.

Two rather more attractive but much smaller mushrooms of lawns and parks are the Pleated Inkcap *Parasola plicatilis* and the Turf Bell *Galerina graminea* (below). With its orange caps and widely spaced gills, the latter is a common mushroom of mossy grasslands, although it is also found in bogs and woodlands among *Sphagnum*.

The Pleated Inkcap thrives in lawns which, apart from being mown fairly often, are otherwise 'neglected'.

With their widely-spaced gills and tiny caps, the tiny but conspicuous Turf Bells are a common sight in mossy lawns and parks.

Popular as ornamental grasses in parks and large gardens are various kinds of imported bamboo. True members of the grass family, Poaceae, some of these bamboos have attracted the attention of fungi whose odours detract noticeably from the olfactory pleasures of a stroll through the flowerbeds.

Both the Stinkhorn *Phallus impudicus* and its more colourful southern-European cousin the Red Cage (also known as the Lattice Fungus) *Clathrus ruber* are found increasingly often under bamboo plants in Britain.

The leaf litter beneath the Golden Bamboo *Phyllostachys aurea* provides a habitat much appreciated by stinkhorns native to Britain and Ireland as well as some new arrivals.

Red Cage *Clathrus ruber* is found increasingly often in many parts of Britain; it appears to be particularly fond of the fallen sheaths and blades of bamboos.

Among the damp longer grass in less-trampled areas of parkland and on lawns that are mown less frequently, a large and striking white (initially) columnar mushroom can appear overnight. Commonly known as the Shaggy Inkcap or Lawyer's Wig, *Coprinus comatus* fruits either singly or in clumps. Although edible when young, the caps soon deliquesce and even if stored in a refrigerator they begin turning into an inky mess within a few hours

If your interest in Shaggy Inkcaps is culinary, they are best gathered before and eaten during breakfast; they certainly do not keep at all well.

Right: this Shaggy Inkcap is beginning to deliquesce, the skirt of the cap turning black as droplets of 'ink' fall to the ground beneath the cap.

Gauging the Goodness of Grasslands

Grasses are rarely the best guide to the fungal diversity and abundance likely to occur on a site, although some grasses give a clue to the factor that matters most: land management.

Yorkshire Fog *Holcus lanatus* is an indicator of poor soil. It is abundant in many of the best grassland fungi sites.

The presence of Wall Barley-grass *Hordeum murinum* is usually indicative of grassland that is not frequently cut or heavily grazed.

The fungus ratings in the table below are based on my own observations. They are merely a rough guide to the relative diversity of large fruitbodies commonly found growing with the grasslands listed. (Be aware that location and weather can make a big difference to the 'goodness of grassland' even if you are there at what is generally the optimal time of year.)

Grassland Habitats	Typical Management Regime	
Unimproved dry acid grassland	Grazing - summer, cattle; winter, sheep	🍄🍄🍄🍄🍄
Old churchyards	Periodic mowing with grass removal	🍄🍄🍄🍄
Chalk downland	Grazing in early spring and late summer	🍄🍄🍄🍄
Mossy, messy garden lawns	Frequent mowing with grass removal	🍄🍄🍄🍄
Dune slacks	Light grazing (or conservation mowing)	🍄🍄🍄
Herb-rich hay meadows	Hay harvested in late summer	🍄🍄
Parkland	Mowing without removal of cut grass	🍄🍄
Limestone pavement	Grazing by goats or sheep	🍄🍄
Wet acidic moorland	Summer grazing	🍄🍄
Semi-stable sand dunes	Fenced off to avoid grazing by livestock	🍄🍄
Posh, weed-free lawns	Mowing; weed-and-feed treatment	🍄
Rye-grass leys	Silage cutting, ploughing, re-seeding	🍄
Lowland permanent pasture	Grazing, slurry spreading	🍄

CHAPTER 8 Grassland Fungi

The marvellous mushrooms of mountains, meadows and moorland

In the Fungal Diversity Stakes, you can safely bet on woodlands leaving grasslands standing, but in a fruitbody beauty contest you would be wise to put your money on grasslands. Even the most glamorous of *Amanita* and *Russula* fungi have to defer to those fungal film stars the waxcaps.

There are real beauties in other grassland fungus families, too, as well as some that are more grotesque than gorgeous and at least one that can only be described as gross.

Because, as we saw in the previous chapter, the way land is managed determines to a large extent the kinds of fungi it supports, some families are almost entirely confined to unimproved grassland while others grow almost exclusively in nutrient-rich land. There are also a few grassland generalists, and then there are what appear to be grassland fungi but in fact they grow on the dung of grazing animals that feed on grass – and so I am covering them in this chapter rather than as 'marginal mushrooms' (the subject of Chapter 9).

The Wonderful World of Waxcaps

Red, orange, yellow, green, brown, purple, black, white – the glossy bold colours of waxcaps have earned them the title 'orchids of the fungal kingdom'. So sensitive are they to unnatural enrichment (particularly by phosphates) or other forms of chemical pollution or disturbance of the soil that they are recognised as indicators of environmental quality. The more waxcap species there are on a grassland site the higher its environmental status.

To turn a fertile farm field into a waxcap wonderland all you have to do is to stop applying fertiliser, herbicides and pesticides and to mow the vegetation regularly in spring and summer, taking away the clippings and with it more and more of the nutrients. Provided nutrients do not pour in from adjoining land, the first waxcaps are likely to appear after one or two decades, but you may have to wait at least 50 and more likely 100 years before it becomes a species-rich waxcap site. Reversing the process, however, takes no time at all!

Many of the best sites in Europe are in Britain and Ireland, and several of them contain in excess of 30 waxcap species – that is around 50% of the total number of waxcap fungi known to occur in Europe. The top sites are visited by mycologists and other fungi enthusiasts the most often, and so inevitably most if not all of the species occurring there will be seen fruiting during one or more of the visits. In one sense that is helpful, because waxcaps, in common with most other fungi, have good years and poor years (at least as far as fruiting is concerned), and therefore the species count becomes more credible if the species richness is assessed over a number of years. On the downside, however, when a new waxcap site is found, its quality as assessed by the number of waxcap species present is likely to be an underestimate. Waxcaps are only visible when fruiting, and they don't all do so at the same time; so, only after many visits over several years can the waxcap score of a site be quoted with any confidence.

With the possible exception of the Meadow Waxcap, *Cuphophyllus pratensis*, there is no strong tradition of waxcap fungi being collected for food, although some books state that the lovely Pink Waxcap *Porpolomopsis calyptriformis* is a good edible species. Please don't eat them; not only are they rare on an international scale but their distribution is also quite localised.

Many of the larger waxcaps are fairly distinctive and most are reasonably easy to identify, but there are also several small yellow, orange and red ones that are superficially very similar to one another. Quite a number of these waxcaps can only be separated by examination of their microscopic features (and even then it is often not at all easy). It takes time to get to know these fungi, as they are capable shape shifters and to make matters worse their colours and sizes are variable too. Fortunately it is not necessary to know the specific name of a mushroom to be able to enjoy its beauty.

Cuphophyllus pratensis (Hygrophoraceae) – Meadow Waxcap

This flamboyant mushroom, with its flesh-coloured cap and paler stem, often occurs in small groups or in lines. Like other large waxcaps, its shape is very variable indeed, and even the cap colours cover quite a range – yet, strangely, once you get to know the Meadow Waxcap it becomes instantly recognisable in all its many shapes, sizes and common colour variations. (If only that could be said of the various red, orange and yellow waxcap species!)

Although somewhat darker than the average Meadow Waxcap, the chunky specimen pictured here is immediately recognisable. A colour variety that can cause a bit of confusion is the Pallid Waxcap *Cuphophyllus pratensis* var. *pallidus,*(below, left) which is white; however, this rarely causes difficulties because Pallid Waxcaps are not at all common.

One of the largest of grassland waxcaps, this species was previously known as *Hygrocybe pratensis*, *Camarophyllus pratensis* or *Hygrophorus pratensis*. Meadow Waxcaps are generally considered to be edible, but by all accounts they are nothing special in terms of flavour; in contrast they can provide stunningly beautiful displays when seen in the autumn sunshine. Even when not jostling with neighbours, this waxcap tends to distort, flaring its skirt and showing off what are decurrent (often deeply-decurrent) gills.

Cap: 7 to 12cm across; initially hemispherical, becoming shallowly convex, or flattening with a broad umbo; various shades of apricot to pale orange; surface smooth and matt; sometimes cracking and flaking with age, mainly at the centre.
Gills: moderately to deeply decurrent; broad; distant; colour as cap but usually somewhat paler.
Stem: 7 to 15cm long and 1 to 1.5cm dia.; white at base, elsewhere usually flushed with the colour of the gills; cylindrical, narrowing at the base; smooth; no ring.
Spores: white.

Gliophorus psittacinus (Hygrophoraceae) - Parrot Waxcap

Previously known as *Hygrocybe psitacina*, the common name arose because caps can be green, orange, purple or yellow depending on age and weather. (NB This is a species group, not a single species.) Variegated forms are common, particularly when overhanging grass shades part of the cap so that an attractive striped marking results. The green pigment is contained in gluten which, during wet weather, washes off the cap and the lower part of the stem but remains visible at the stem apex.

Cap: 1 to 4cm across; hemispherical, becoming shallowly convex or flattening, sometimes with a broad umbo; margin splitting in dry weather; green with buff, yellow, orange or purple patches; smooth; very greasy.
Gills: adnate; broad; yellowish, tinged green near stem.
Stem: 4 to 7cm long and 3 to 6mm dia.; yellow near base, but increasingly greener towards the apex; cylindrical; smooth and very slimy; no ring.
Spores: white.

Gliophorus laetus (Hygrophoraceae) - Heath Waxcap

In unimproved, sheep-grazed hill and mountain grassland and on mossy acid heath these little orange waxcaps frequently occur in great numbers. Sometimes they are packed together in such dense tufts that many of the caps are distorted by pressure from their neighbours.

In form these fungi are rather like miniature Meadow Waxcaps, but in addition to their relatively feeble stature the very viscid, striate caps and pallid gills of the Heath Waxcaps distinguish them at once from small specimens of *Cuphophyllus pratensis*.

Cap: 1.5 to 3cm across; initially convex, flattening and sometimes developing a slight depression; smooth and very greasy; deep striations cover the outer two-thirds of the cap; margin becomes slightly toothed with age; brownish- orange or tawny with a paler margin.
Gills: decurrent; gill edges very viscid; pale grey, turning salmon pink as the fruitbody ages.
Stem: 3 to 6cm long and 2 to 4mm dia.; colour as cap or slightly paler; cylindrical; smooth; very slimy; no ring.
Spores: white.

Note: Viscid cap and pallid gills distinguish this species from other red-orange waxcaps.

Hygrocybe aurantiosplendens (Hygrophoraceae) - Orange Waxcap
A waxcap of unimproved grassland, *Hygrocybe aurantiosplendens* is a rare find in most parts of Britain and Ireland. Unfortunately this is not an easy species to pin down from macroscopic characters alone, and like so many other waxcaps microscopic examination is usually necessary to be certain of the identity of a candidate specimen. The cap colour, although generally reddish orange, is rather variable; so, too, is the shape, with some specimens remaining broadly conical while others open up more and become umbonate, developing wavy margins.

Cap: 2.5 to 5cm across; initially conical, sometimes becoming shallowly convex with a slight umbo; margin sometimes splitting; yellowish-orange to reddish orange, drying a paler orange; more yellow towards shortly striate margin; smooth; greasy or viscid.
Gills: adnate; fairly distant; yellowish-orange with much paler edges.
Stem: 5 to 8cm long and 8 to 15mm dia.; yellow; cylindrical or slightly clavate; smooth or finely fibrillose; no ring.
Spores: white.

Hygrocybe cantharellus (Hygrophoraceae) - Goblet Waxcap

The specific epithet suggests that the caps will be infundibuliform (funnel-like) and indeed sometimes they are – hence the common name Goblet Waxcap; however, more often than not the caps remain convex or merely become flat. If you look underneath you will see that the gills are decurrent, giving these waxcaps goblet-like silhouettes (even though there is little or no room for the wine!). Despite their liking for boggy grassland, the caps of Goblet Waxcaps are dry and scaly rather than greasy or viscid.

Occasionally seen singly, more often these neat little mushrooms grow in small clusters.

Cap: 1 to 3.5cm across; initially convex, becoming flat-topped and eventually developing a slight depression; various shades of reddish-orange, scales drying to almost white; incurved margin becomes crenate at maturity and is usually paler than the rest of the cap.
Gills: slightly decurrent (right) to deeply decurrent; initially almost white, becoming yellow.
Stem: 3 to 6cm long and 1.5 to 3mm dia.; dry and silkily fibrillose; orange, becoming paler towards base; cylindrical; no ring.
Spores: white.

Hygrocybe chlorophana (Hygrophoraceae) - Golden Waxcap

In the majority of waxcap sites in Britain and Ireland this is one of the most common 'yellow' species. Varying from lemon-yellow to a deep golden orange-yellow, this species cannot be separated from other yellowish waxcaps simply on cap size, shape and colour; it is crucial to note the texture of the cap and the stem. These lovely fungi are often found in small groups. They can occur in churchyards, but sheep-grazed upland commons are generally better places to try.

Cap: 2 to 6cm across; initially domed or convex, becoming flattened and occasionally centrally depressed and slightly umbonate; smooth; yellow or orange-yellow; viscid; slightly striate, most noticeably at margin; not blackening with age or when handled.
Gills: adnexed, almost free; broad; white at first becoming almost the same colour as the cap but usually somewhat paler.
Stem: 4 to 8cm long and 3 to 6mm dia.; yellow; cylindrical; slimy when moist; smooth; no ring.
Spores: white.

Note: *Hygrocybe ceracea* is similar but usually smaller; its gills are adnate or slightly decurrent.

Hygrocybe quieta (Hygrophoraceae) - Oily Waxcap

In all but the wettest of weather mature caps of Oily Waxcaps are dry with a dull matt appearance. Fairly common, these medium-sized waxcaps appear in all kinds of unimproved grassland. A smell of bed bugs is said to be one of their distinguishing features… a point worth remembering, but only if you are an expert on bed bugs!

Cap: 3 to 5cm across; initially convex or bell-shaped, flattening, sometimes with a shallow depression (right); slightly greasy when young, then dry; smooth and matt; yellowish-orange.
Gills: adnate; broad; distant; sometimes a deeper orange than the cap.
Stem: 4 to 9cm long and 4 to 8mm dia.; smooth or finely fibrillose; yellowish-orange, paler towards the base; cylindrical.
Spores: white.

Hygrocybe acutoconica (Hygrophoraceae) - Persistent Waxcap

In wet weather easily mistaken for a young Blackening Waxcap, *Hygrocybe conica,* in its yellow form, the Persistent Waxcap does not blacken. As the name implies, the fruitbodies are relatively long lasting.

Most often found on sandy soil on limestone or chalk substrates, these attractive medium-sized waxcaps are infrequent or rare in many areas where other *Hygrocybe* species are abundant. On mainland Europe I have found the Persistent Waxcap as far south as the Algarve Coast, in southern Portugal. (Until very recently most field guides recorded this species under the synonym *Hygrocybe persistens.*)

Cap: 3 to 6cm across; initially acutely conical, expanding to become umbonate; margin irregularly lobed and tending to split as cap expands; yellow, tinged with orange; viscid at first with a translucent striate margin, drying silky smooth or with very fine radial fibrils.
Gills: adnexed to free; broad; fairly distant; pale yellow.
Stem: 5 to 9cm long and 5 to 8mm dia.; yellow tinged with orange; tapering towards apex; often with one or more longitudinal grooves; dry and finely fibrillose; no ring.
Spores: white.

Hygrocybe spadicea (Hygrophoraceae) – Date Waxcap

Date coloured the cap may be, but don't wait until Christmas to go on the hunt for these elusive waxcaps of unimproved grasslands. The common name is to do with the colour of the fruit, of course, not the calendar! This is a rare mushroom, a UK Biodiversity Action Plan species in fact, and it is found mainly on limestone pastures with a southern aspect; however, it has also been recorded from calcareous dunes and from mown parkland. There are known Date Waxcap sites in upland Wales, England and Scotland and on one of the Channel Islands.

Cap: 4 to 7cm across; initially conical, expanding to become umbonate; brown; margin irregularly lobed, splitting to show yellow cap flesh; viscid at first, drying silky smooth with radial fibrils.
Gills: adnexed to free; undulating or serrated; bright yellow.
Stem: 4 to 7cm long and 7 to 14mm dia.; yellow, flushed with longitudinal brown fibrils; dry; fibrous and brittle; cylindrical; no ring.
Spores: white.

Note: Formerly better known as *Hygrocybe spadicea*, in Britain this lovely waxcap is classified as 'vulnerable'; it has been included on the European provisional Red Data list.

Porpolomopsis calyptriformis (Hygrophoraceae) – Pink Waxcap

One of the most beautiful and among the rarest of waxcaps, this distinctive mushroom (syn. Hygrocybe calyptriformis) is extremely sensitive to chemical pollution and nutrient enrichment. A large proportion of the known European sites for this species are in Britain and Ireland. Recent concern over its conservation status prompted more intensive surveys, and as a result the number of known sites in Britain increased substantially; nevertheless, it is still very uncommon and one of the most gorgeous of mushrooms.

No matter how difficult you find the waxcaps, this is one that you will always be able to identify with complete certainty. Pink fungi are very unusual, which also adds to the attraction of this particular species.

Cap: 3 to 7cm across; initially sharply conical with an irregularly lobed margin that splits as the cap broadens, sometimes flattening completely with no central umbo; smooth; dry or only slightly greasy; with very fine radial fibrils; rosy pink to pale pink, often paler at margin.
Gills: free or weakly adnexed; pale pink – always paler than the cap.
Stem: 6 to 12cm long and 8 to 10mm dia.; white, sometimes flushed pale pink near apex; cylindrical; smooth or very finely fibrillose; no ring.
Spores: white.

Notes: Known to be edible (which may even have contributed to its scarcity), in the fairly recent past *Hygrocybe calyptriformis* , as it was generally referred to, was sometimes called the Ballerina Waxcap, and it is easy to see why.

Hygrocybe helobia (Hygrophoraceae) - Vermillion Waxcap

This distinctive little waxcap has a dry, finely scurfy cap that is usually brilliant scarlet but occasionally nearer to orange. Its small size, cap texture, incurved margin and habitat preference are aids to identification.

Cap: 0.7 to 2cm across; convex with an incurved margin; dry; finely scurfy; scarlet or reddish-orange.
Gills: broadly adnate or very slightly decurrent; pale yellow, becoming flushed red.
Stem: 2 to 4cm long and 2 to 5mm dia.; reddish-orange; cylindrical; smooth; no ring.
Spores: white.

Occasionally found on heathland but equally common in grassy woodland clearings and occasionally on mossy banks beneath hedgerows, the Vermillion Waxcap can be confused with the Goblet Waxcap, a mushroom of wet grassland whose gills are always decurrent. Microscopic and macroscopic features assessed together are often the only way to separate small red waxcaps with any degree of certainty.

Hygrocybe coccinea (Hygrophoraceae) - Scarlet Waxcap

In most waxcap sites this is the most common and abundant of the small to medium-sized deep-red *Hygrocybe* species, but there are others with which it can be confused. Fortunately its greasy cap and dry stem together with broadly adnate gills are very helpful identification features – and we need all the help that we can get when trying to sort out the many small red waxcaps. For this reason it is really important to note the texture of cap and stem as well as the form of the gill attachment.

Many of the larger red waxcaps have stems that are much paler than their caps, but the Scarlet Waxcap really is scarlet all over, the vibrant deep red fading only when the caps become old.

Cap: 2 to 5cm across; initially bell shaped then convex, flattening sometimes with a slight umbo; scarlet, fading from margin with age; smooth and greasy.
Gills: broadly adnate; distant; colour as cap but with paler gill edges.
Stem: 3 to 6cm long and 4 to 9mm dia.; scarlet, often fading to yellow close to base; cylindrical or sometimes slightly compressed laterally; smooth and dry; no ring.
Spores: white.

Hygrocybe splendidissima (Hygrophoraceae) - Splendid Waxcap

The Splendid Waxcap can be distinguished from the Crimson Waxcap by its dry cap and the smell of honey that is given off when the fruitbodies are dried... but how can you make use of that character is a non-destructive way? *Hygrocybe splendidissima* usually has a slightly (and often very substantially) flattened stem, particularly near to the base, whereas the stem of *Hygrocybe punicea* is more or less round in cross section.

The Splendid Waxcap is a rare find in most parts of Britain and Ireland, but there are damp grassland and moorland sites in West Wales and in Scotland where it is fairly common.

Cap: 5 to 10cm across; initially conical, becoming shallowly convex or flattening with a broad umbo; scarlet; smooth; dry or only very slightly greasy.
Gills: adnate; distant; colour as cap but usually somewhat paler.
Stem: 7 to 10cm long and 1 to 2cm dia.; yellow flushed with cap colour, but paler near base; irregularly flattened and longitudinally grooved, narrowing near base; smooth; no ring.
Spores: white.

Hygrocybe punicea (Hygrophoraceae) - Crimson Waxcap

This is the largest waxcap found in Britain and Ireland, but it is all too often misidentified as the much rarer Splendid Waxcap *Hygrocybe splendidissima*. (These two large red waxcaps have been treated as varieties of one species by many authors.)

Initially a deep blood red, soon fading, as so many red waxcaps do, to more of an orange-red, the Crimson Waxcap is able to tolerate small amounts of fertiliser that would wipe out most other red waxcaps.

Cap: 7 to 15cm across; initially convex, flattening with a broad umbo; crimson, usually tinged with brown; margin yellowish; greasy.
Gills: adnate; distant; yellow, developing a reddish flush; gill edges pale.
Stem: 6 to 10cm long and 1 to 2cm dia.; yellow flushed with red, paler near to base; dry; coarsely fibrillose; cylindrical, usually narrowing to a point at base; no ring.
Spores: white.

Hygrocybe conica (Hygrophoraceae) - Blackening Waxcap

Cap colour is not a defining feature of this very common and widespread waxcap, as it can be red, orange or yellow when fresh. Several of the waxcaps darken as they age, but this species truly deserves its common name. Within a few days of the caps expanding the whole mushroom turns jet black, but it is then very slow to decay, and as a result displays of old black fruitbodies are interspersed with colourful 'youngsters'.

Cap: 4 to 8cm across; acutely conical, expanding with a distinct umbo; red or orange; a yellow form *H. conica* var. *chloroides* (right) is also fairly common in some areas, but microscopic examination may be necessary to confirm its identity; margin wavy and usually irregularly lobed; viscid, drying silky matt with radial fibrils.
Gills: free or adnexed; pale greyish-yellow, blackening with age.
Stem: 4 to 8cm long and 8 to 10mm dia.; yellow, blackening from apex or where bruised by handling; cylindrical; smooth; no ring.
Spores: white.

Cuphophyllus virgineus (Hygrophoraceae) - Snowy Waxcap

Although there are several white waxy mushrooms, most of them are woodland fungi (*Hygrophorus* species). In grassland habitats one whitish waxcap is far more common than any other pallid species – in fact on most waxcap sites it is the most plentiful species by far – and that is the Snowy Waxcap. Formerly known as *Hygrocybe virginea*, the only significant identification challenge is with its infrequent colour varieties whose caps are fawn centred or sometimes fawn all over (var. *fuscescens*).

Cap: 1 to 4.5cm across; initially broadly convex, flattening, sometimes eventually becoming infundibuliform (pictured above); white or ivory or occasionally fawn; smooth and greasy when wet, drying silky.
Gills: decurrent (right); distant; white or ivory.
Stem: 3 to 5cm long and 2 to 4mm dia.; white or ivory; tapering towards base; dry; finely fibrillose; no ring.
Spores: white.

Note: These easy-to-spot waxcaps often appear in tufts and occasionally in large trooping groups.

Gliophorus irrigatus (Hygrophoraceae) - Slimy Waxcap

Gliophorus irrigatus (formerly known as *Hygrocybe irrigate or Hygrocybe unguinosa*) is one of the less common waxcaps of unimproved grassland and one that fully deserves its common name. It is *very* slimy, even during long spells of dry weather.

The subdued but very variable cap and stem colours of the Slimy Waxcap make it particularly difficult to spot on dull days. In bright sunshine, however, the caps glisten like domed mirrors, and at such times they are much more likely to catch your eye as you amble past.

Cap: 2 to 4.5cm across; initially bell shaped, later convex and sometimes becoming broadly umbonate; various shades of fawn or grey brown; margin usually translucent striate (right); smooth and very slimy.
Gills: adnate or shortly decurrent; very pale grey.
Stem: 4 to 10cm long and 3 to 6mm dia.; pale grey-brown; slimy; no ring.
Spores: white.

Pinkgills in Pastures

Although a few *Entoloma* species (commonly referred to as pinkgills) occur in woodland, the majority are grassland mushrooms and most are restricted to unimproved permanent pastures. With (fortunately) a few notable exceptions these are not very colourful fungi and many of them produce small, low-profile fruitbodies that are easily missed on all but the shortest of swards. Some of the best places for finding pinkgills are sheep-grazed grassland on coastal cliffs and on steep hill slopes – partly because on steep inclines it is almost impossible to use machinery for ploughing, re-seeding or applying fertiliser, and partly also because rank vegetation does not tend to grow in these places and hide any fruitbodies from sight. The downside is that sheep are particularly good at kicking over and treading on mushrooms, and (in my experience) they seem to have an uncanny knack of homing in on anything that is rare or unusual.

Parkland, churchyards and traditionally-managed lawns and outlying areas of golf courses are also potential sites for pinkgill mushrooms, as indeed they are also for *waxcaps*. The best waxcap sites are not necessarily perfect for pinkgills but they are often pretty good, and so the easy-to-spot 'orchids of the fungi world' can act as beacons for the generally more sombre *Entoloma* species, in much the same way as in woodland habitats Fly Agarics can act as sentinels for Ceps.

Worldwide there are some 1000 known *Entoloma* species, a third of which occur in Europe. (The genera *Leptonia* and *Nolanea,* which together contained more than 100 small pink-spored agarics, have now been consolidated into the much larger genus *Entoloma*.) Pinkgills are not the easiest of mushrooms to spot, and the majority of species are rare and localised. Here are details of a few that turn up fairly frequently in grassland fungal forays:

Entoloma serrulatum (Entolomataceae) – Blue Edge Pinkgill

Blue-black is an unusual colour for a mushroom, and the radially fibrillose cap that often breaks up into fine scales near the centre helps distinguish this *Entoloma* from other bluish species. The identification can be clinched by studying the gills, which have blackish edges. (Such a characteristic is described in technical terms as 'marginate'.)

Uncommon to rare in southern mainland Europe and in southern parts of Britain and Ireland, this neat little grassland mushroom is fairly common in Scotland.

Cap: 1.5 to 3.5cm across; initially convex, expanding to become broadly convex or umbilicate; blue-black, becoming brown when old; radially fibrillose; silky or finely scaly.
Gills: adnexed sometimes with a decurrent tooth; distant; with serrated or jagged edges; pale bluish-white turning flesh pink, with blue-black edges (right).
Stem: 4 to 7cm long and 2 to 3mm dia.; silky with blackish dots near apex, smooth and blue-black below; hollow; cylindrical; no ring.
Spores: pink.

Note: *Entoloma serrulatum* was formerly classified as *Leptonia serrulata*.

Entoloma conferendum (Entolomataceae) – Star Pinkgill

Star Pinkgills fruit from spring right through to the onset of winter. The spores, which tend to be irregularly star shaped, give this little pinkgill its common name. Star pinkgills often occur in picturesque groups in parkland and in pastures, but occasionally you may also come across these neat little mushrooms in grassy woodland clearings.

Formerly this species was included in the now defunct genus *Nolanea*, under the scientific name *Nolanea staurospora*.

Cap: 1.5 to 3.5cm across; initially convex or bell shaped, becoming broadly umbonate with a slightly incurved margin, expanding to become wavy edged; hygrophanous, dark brown at first, becoming much lighter once the caps dry out; margin translucent striate; surface finely fibrillose.
Gills: sinuate; white at first, becoming pink.
Stem: 4 to 7cm long and 1.5 to 3mm dia.; colour as cap; silkily fibrillose; cylindrical; no ring.
Spores: pink.

Entoloma griseocyaneum (Entolomataceae) – Felted Pinkgill

While the majority of grassland pinkgills have smooth or silky caps there are exceptions, and *Entoloma griseocyaneum* is one of them. Its finely scaly cap is initially bell-shaped but ,while expanding to become broadly convex ,it does not flatten or become noticeably umbonate as many other grey-brown pinkgills do. Although microscopic study is necessary to identify most *Entoloma* species, once you have found a few of these uncommon little mushrooms you may feel confident enough to base your identification on macroscopic characters alone.

Cap: 2 to 3cm across; initially conical, expanding to become broadly convex; fibrous and scaly, the scales being smaller near to the margin.
Gills: adnate; fairly distant; whitish at first becoming pink (right) at maturity.
Stem: 4 to 8cm long and 3 to 6mm dia.; whitish with longitudinal blue-grey fibrils, paler towards base; fibrous; cylindrical; no ring.
Spores: pink.

Note: This pinkgill is fairly common in upland sheep-grazed pastures.

Entoloma porphyrophaeum (Entolomataceae) – Lilac Pinkgill

Quite a common mushroom of lawns and parkland, the Lilac Pinkgill often appears in trooping groups. The fruitbodies are slow to decay, so that lawns rich in Lilac Pinkgills can get to look like fungal warzones.

Despite its subdued colours this is one of the easier pinkgills to spot because the caps are large and at maturity the margins tend to curl upwards revealing the rather paler gills.

Cap: 3 to 9cm across; initially conical, expanding to become sharply umbonate, sometimes with an upcurved margin; hygrophanous, medium to dark grey-brown, often tinged with purple, drying paler; margin sometimes splitting at maturity; viscid at first, drying silky smooth with radial fibrils.
Gills: adnexed; distant; white at first (right) becoming dark flesh pink.
Stem: 4 to 8cm long and 5 to 10mm dia.; colour as cap but paler towards base; with longitudinal grey-brown fibrils; cylindrical; no ring.
Spores: pink.

Entoloma sericeum (Entolomataceae) – Silky Pinkgill

Varying from the palest shade of brown to the darkest, this grassland mushroom has one redeeming characteristic: its wonderfully silky cap is an aid to identification.

Cap: 2.5 to 5cm across; initially conical, developing an umbo as it becomes broadly convex; hygrophanous, darker brown when wet and much paler, often streaky buff, when dry; surface smooth with silky radial fibrils.
Gills: sinuate; pale grey at first, becoming pinkish grey and eventually brown.
Stem: 3 to 6cm long and 4 to 10mm dia.; colour as cap but paler towards base; with longitudinal silky fibrils; cylindrical; no ring.
Spores: pink.

Grassland Fairy Clubs, Corals and Earthtongues

Fairy clubs and corals are usually brightly coloured and easy to spot, while earthtongues are much more sombre in appearance and can be difficult to find even when you are standing right on top of them. These non-agaricoid groups are represented in the mycota of unimproved grasslands, and it's usually possible to locate three or four species during an autumn grassland fungal foray. Microscopically, the differences between these two groups of fungi could hardly be greater: fairy clubs and corals are basidiomycete fungi, while earthtongues belong to the ascomycetes. One thing they do have in common is a taste for good clean grassland free from artificial fertiliser and herbicides; they disappear whenever the land that they are growing in gets 'improved'.

Clavaria fragilis (Clavariaceae) – White Spindles

Simple, unbranched clubs but often in bunches, like eels with their tails twisting upwards as they fight over a morsel buried in a riverbed, White Spindles is the most common of the many fairy clubs and corals that pop up in unimproved grassland. (Their worm-like appearance is reflected in their synonym *Clavaria vermicularis*.) This, the type species for the *Clavaria* genus, is easy to spot... but only when growing in short grass.

Some club-like and coral-like fungi are ascomycetous, but fairy clubs of *Clavaria* and related genera belong to the Basidiomycota.

Fruitbody: 2 to 12cm tall and 4 to 5mm across, often somewhat laterally flattened and sometimes longitudinally grooved; sometimes straight but more often wavy; occasionally forked near tips, but most often simple clubs with rounded tips; white, the tips yellowing and eventually turning brown with age.
Spores: white.

Clavulinopsis fusiformis (Clavariaceae) – Golden Spindles

Golden Spindles are, well... gold and spindly - but then so are several close relatives. Nevertheless there is something about the tightly clustered form of these fruitbodies that makes them quite distinctive. They are found in unimproved acidic grassland and are most common in upland areas of northern and western Britain and in western Ireland. The specific epithet is refers to the fact that, unlike many other yellow fairy club fungi, the spindles are usually conjoined at the base and hence very densely packed together.

Fruitbody: unbranched wavy spindles 2 to 12cm tall and 3 to 8mm across, rounded or more often laterally compressed with longitudinal grooves; golden yellow; narrowing towards base; narrow rounded tips turn brown with age.
Spores: white.

Clavulinopsis corniculata (Clavariaceae) – Meadow Coral

This coral fungus is common in unimproved grassland, including old lawns. Because it also occurs in woodland clearings, there is a chance that it could be confused with Yellow Stagshorn, *Calocera viscosa*; however, the latter is a rubbery fungus that grows on conifer stumps, whereas Meadow Coral grows among grass and emerges from the soil. In long grass the fruitbody is often tall and sparsely branching, whereas in close-cropped turf it is much more coral like.

Fruitbody: branching stems 4 to 8cm tall arising from a common thickened base; stems usually branch dichotomously each branch eventually terminating in two (very occasionally more) blunt tips; yellow, maturing ochre or tan-brown; base paler and downy.
Spores: white.

Clavulinopsis umbrinella (Clavariaceae) – Beige Coral

Also known as *Ramariopsis umbrinella*, and formerly recorded as *Clavulinopsis cineroides*, this rather rare coral fungus is found mainly in neutral or basic grassland.

Fruitbody: branching stems 4 to 8cm tall arising from a common thickened base; stems usually branch dichotomously each branch eventually terminating in two (but occasionally more) blunt tips; pinkish beige, maturing tan-brown; base paler.
Spores: white.

Geoglossum cookeanum (Geoglossaceae) – No Common Name

Sometimes mistakenly recorded as Dead Man's Fingers, this earthtongue has some even closer lookalikes, including *Trichoglossum hirsutum*, Hairy Earthtongue. (The stem of the latter is minutely hirsute, but in other macroscopic characters it matches the description of *Geoglossum cookeanum* very closely.)

This common earthtongue is found mainly in mossy, sandy grassland, often in dune slacks or on the edges of coastal pine forests.

Fruitbody: 3 to 7cm tall; black, longitudinally indented fertile section above a more or less cylindrical stem;
Fertile surface: black, shaped like a flattened club; covering the upper 50 to 70% of the fruitbody,
Spores: white.

Lookalikes

There are dozens of earthtongue species and most are black or brown and look much the same as this one. A microscope is therefore essential for confident identification of these difficult fungi. Sometimes the difference is so subtle that you could end up, as I did, taking photographs of what you are convinced is *Geoglossum cookeanum* only to discover that it is actually something visually almost identical and yet genetically quite different.

The photogenic pair of earthtongues pictured on the right, nestling in mossy, sandy grassland as all good earthtongues should, can be separated from *G. cookeanum* by molecular analysis, which would show that its DNA is identical to that of *Bos taurus*, otherwise known as the Dairy Cow. (Rather than go to all the cost and trouble of DNA analysis, I dug them up to take samples home for further study.)

Yes, I have to admit that I was completely fooled by this discarded handle from some kind of leather bag… and I have plenty more pictures to prove it!

Not all earthtongues are as drab as *Geoglossum cookeanum*. The rare Green Earthtongue *Microglossum olivaceum* has a green stem and a matt olive fertile head. Not only is it very rare (it is a UK BAP species) but it is also far from easy to spot.

Nutrient-tolerant Grassland Fungi

The CHEG fungi – Clavariaceae, *Hygrocybe, Entoloma* and Geoglossaceae – are indicators of grassland quality (in the sense of not being unnaturally enriched with fertilisers - phosphorus in particular - or polluted with other chemicals such as herbicides and pesticides). Many other kinds of fungi are less sensitive than CHEG species to such contaminants. As a result, some species that occur in unimproved grassland are also found in pastures subject to small or moderate amounts of enrichment – environments that are inhospitable to many of the more sensitive CHEG species. Among these are some very good edible species from the family Agaricaceae as well as one or two notoriously hallucinogenic LBMs.

There are also plenty of fungi that seem to thrive on high levels of nitrates and cope well with phosphorus and potassium salts, and they are found only or mainly in intensively farmed fields. Included in this group are fungi that live on animal dung – but of course a light stock level of suitable grazing animals during spring and summer is one of the most cost-effective ways of managing waxcap grasslands, and for this reason many of the dung-loving (coprophilous) fungi can also be found in unimproved grassland sites that are grazed by sheep, horses, rabbits etc.

Let's start with grassland fungi that live on and in the grass itself, and then move on to the dung fungi that could perfectly well live without grass – except, of course, that their dung suppliers would be unable to produce the goods…

Agaricus campestris (Agaricaceae) – Field Mushroom

The one mushroom that most people have seen in the wild, this is what many believe to be the origin of the cultivated white button mushrooms that are sold in shops. In fact it is not: the much rarer (in the wild!) lookalike and close relative *Agaricus bisporus* owns that claim to fame. Field Mushrooms are very variable in appearance, with caps that may be white or brown, smooth or scaly.

Cap: 4 to 10cm across; initially concave with an inrolled margin and a partial veil that covers the gills for quite a while before the cap flattens; white or various shades of brown, often developing scales, usually small and pale but in some varieties larger and darker brown.
Gills: free; crowded; pink, maturing dark brown. (Right: young and older gills.)
Stem: 4 to 8cm long and 0.8 to 1.8cm dia.; white; smooth above ring, woolly below; cylindrical; small, fragile, with an ephemeral white ring.
Spores: chocolate-brown.

Note: Field Mushrooms appear in pastures during summer and autumn, producing good harvests some years and very few fruitbodies in other years.

Agaricus arvensis (Agaricaceae) – Horse Mushroom

Climbing the brow of a grassy hill and finding a ring of Horse Mushrooms is always a joy, for these large and chunky mushrooms are very good to eat. They don't always produce rings; sometimes a meadow will be dotted with singletons or, more often, small groups. A strong smell of aniseed distinguishes the Horse Mushroom from the smaller Field Mushroom, as also does it unusual stem ring.

Cap: 8 to 18cm across; initially hemispherical, becoming broadly convex but not completely flat; white or pale cream; surface covered in fine scales.
Gills: free; crowded; pale pink at first, becoming dark purple-brown.
Stem: 7 to 12cm long and 2 to 3cm dia.; white or pale cream; smooth, sometimes finely scaly below ring; cylindrical with a slightly clavate base; pendulous ring distinguished by cog-wheel pattern on underside.
Spores: chocolate-brown.
Odour: strong, of aniseed.

Agaricus bisporus (Agaricaceae) – Cultivated Mushroom

Although it is a rare find in the wild, *Agaricus bisporus* is the most common and widespread member of the genus *Agaricus* in the Western World. The most common cultivated form of this mushroom has a white cap, but brown-capped forms (known as Chestnut Mushrooms) are also grown commercially and this is the form most likely to be found in the wild. (The white button mushroom stocked by every supermarket and grocery shop was cultivated from an unusual pale form of *Agariicus bisporus*.)

The specific epithet deserves some explanation. Other members of the genus *Agaricus* produce their spores (basidiospores, of course, because these fungi are part of the Basidiomycota) on basidia that have four sterigmata; spores are thus produced in fours. Not so with *Agaricus bisporus*, which has two-spored basidia. (When studying basidia under a microscope it is important to look at several samples, because many fungi have some atypical basidia with either more or fewer spores than the norm for the particular species concerned.)

Cap: 5 to 15m across; initially hemispherical, expanding to become convex and eventually flat; white or brown; smooth or finely scaly.
Gills: free; crowded; white at first becoming greyish pink and finally dark chocolate-brown.
Stem: 3 to 5cm long and 8 to 15mm dia.; white; smooth, sometimes finely scaly below ring; cylindrical; white persistent ring.
Spores: chocolate-brown.
Odour: perhaps best described as 'mushroomy'.

***Macrolepiota procera* (Agaricaceae) – Parasol**

Such a distinctive (and distinguished) mushroom, tall and with a ragged tidiness, the Parasol is just as its common name implies – a lovely sunshade (in this instance apparently protecting its little brother or sister from the drying effects of the summer sunshine). Often as here, they can be seen lining roadside verges, but in such places they are likely to contain high levels of contaminants, perhaps including lead. These good edible mushrooms are best gathered from fields, where they commonly spring up on well-drained gentle slopes as well as on banks beside hedgerows and footpaths.

Look out for Parasols also in woodland clearings and on grassy coastal slopes.

Cap: 10 to 25cm across when fully expanded; initially oval (left), expanding until eventually flat with a distinct umbo; white or very pale buff background with a reddish-brown central region; surface breaks up into scales surrounding a smooth central disc.
Gills: free; crowded; white at first, becoming pale cream and later turning brown.
Stem: 15 to 30cm long and 1 to 1.5cm dia.; fawn background covered in a snakeskin-like pattern of fine brown scales, larger scales towards the base; cylindrical, widening slightly near base; thick, collar-like ring becomes moveable and sometimes slips gradually down the stem.
Spores: white or pale cream.

***Chlorophyllum rachodes* (Agaricaceae) – Shaggy Parasol**

More ragged and generally stockier than the Parasol, and lacking the snakeskin patterning on its stem, this mushroom seems most at home in woodlands; it is sometimes found in fields, parks and gardens. (Even well cooked it can cause severe allergic reactions.)

Cap: 6 to 18cm across; initially oval, expanding until almost flat (without an umbo); pale buff surface covered in large brown upturned scales.
Gills: free; crowded; white at first becoming pale cream and later turning brown.
Stem: 6 to 15cm long and 1 to 1.5cm dia.; white, soon discolouring brown; smooth; cylindrical; thick double ring is moveable.
Spores: pink.

Leucoagaricus leucothites (Agaricaceae) – White DApperling

Looking something like a cross between a Parasol and a Field Mushroom, the White Dapperling differs from both in having very much paler gills at maturity and white spores.

Although fairly common, these larger than life dapperlings tend to be localised. In fields where they occur there are often large numbers of them scattered around in groups.

Some authorities say that White Dapperlings are slightly poisonous, so stick with the guideline of shunning all white-gilled fungi.

Cap: 3 to 9cm across; initially convex, expanding to become almost flat; white, gradually becoming flushed pale cream-ochre or flesh-coloured; smooth and silky.
Gills: free; crowded; white at first becoming pale flesh pink.
Stem: 6 to 8cm long and 0.8 to 1.8cm dia.; white; smooth above ring, longitudinally fibrillose below; cylindrical with a bulbous base; white ring sometimes becomes moveable.
Spores: white.

Cystoderma amianthinum (Agaricaceae) – Earthy Powdercap

These colourful little mushrooms turn up in all sorts of grassy-mossy places, but they are most common on acid moorland and heathland. On lawns they sometimes produce fairy rings several metres in diameter.

Powdercaps usually do have granular cap surfaces, but their most distinctive feature is the marked contrast between the smoothness of the stem above the ring and its scaly surface below. The overall impression is of a mushroom wearing an ill-fitting stocking.

Cap: 2 to 5cm across; initially convex, becoming broadly convex or flat; colour variable from pale ochraceous yellow to reddish brown (centre darker and umbonate in *Cystoderma amianthinum* var. *rugosoreticulatum*); surface finely granular, sometimes radially wrinkled.
Gills: adnate or adnexed; crowded; white at first, becoming cream.
Stem: 3 to 5cm long and 4 to 8mm dia.; colour as cap but paler above ring; smooth or very finely granular above ring, scaly below; cylindrical; small collar-like persistent tan ring.
Spores: white.

Note: The Earthy Powdercap is the only member of its genus that can be considered 'very common and widespread' in Britain and Ireland.

Calvatia gigantea (Agaricaceae) – Giant Puffball

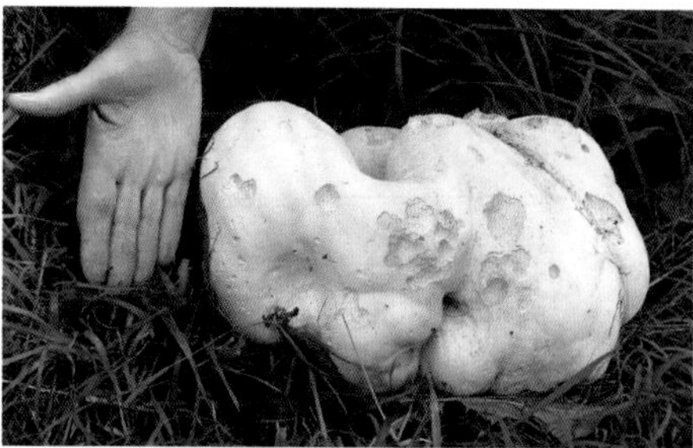

Setting off in search of Giant Puffballs when you don't know where they live is a recipe for failure. Finding these monster fungi from time to time should be considered a bonus, a delightfully serendipitous accident. But once you find a Giant Puffball site, you should be able to return year after year, for the underground mycelium is long lived – indeed these fungi sometimes produce fairy rings tens of metres in diameter.

Fruitbody: 20 to 70cm across; initially rounded or an elongated ovoid form, sometimes developing folds and irregular bumps; surface white and smooth, turning slightly brown; internally white at first, turning olive and finally brown as the spore mass matures; fruitbody disintegrates allowing wind and rain to disperse spores
Spores: brown.

Note: Giant Puffballs are edible only when young and white throughout. If you like them, just one large fruitbody can provide you with several kg of ingredients for soups, risottos, quiches and many other meals. Small chunks of Giant Puffball can be used in place of 'button mushrooms' in just about any recipe where they are to be cooked, but unlike button mushrooms they should not be eaten raw. These and most other puffball fungi have very little flavour of their own, but (like tofu) they are very good at soaking up flavour from good things that they are cooked with.

Lycoperdon pratense (Agaricaceae) – Meadow Puffball

Another of the common puffball fungi frequently found in meadows, *Lycoperdon pratense* looks rather like a baby Giant Puffball when viewed from the top, although in the early stages of development its skin is scurfy whereas its larger cousins have smooth skins. Both the Meadow Puffball and the Giant Puffball are edible, so confusing the two is not disastrous. To differentiate these puffballs look underneath: the Meadow Puffball has a stump-like stem whereas there is no stem at all on a Giant Puffball.

Fruitbody: 4 to 8cm across and 2 to 4cm tall; an elongated ovoid form with a short sterile stem typically half the width of the fruitbody; stem separated from fertile upper section by a skin-like membrane; outer surface white and scurfy when young, becoming smooth; eventually turning brown and rupturing at the apex; internally white at first, turning olive and finally brown as the spore mass matures; spores disperse through a large apical hole.
Spores: brown.

Note: Synonyms for this species include *Vascellum pratense* and *Lycoperdon depressum*.

Marasmius oreades (Marasmiaceae) – Fairy Ring Champignon

When you see them pouring across grassland in great crowds, jostling one another like excited football fans queuing for the Big Match, you could (almost) forgive the anthropomorphic attribution to these mushrooms of the cry 'We are the Champignons'. As the common name suggests, sometimes they create fairy rings (of the turf-killing kind that gardeners are not at all keen on). These grassland mushrooms' other main claim to fame is that they are edible, although the stems are very tough and so cooks who know about this problem simply retain the caps.

Cap: 2 to 5cm across; initially convex, flattening with a broad umbo; hygrophanous, orange-ochre or tan, drying buff or pallid cream; smooth, sometimes with faint marginal striations.
Gills: adnexed or free; distant; white at first, becoming cream.
Stem: 4 to 8cm long and 2 to 6mm dia.; tough and pliant; white or buff, darkening towards base; smooth and dry; cylindrical, base sometimes slightly swollen; white and downy at base.
Spores: white.

Volvopluteus gloiocephalus (Pluteaceae) – Stubble Rosegill

Amanita fungi are not the only ones that produce a volva from the lower part of the partial veil; mushrooms in the genus *Volvopluteus* do so as well. *Volvopluteus gloiocephalus* (syn. *Volvariella speciosa*) does indeed grow in fields where crops have been harvested to leave stubble (and it doesn't have to be grass or cereal crops; I have seen cleared cabbage field dotted with hundreds of these large white mushrooms). Grassy roadside verges and permanent pastures are also places where this rather handsome mushroom is apt to appear.

Cap: 8 to 14cm across; initially oval becoming convex but not often flattening completely; white or pale grey, becoming cream and later ochre; sticky when moist, silkily smooth when dry.
Gills: free; crowded; white at first, becoming pink.
Stem: 10 to 15cm long and 1 to 1.5cm dia.; white; bag-like volva (right) at base; tapering towards apex; no ring.
Spores: pink.

Parasola plicatilis (Psathyrellaceae) – Pleated Inkcap

Often referred to as the Little Japanese Umbrella (no explanation needed, surely!), this dainty inkcap is very common in unimproved grassland, but it quickly disappears from lawns treated with 'weed-and-feed'. Formerly *Coprinus plicatilis*, it is now the type species of the genus *Parasola*.

Following overnight rain, Pleated Inkcaps can appear at dawn, opening fully by mid morning and collapsing to nothing before sunset. Unlike most ink caps, this delicate little fungus has a cap that flattens and then shrivels rather than its gills deliquescing (turning to a black inky liquid). In damp summers a new array of caps usually appears each morning.

Cap: 1 to 2cm across; initially egg-shaped, then convex and finally flat; heavily ribbed from margin to edge of central 'eye'; pale grey with a tawny eye.
Gills: free, usually radiating from a collar around the top of the stem; white, turning grey and then black; thin; distant; not deliquescing significantly.
Stem: 3 to 6cm long and 2 to 3mm dia.; white; silky smooth; cylindrical; no ring.
Spores: black.

Bolbitius titubans (Bolbitiaceae) – Yellow Fieldcap

Well known by its synonym *Bolbitius vitellinus*, the Yellow Fieldcap has a wealth of common names including Egg-yolk Fungus, Cow-pat Mushroom and (guess where!) Sunny Side Up. Enriched grassland is its favoured habitat, and where better to find that than beside (rarely on) well-rotted cow-pats.

When grassy roadside verges are mown and the cut material left to rot, Yellow Fieldcaps often call in for breakfast. By lunchtime, however, all but the late risers are fading.

Cap: 2 to 4cm across; initially oval, expanding to become flat; hygrophanous, bright yellow, drying cream before turning ochre and shrivelling with 24 hours; margin striate, tending the split in dry weather.
Gills: adnexed or free; pale ochre turning rusty brown.
Stem: 5 to 9cm long and 2 to 4mm dia.; pale yellow, covered in fine white powder; cylindrical; no ring.
Spores: rust brown.

Agrocybe praecox (Strophariaceae) – Spring Fieldcap

One of the most common of the fieldcaps, and appearing from spring through to the end of summer, *Agrocybe praecox* has catholic taste when it comes to setting up home. Grassy roadside verges, scrubby wasteland, riverside fields where plenty of dead leaves and twigs get washed up, and even mulched shrubberies suit this gregarious fungus. Only when thoroughly cooked are Spring Fieldcaps reputed to be edible – hardly worth the risk!

Cap: 3 to 6cm across; convex, expanding to become broadly umbonate; ochre or pale tan, often slightly darker in centre; smooth, cracking in dry weather.
Gills: adnate; crowded; pale buff at first, becoming brown as the spores mature.
Stem: 4 to 8cm long and 5 to 9mm dia.; cream, turning brown with age; cylindrical, base slightly swollen; fragile ring, often ephemeral.
Spores: dark brown.
Odour: farinaceous.

Note: Many other *Agrocybe* species similar in size, colour and form to *Agrocybe praecox* occur mainly on wood mulch. Within this group are *Agrocybe molesta*, *Agrocybe pediades* and *Agrocybe rivulosa*, all of which are less common that the Spring Fieldcap and usually appear later in the year.

Stropharia coronilla (Strophariaceae) – Garland Roundhead

In lowland pastures and on lawns, this occasional roundhead appears sometimes in small groups but more often singly and widely scattered. Bold striations on the upper surface of the stem ring distinguish the Garland Roundhead from other yellow-ochre mushrooms of similar size. It is not unusual for these chunky little mushrooms to be mistaken for small *Agaricus* species, but as they are edible (not to be confused with 'nice to eat') the consequence is not too bad.

Cap: 2.5 to 4cm across; initially convex, becoming flat; surface felty or finely scaly; yellow-ochre, often slightly darker towards centre.
Gills: adnate; fairly crowded; pale grey-brown, becoming purple-brown at maturity.
Stem: 2 to 5cm long and 6 to 8mm dia.; white, yellowing with age; smooth at apex, finely fibrillose below ring; small white persistent ring with a striate upper surface.
Spores: purple-brown.

Note: Most *Stropharia* species occur on rotten wood, well-rotted vegetation or animal dung, but the Garland Roundhead is one of a select few that grow in grass (albeit usually on nutrient-rich soil) in meadows, parks and gardens.

Psilocybe semilanceata (Strophariaceae) – Magic Mushroom

Commonly referred to in the USA as Liberty Caps, these notorious little mushrooms are not quite as easy to identify as some people think. As a result several serious doses of mushroom poisoning have been suffered by sad people seeking the solace of this hallucinogenic species.

Cap: 0.6 to 1.5cm across; conical, with a sharp central pip-like umbo (never flattening); margin striate when wet; initially smooth, covered in a thin gelatinous pellicle; quickly becoming wrinkled during dry weather; hygrophanous, yellow-brown drying pale ochre.
Gills: adnate to narrowly adnexed; light brown with pale felty edges, becoming purple-brown as spores mature.
Stem: 4 to 8cm long and 2 to 4mm dia.; white, discolouring brown; cylindrical; nearly always wavy rather than straight; short-lived cobweb-like partial veil leaves a faint ring-zone on the stem.
Spores: purple-brown.

Note: In the UK, fungi (fresh or 'prepared' by drying, cooking etc) containing psilocybin are scheduled Class A drugs, and so it is an offence to possess any of these species.

Panaeolus fimicola (Strophariaceae) – Turf Mottlegill

It's hard to imagine a duller mushroom, but this very dark mottlegill somehow manages to make itself conspicuous on lawns after rain. The dark-brown caps – sometimes almost black – fade with age, covering a huge range of shades of brown. You may find it listed in some field guides as *Panaeolus ater*.

There can be small amounts of the hallucinogen psilocybin in these fungi, which lack the umbonate pips of Magic Mushrooms *Psilocybe semilanceata* (above).

Cap: 1.5 to 4cm across; initially hemispherical or convex, expanding to become broadly convex; hygrophanous, dark reddish-brown, sometimes tinged with purple, drying paler brown; smooth, satin surface.
Gills: adnate; grey-brown with white, toothed edges at first (right) becoming black as spores mature.
Stem: 4 to 8cm long and 3 to 5mm dia.; dusted with a white bloom at apex, the middle and lower stem colour is as the cap; cylindrical; no ring.
Spores: black.

Note: Approximately 100 *Panaeolus* species are known, and the majority have brown caps. Identification on macroscopic features alone is therefore a risk-ridden process. Several members of this genus contain hallucinogens, and so none should be eaten.

***Panaeolina foenisecii* (Strophariaceae) – Brown Mottlegill**

Also commonly referred to as the Mower's Mushroom and the Haymaker, *Panaeolina foenisecii* springs up on any lawn that is regularly mown but not intensively dosed with selective herbicides. It is probably the most common of the 'common or garden' lawn mushrooms, and unfortunately it is inedible and can cause sickness if eaten. The hygrophanous nature of the cap means that colour cannot be considered to be a significant identifying feature.

Cap: 1 to 2cm across; initially bell-shaped or conical, expanding to become broadly convex; hygrophanous, medium to dark brown when moist, drying from the centre outwards to a creamy-beige.
Gills: adnate; pale brown at first becoming mottled dark brown.
Stem: 4 to 7cm long and 3 to 5mm dia.; cream flushed towards base with mid brown; cylindrical; finely fibrillose; no ring.
Spores: dark brown.

***Lepista personata* (Tricholomataceae) – Field Blewit**

This edible mushroom (syn. *Lepista saeva*) is found in pastures and on woodland edges. You might even see fairy rings of Field Blewits on scrubby roadside verges. It is a calcium-loving mushroom and more common on chalk downland and on pastures overlying limestone than on acid moorland and heath.

Even when properly cooked, Field Blewits are known to cause allergic reactions in some people. They should never be consumed raw, and old specimens are nearly always infested with maggots, so check carefully. In most areas Wood Blewits *Lepista nuda* are more common than Field Blewits. Shop-bought blewits are usually Wood Blewits.

Cap: 6 to 12cm across; initially convex, flattening and sometimes developing a central depression, the margin becoming wavy; hygrophanous, pale brown or beige, becoming gradually paler as they dry out.
Gills: sinuate, crowded; white or pale beige.
Stem: 4 to 8cm long and 1.5 to 2.5cm dia.; pale background covered with violet to bluish-lilac longitudinal fibrils (usually paler than the stem of a Wood Blewit); cylindrical, but with a swollen base; no ring.
Spores: pale pink.

Fungi on Dung

As well as fungi of unimproved grassland and those species that tolerate moderate amounts of natural or artificial enrichment, the fungal kingdom has also spawned (oops!) a fair selection of dung-loving (coprophilous) fungi to capitalise on the increasing abundance of mammalian droppings since the first hairy beasts evolved nearly 200 million years ago. In the past few millennia farming has resulted in a huge increase in the amount of dung available for fungal consumption, and were it not for the sad fact that individual mammalian species (no doubt including *Homo sapiens*) become extinct within a few million years of their emergence, it would probably be worthwhile for the Mycota Kingdom to produce even more of these specialised dung-hungry fungi.

Muntjac and other farmed animals produce lots of dung for all sorts of weird fungi to fight over.

Protostropharia semiglobata (Strophariaceae) – Dung Roundhead

The most common of the large agaricoid fungi found on dung, this tidy toadstool earns its specific epithet in infancy, when the cap is a perfect, shiny hemisphere. Later, when fully expanded, it not only ceases to be semiglobose but it tends to lose a lot of its gloss and so blends in better with its lacklustre background.

Because this fungus is coprophilous, its occurrence is not related to the soil chemistry; Dung Roundheads are therefore more or less as common on chalky soil as they are on upland acid hillsides.

Cap: 2 to 4cm across; initially hemispherical, expanding to become broadly convex; surface sticky when wet, drying smooth and silky; creamy yellow-ochre, becoming mid brown in patches.
Gills: adnate; broad, pale grey maturing purple-brown.
Stem: 6to 10cm long and 2 to 3mm dia.; colour as cap but paler towards apex; dry above ring zone, slimy below and with fine brown fibrils; cylindrical; ephemeral ring zone.
Spores: purple-brown.

Panaeolus papilionaceus (Strophariaceae) – Petticoat Mottlegill

A neatly serrated edge to the cap margin, consisting of remnants of the partial veil, makes this a rather attractive dung fungus and is the source of its common name. Among its many synonyms this species is also recorded as *Paneaeolus campanulatus* and *Panaeolus sphinctrinus*.

A late coloniser of dung in farm fields, this mushroom often appears in groups and is most commonly seen where dung has rotted down and become overgrown with grass.

Cap: 2 to 4cm across; initially conical, expanding to become bell shaped but never flattening; hygrophanous, pale brown or grey-brown with a darker centre, drying pallid grey; smooth and silky, sometimes cracking radially in dry weather; with tooth-like velar remains around rim.
Gills: adnate; pale grey-brown with white edges, becoming mottled dark brown and then black at maturity.
Stem: 6 to 12cm long and 4 to 8mm dia.; colour as cap but covered in a fine white powder; cylindrical; no ring.
Spores: black.

Panaeolus semiovatus (Strophariaceae) – Egghead Mottlegill

Fairly common on all sorts of dung (including cow-pats) in meadows but seemingly particularly partial to horse manure, the Egghead Mottlegill is commonly confused with the Dung Roundhead. This black-spored fungus produces elongated caps that do not flatten anything like as much as the purple-brown-spored Dung Roundheads do, but in other respects there is a lot of similarity between these two species.

Cap: 3 to 6cm across; egg-shaped or bell shaped; light ochre or grey-brown; surface greasy at first, becoming shiny and wrinkled.
Gills: adnate; white, becoming mottled dark brown and then black at maturity.
Stem: 7 to 15cm long and 4 to 6mm dia.; colour as cap but darker brown towards base; cylindrical, base slightly swollen; white ring.
Spores: black.

The Basidiomycota do not have sovereign rights over animal dung, by any means. In fact almost invariably when you come across coprophilous (dung eating) agaricoid fungi there will be representatives of the Ascomycota present too, and although generally producing small fruitbodies they nevertheless tend to 'munch their weight' by sheer force of numbers. Many of these small or very small fungi belong to the order Pezizales, and they produce cup-like or disc-like fungi in a great variety of colours, although unfortunately brown does seem to feature rather a lot. This means that you are unlikely to spot them unless you go seriously scouring animal droppings for fungi – not everybody's favourite pastime. Here are details of two of the many ascomycetes – the first very common and the second much less so – that can be found only on animal droppings, and in each instance it has to be the right kind of dung. A chapter on dung recognition is *not* included in this book!

Cheilymenia granulata **(Pyronemataceae) – No Common Name**

Cow-pats and bedding from cow sheds are home to a host of macro and micro fungi, but one of the early colonisers of cow-pats, moving in as soon as there is a surface crust, in *Cheilymenia granulata* (syn. *Coprobia granulata*). This tiny disc-like ascomycete fungus belongs to the order Pezizales.

Fruitbody: a flat or shallowly concave disc, 1 to 2mm across and 0.5 to 1.5mm tall; orange; sessile; usually in groups and sometimes in huge swarms on cow-pats.
Fertile (upper) surface: orange; smooth in centre but granular near rim.
Spores: white.

Poronia punctata **(Xylariaceae) – Nail Fungus**

Type 'nail fungus' into Google and you soon become aware of the damage and destruction that dermatophytic micro fungi inflict upon the toenails and fingernails of some unfortunate people. What you are less likely to learn about is an ascomycete that masquerades as an agaric – at least in so far as it has a clearly defined cap and a stem. Nail Fungus grows on pony dung and looks like a broad-headed nail of the type used when securing bituminous felt to weatherproof the roof of a garden shed. Nail Fungus, a rare find in Britain and Ireland, is a UK BAP species.

Fruitbody: a flat, round or oval disc, 0.4 to 1.5cm across, sometimes developing a slightly raised margin at maturity; seated more or less centrally on a grey stem 0.5 to 1.5cm tall and 2 to 4mm in diameter.
Fertile (upper) surface: white, becoming brownish particularly at the rim; matt; irregularly spotted with black pore openings.
Spores: creamy white.

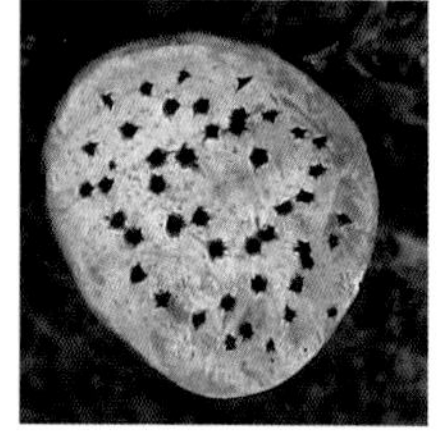

Claviceps purpurea (Clavicipitaceae) – Ergot

Only seen on grasses (including in the past some cereal crops) the common name Ergot is applied to a group of similar tiny ascomycetes fungi with complex lifecycles. The sclerotia develop in place of the seeds once spores of a *Claviceps* fungus have infected grass flowers. Rye and ryegrasses (*Lolium* spp.) are particularly susceptible because of their open flower form. The Ergot mycelium then destroys the flower ovary and ultimately produces vast numbers of conidia (asexual spores) that can infect grass florets. Visible eventually as blackened sclerotia in the husks of the florets, they contain toxic alkaloids. When eaten with grain these sclerotia are the cause of the illness known as ergotism, with such notorious symptoms as St Anthony's Fire. (The name is a reference to The Brothers of St. Anthony, who developed treatments for victims of this ailment, and to the burning sensation in limbs resulting from eating Ergot-infected cereals.)

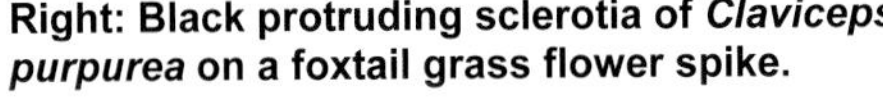

Right: Black protruding sclerotia of *Claviceps purpurea* on a foxtail grass flower spike.

Sclerotium: banana-shaped; purple, becoming black; 1 to 2mm dia., and 1 to 1.5cm long; falling to ground in winter, at which point the sexual stage of the lifecycle begins.

Fungi Don't Read Field Guides

Field guides to fungi tell us where we should expect to find each species. It is important to remember that guides are only for guidance; they are not rules written by the rulers of the fungal kingdom. Fungi are not as agile as birds or mammals, but they are quite capable of playing truant and turning up where you least expect them. For example, grassland fungi can occur in woodlands, and vice versa.

In North America, waxcaps are generally considered to be woodland fungi. It is possible that in Europe they are woodland species that have survived in grasslands after the trees were felled – or maybe they just moved in to pastures new and they liked it there and have now settled down. (In Ireland, unlike in most of Britain, waxcaps are found as often in woods as they are in meadows.) We do not yet understand the complex relationships between many grassland fungi and the mosses in particular that seem to make a grassy area good for fungi. It may be that suitable soil, plants and mosses coexist in certain kinds of woodlands as well as in certain kinds of grasslands. Where the habitat has been changing gradually, it may be that the fungi, unable to evolve as rapidly, have simply moved home. (They may well still be on the move.) Animals – mainly but not exclusively *Homo sapiens* – occasionally help in this process. They bury timber in grassland (or timber dropped there becomes overgrown with vegetation that later decays so that gradually the wood is buried); then all sorts of wood-rotting fungi can emerge, giving the false impression that they are growing in and on the grass itself.

Chapter 9 – Mushrooms on the Margin

Is nowhere fungus-free?

Somebody should have explained to these Oyster Mushrooms *Pleurotus ostreatus* that they are supposed to grow on trees. Here in the foundations of a hospital building there must be some buried timber. Let's hope that its structural role is non critical!

No forest is free from fungi; in few fields will you fail to find fruitbodies (although many meadows are merely mediocre); but there's more to our world than forests and fields, and if you can't get out into prime fungi foray locations it's still worth keeping your eyes open, because fungi can fruit in the most surprising places.

This chapter is about some of those marginal places where our intuition might say 'don't even bother to look'. Some of the mushrooms and other fungi that grow there are scarce and difficult to find in the more popular haunts of fungi hunters. Your garden, your home, your High Street – nowhere is sacrosanct when fungi need accommodation.

Many years ago an elderly friend asked me to help him paint the 'high bits' in his kitchen. (The high bits turned out to be the ceiling, walls, windows, doors, skirting boards…) It was an old house with a gas pipe running up one wall, and near to the top the pipe was connected to what appeared to be the hand-wheel of some sort of valve. Down the decades it had been coated with layer upon layer of paint. Deciding that in case the valve should ever need to be turned off in an emergency it would be a good idea to scrape off the paint and free up the mechanism, I dug a scraper in to the tough magnolia surface. Half of the cap of a paint-encrusted gilled mushroom flew across the room. How many painters and decorators had helped to preserve that ancient agaric since it had first emerged from a damp spot in the plaster?

Ceps and the City

There's a well-worn saying that grass doesn't grow on a busy street. For sure the High Street is no mycological Mecca, but if there are roadside trees it's a certainty that they will have battle-scarred trunks, and damaged bark is an open invitation to a whole host of fungi. I have seen mushrooms on main streets in London, Washington and Buenos Aires.

City-centre gardens, parks and cemeteries are good places to look, the only problem being that other people tend to spot metropolitan mushrooms, and not everyone treats them with respect. (Smaller fruitbodies and those well camouflaged on tree trunks or among leaf litter may escape attention.) I have even found Ceps in city parks, whereas in the countryside I seem to have an uncanny knack of treading forest footpaths mere minutes behind groups of mushroom hunters who have picked the area clean. Back at the car park I see them loading their car boots with baskets piled high with Chanterelles, Ceps, Wood Blewits and other choice edibles – and all I wanted was to take a few photographs. (Maybe I, too, would have found the temptation irresistible.)

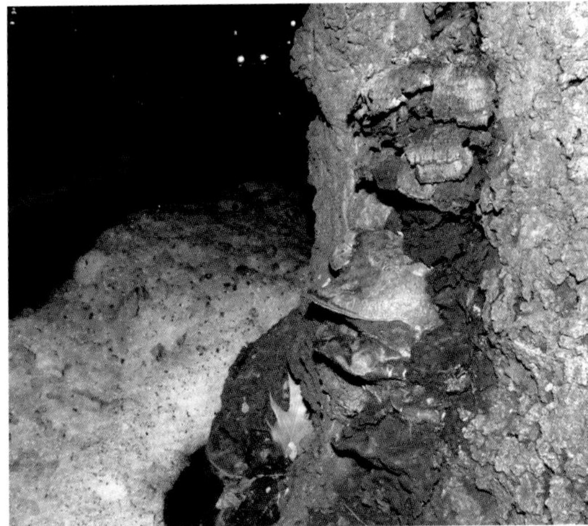

Mushrooms on Main Street. Late on Christmas Eve 2009 I came across these tough red bracket fungi on the gnarled base of an old tree on one of Washington DC's busiest streets. How many cars (sorry, that should be automobiles) have bounced off or sliced into the bole of this old tree, allowing fungal spores to enter and set up home there?

Urban fungi are not restricted to trees and grassland habitats. Here are two intrepid species that are undeterred by tarmac or even concrete paving slabs:

Agaricus bitorquis (Agaricaceae) – Pavement Mushroom

As the common name suggests, this is a mushroom that thrives in the compacted soil beside (and occasionally even beneath) urban footpaths. Sometimes the fruitbodies emerge in the gaps between paving slabs; more often they are found in dry, hard soil that defies even the most determined of urban weeds. Like others that hang around in gangs on street corners, Pavement Mushrooms are not the most photogenic of subjects. Although edible, these roadside mushrooms are often dirty and maggoty. Eating them is inadvisable.

Cap: 6 to 12cm across; initially spherical or hemispherical, flattening and sometimes becoming centrally depressed; margin slightly inrolled; surface pale grey, often partly obscured by debris pushed up as cap emerges from soil; yellowing with age and turning reddish when cut or bruised; smooth or somewhat scaly.
Gills: free; pink, turning dark chocolate-brown with age.
Stem: 4 to 8cm long, 1 to 2cm dia.; with a white double ring.
Spores: chocolate brown.

Pisolithus arhizus (Sclerodermataceae) - Dyeball

This mycorrhizal earthball (picture, left), is a forest fungus and so it has been described in Chapter 4. Normally these large fruitbodies, looking very much like dollops of horse dung, push up in the soft sandy soil of coastal pine forests, shoving large rocks aside if necessary. Even given that it has such a pedigree, it may surprise you to learn that this tough cookie is undeterred by the tarmac surface of an urban street.

Unfortunately one of these remarkable fungi came as quite a surprise to my wife and me when, having failed to spot the hazard in time, we ran it over and our car lurched violently. The impact seemed to have made very little impression on the Dyeball, which had displaced some quite sizeable lumps of tarmac and created a raised area that stood up well above the surrounding road surface (picture, right). Once the spores ripen, the whole of the fruitbody turns into a fine brown powder that is whisked away on the breeze during dry weather or washed away as spore soup when it rains, leaving a nasty pothole.

Seashore Surprises

Seashores are salty, sandy places, and salt is a hostile environment for most organisms. Sand drains and dries out quickly, and mushrooms cannot live without water. You might think, therefore, that beaches would be mycological deserts. They are not... well, not quite. Just as some plants have evolved to cope with a seashore climate and habitat, so also have a select band of fungi. Here are details of some that are worth looking out for:

Psathyrella ammophila (Psathyrellaceae) – Dune Brittlestem

Dune Brittlestems are saprotrophic on Marram Grass (*Ammophila arenaria*), and these little mushrooms can sometimes be found remarkably close to the littoral line, although stable dune slopes and dune slacks are the best places to look for them. Very variable and often swarthy, Dune Brittlestems occur singly or in small groups.

Cap: 3 to 5cm across; initially bell-shaped, flattening; margin not striate; surface pale brown, tan or mid brown, paler in dry weather but usually blackening when very old; smooth, but often coated in sand particles.
Gills: adnate, fairly crowded; dingy brown becoming chocolate brown; drying very dark brown, almost black.
Stem: 3 to 7cm long above the surface, but usually a further 2 to 4cm buried in sand; 2 to 5mm dia.; rooted among Marram Grass; whitish, turning brown with age; no ring.
Spores: brown.

Tulostoma brumale (Tulostomataceae) – Winter Stalkball

Looking like a miniature puffball on a stick, the Winter Stalkball is a most distinctive fungus. Unlike its close relatives the earthballs (*Schlerodera* spp.) it matures below ground out of harms way, only extending its stalk and raising its head above the parapet once the spores within its spherical spore sac are ripe and ready for propagation.

It is unusual to find Winter Stalkballs very far from the sea. (The furthest inland I have seen them is 2km from the shore.) The most likely places for spotting these gregarious fungi are not on the beach itself nor on the sides of sand dunes but among moss lying up against the first line of stable dunes and in lime-rich mossy dune slacks between young dunes nearest to the sea. Scrubby older dunes and slacks are often acidic and as a result devoid of calcium-loving Winter Stalkballs.

Spore sac: 1 to 2cm across; white, matt-surfaced sphere with a small raised apical ochre-sided pore; raised above sandy ground only when spores ripen.
Stem: 2 to 5cm long, 3 to 4mm dia.; ochre to mid brown; fibrous; base swollen.
Spores: brown.

***Phallus hadriani* (Phallaceae) – Sand Stinkhorn**

Slightly smaller, typically, than the Stinkhorn *Phallus impudicus* and differing visually by its volva being lilac-pink rather than white, the Sand Stinkhorn occurs only in sand dunes near to the sea. In the UK and Ireland this is a very rare species.

Egg: 3 to 5cm across and 4 to 6cm tall; lilac-pink; surface smooth and leathery.
Cap: thimble-like, ridged and pitted; covered in dark olive spore-laden gleba, whose foetid smell attracts insects; once insects have taken away all gleba the white, honeycombed surface of the cap is visible.
Stem: 12 to 18cm long, 2 to 3cm dia.; white; spongy; base and remains of egg surrounded by lilac-pink thin and papery volva.
Spores: olive-brown.

Note: Like other stinkhorns, *Phallus hadriani* occurs either singly or in small groups.

Saprophytic on dune grasses in Britain and Ireland, the Sand Stinkhorn is reportedly a symbiot of certain grasses in dry parts of Poland. There is still much to learn...

***Hygrocybe conicoides* (Hygrophoraceae) – Dune Waxcap**

With all the wonderful wildflowers that sand dunes sport in springtime, it's only fair that they should also have some colourful fungi later in the year, and with the Dune Waxcap they certainly do! With strident orange-red conical caps and yellow stems, these autumn gems sometimes fruit in large groups.

Like the Blackening Waxcap that is characteristic of unimproved grassland further from the shoreline, Dune Waxcaps blacken gradually with age, mainly in their stems, but nowhere near as much or as rapidly as Blackening Waxcaps do.

Cap: 1 to 4cm across; conical or convex with a central umbo; finely silky surface, greasy when wet; margin sometimes lobed but not striate; initially red or orange, gradually blackening with age.
Gills: adnate or adnexed; crowded; yellow, tinged with cap colour near stem.
Stem: 2 to 7cm long and 2 to 5mm dia.; finely striate; yellowing, blackening with age.
Spores: white.

Agaricus bernardii (Agaricaceae) – Salty Mushroom

Distinctive large brown cap scales and a coastal grassland habitat make this a fairly easy species to identify, and being remarkably tolerant of salt-laden air this large edible mushroom is often seen in grassland very close to beaches; it can also occur on the grass verges of roads that have been heavily salted in winter. These mushrooms can occur as solitary specimens, but more often they are in groups jostling one another for space.

Cap: 7 to 15cm across; initially hemispherical, becoming convex; surface background white, covered in coarse brown scales that give it a cracked appearance; white flesh turns reddish when cut.
Gills: free; crowded; pink, becoming chocolate-brown as the spores mature.
Stem: 4 to 8cm long and 2 to 4cm dia.; narrow sheathing ring with an upturned rim.
Spores: chocolate-brown.

Peziza ammophila (Pezizaceae) – Dune Cup

Cup fungi, and brown ones in particular, are very difficult to identify with certainty; however, the Dune Cup is distinctive not merely because of its growing habitat but also because of the way it develops. A globose fruitbody grows beneath the sand, breaking the surface when fully developed; then the peridium splits into between five and ten pointed petals, which peel backwards to expose the inner surface of the cup. At this stage the Dune Cup looks like an earthstar that has lost its central spore sac. The fertile surface is inside the cup, as with all *Peziza* species. (The first time I saw one of these strange fungi I assumed that it was the empty dried-up case of an earthball, but there was no sign of any of the spore mass inside and yet clearly it was not a particularly old fruitbody.)

As dry sand blows across the dunes, specks inevitably fall into the cup and trigger the discharge of ripe spores; these are then carried away on the breeze – quite a cunning system for releasing spores at times ideal for their long-range distribution!

Fruitbody: 2 to 4cm across and 1.5 to 3cm tall; globose at first, opening into a crown-like form as several pointed star-like rays fold back to reveal the inner surface of the cup. Outer and inner surfaces are various shades of ochre or brown.
Stem: sometimes cups sit on pseudostipes consisting of sand grains bound together by mycelium; more often there is no stem.
Spores: white.

Note: The Dune Cup is saprophytic and, as the specific epithet implies, it is usually found with Marram Grass, *Ammophila arenaria*.

Pholiota tuberculosa (Strophariaceae) – No Common Name

Pholiota fungi feed on wood and occasionally on other kinds of plant debris. This particular species is rather partial to dead pine wood, although it can also be found on oak and many other kinds of timber. It seems that a slightly salty diet of flotsam, just above the high-tide line, suits it well - as the picture below indicates. *Pholiota curvipes* is one of its many synonyms, the specific epithet referring to its stem, which is often curved at the base.

Cap: 1.5 to 5cm across; subglobose becoming convex and then flattening with a broad umbo; brilliant yellow to rusty or reddish brown; surface dry, broken into small flat or upturned scales, centre scales often small and inconspicuous; rim sometimes bearing ragged velar remains; flesh yellow.
Gills: adnate; yellow and finally cinnamon as spores mature.
Stem: 1 to 3cm long and 3 to 9mm dia.; smooth and yellow or rusty brown above ring zone; rusty brown, below; ragged woolly threads of veil remnants form a transient ring; clavate and often curved near base; hollow.
Spores: rusty brown.

Battarrea phalloides (Tulostomataceae) - Sandy Stiltball

Not just an oddity but also a real rarity in Britain and Ireland, the Sandy Stiltball begins life (as we know it!) as a white or pale-buff egg. When fully developed the egg bursts open and a tall stem quickly emerges, on top of which is a cap-like structure; however, the fertile surface is not underneath the cap but on top. The brown powdery spore-laden material on top of the cap blows away on the breeze or is washed into the surrounding sand by rain.

Spore sac: cap-like, emerging from an egg 1 to 3cm across; conical, becoming convex with an incurved margin; tough; fertile upper surface covered in rust-brown sticky spore-laden gleba; sterile lower surface matt, buff.
Gills: none.
Stem: 12 to 30cm long and 0.4 to 1.5cm dia.; pale brown to mid brown; fibrous; hollow.
Spores: rust-brown.

Note: This remarkable mushroom, looking like a fossil even when it is newly emerged from its egg, occurs in dry soil, including sand dunes. Such a find is a wonderful surprise, because of its rarity, but do not be any more surprised if you come across Sandy Stiltballs under dry hedges or in deciduous broadleaf woods or conifer forests on dry sandy soil, because they are certainly not confined to coastal areas.

Pioneering Parasites

In Chapter 1 much was made of the lifestyle differences between organisms in the kingdoms of plants, of animals and of fungi; however, their chemical and hence culinary differences are not so great. All three kingdoms provide us – and of course other animals too - with plentiful sources of good wholesome food. Some plants parasitise fungi, just as some fungi feed on living and dead trees, shrubs and other kinds of plants. But (is it any surprise?) there are plenty of fungi with appetites for animals - the living as well as the dead - and others that feast on fellow fungi. Most of these are microfungi, but here are details of four common macrofungi that live on (or off!) either fungi or animals. The first three are found only in woodlands and the fourth more often in grassland.

Asterophora lycoperdoides (Lyophyllaceae) – Powdery Piggyback

Formerly *Nyctalis asterophora*, this little white mushroom has a taste for decaying brittlegill fruitbodies, and in particular the Blackening Brittlegill *Russula nigricans*.

Although a member of the Basidiomycota, *Asterophora lycoperdoides* does not often produce basidiospores; it is one of the basidiomycetes that produce asexual spores. On the upper surface of the cap, powdery chlamydospores develop in vast numbers giving it the appearance of a puffball disintegrating in a mass of spores (although puffballs produce sexual spores). The thick-walled chlamydospores are star shaped – hence the generic name. The specific epithet reflects its behavioural similarity to the *Lycoperdon* puffballs.

***Asterophora lycoperdoides* on the decaying cap of a brittlegill mushroom**

Cap: 0.5 to 2cm across; globose or convex; white, turning pale brown with age; increasingly covered in fine powdery chlamydospores that also turn light brown.
Gills: very pale grey; adnate; thick and distant; often incomplete or malformed.
Stem: 1 to 3cm long and 2 to 4mm dia.; white, browning with age; surface finely woolly; nearly always curved; no ring.
Chlamydospores: cream to pale brown.

Asterophora parasitica (Lyophyllaceae) - Silky Piggyback

This little mushroom is very similar to *Asterophora lycoperdoides*, but its cap is covered in fine radial fibrils, giving it a silky appearance. Unlike the Powdery Piggyback the gills, upon which white chlamydospores develop along with basidiospores, are usually fully formed. The cap expands until it is broadly concave or almost flat.

The Silky Piggyback feeds on decaying caps of several kinds of brittlegills (*Russula* species) and occasionally also some of the milkcaps (*Lactarius* species).

Pseudoboletus parasiticus (Boletaceae) – Parasitic Bolete

Arguments continue to rage about whether this small and rather dull-looking bolete is truly parasitic, but whatever the case there is no doubt that its habitat is marginal. Only hard against the Common Earthball, *Scleroderma citrinum*, will you ever see these boletes growing. The deformed nature of earthballs living with Parasitic Boletes as neighbours suggest an interaction that could be seen as something other than benign. Common Earthballs are far more common than their parasitic associates.

Like Major Major in Joseph Heller's *Catch 22*, this is such an undistinguished bolete that it is instantly recognisable by its nondescript appearance. Any lingering doubt is immediately settled if it is accompanied by a Common Earthball.

Cap: 1.5 to 4cm across; hemispherical, becoming convex and sometimes flattening; olive-brown to olive-yellow; surface dry and matt or very finely velvety.
Tubes: ochraceous; not discolouring significantly when cut; adnate or slightly decurrent.
Pores: yellow, turning ochre-brown at maturity; not discolouring when bruised.
Stem: 2 to 4cm long and 7 to 10mm dia.; olive with rusty longitudinal fibrils near base; usually curved beneath its host earthball at base; no ring.
Spores: olivaceous-brown.

Cordyceps militaris (Clavicipitaceae) – Scarlet Caterpillarclub

The Scarlet Caterpillarclub is found mainly in grassland and on woodland edges but also occasionally pushing up through bare soil during late summer and autumn. Restricted to a very specific habitat – underground larvae of moths – this sinister little fungus parasitises and kills its host, turning it into a mushy mess and then pushing up through the turf as a bright orange club. In China related species are highly prized as edible fungi and are used to make soup. All sorts of performance enhancing properties (sporting and otherwise) are claimed for treatments based on *Cordyceps* fungi.

Fertile Head: 0.5 to 4cm long and 2 to 4mm dia.; bright orange or scarlet-orange; club-shaped and slightly swollen; rarely branching; granular, covered in raised pores.
Infertile stem: 1 to 3cm long and 1 to 1.5mm dia., usually somewhat wavy; paler orange than the head; attached to a moth pupa below ground.
Spores: white or cream.

Careful excavation reveals that the Scarlet Caterpillarclub is attached to and feeding upon a mummified insect larva – usually of a moth or occasionally a butterfly.

Some 400 or so *Cordyceps* species have so far been identified and described, but given their cryptic nature it's likely that many more remain undiscovered. These are all flask fungi, belonging to the phyllum Ascomycota.

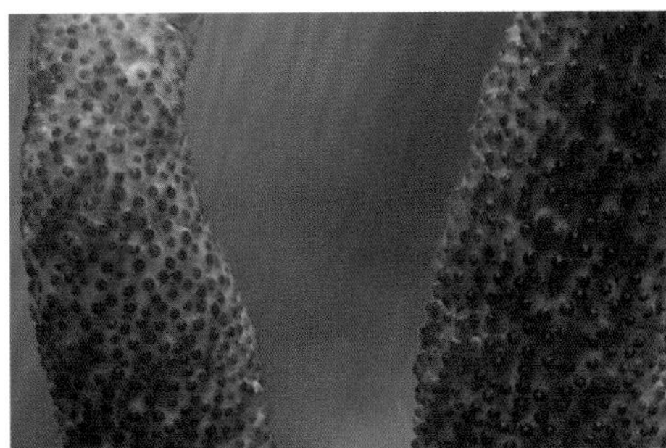

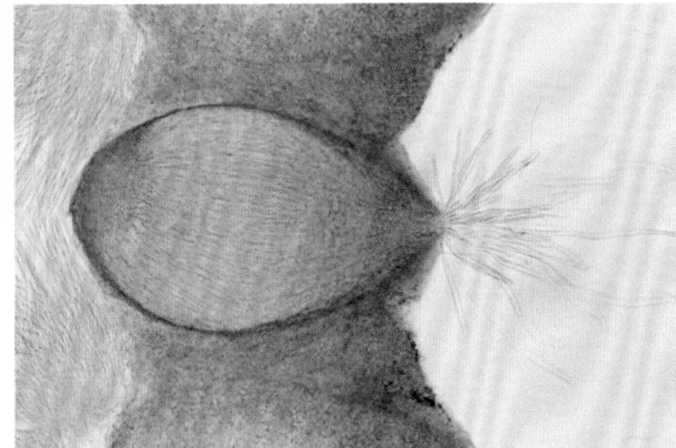

Left: Close inspection of the surface of a Scarlet Caterpillarclub reveals tiny raised pores at the tops of spherical perithecia (an example, greatly magnified, is shown on the right). The flask-like perithecia are lined with asci, within each of which sets of eight ascospores develop.

Thoroughly Modern Mushrooms

Modern farm practices, and in particular the use of herbicides and fungicides, have not created many new habitats hospitable to fungi; however, nature abhors a vacuum, and when a new niche appears a mushroom is usually waiting to colonise it. That certainly has been the case with big-bale silage, where even the smallest slit in the plastic covering provides a convenient access point for fungal spores, and the fermenting grass provides all the warmth and moisture necessary for mycelial growth and eventual fruiting of fungi. The species most commonly seen exploiting these particular opportunities is the Split Gill *Schizophyllum commune*.

Please Do Disturb
Although most fungi need undisturbed places where they can stretch their mycelial muscles, there are some notable exceptions that not only cope with disturbance but really seem to thrive on occasional upheaval, such as the seasonal routine of activities necessary for managing a productive vegetable garden.

There are fungal hot spot in gardens. Wherever you have warm, damp soil rich in organic matter you can expect a succession of unidentifiable fungi. Greenhouses and cold frames are favourite haunts of exotic fungi brought in with plants native to warmer climes, and if you operate a rotation system with three compost heaps - one bay being filled up as you weed, prune and clear out plots, a second rotting down, and the third bay well rotted and ready for use as required – lifting the covers can produce startling surprises.

Some lucky people find Morels *Morchella esculenta* in their compost heaps in springtime. Stinkhorns *Phallus impudicus* are also fond of well-rotted compost as are some of its more colourful but equally pongy imported cousins. Even more common as compost colonisers are various inkcaps, including the large (and edible) Shaggy Inkcap *Coprinus comatus*. Look out, also, for this little beauty:

Coprinopsis nivea **(Psathyrellaceae) – Snowy Inkcap**
If you add horse dung to your compost heap, this pure-white inkcap is quite likely to move in.

Cap: 1.5 to 4cm across; initially egg-shaped, becoming conical and eventually bell-shaped with a curled-up margin that usually splits; entire cap covered in fleecy white fibrils that eventually fall away to leave a grey, smooth or very slightly striate surface.
Gills: adnate or free; initially white, maturing black and finally deliquescing.
Stem: 4 to 8cm long and 1.5 to 3mm dia.; white, covered in fine woolly fibrils.
Spores: black.

Seifertia azaleae **(Ascomycetes) – No Common Name**

Soil fungi are essential for successful gardening, because nearly all plants need mycorrhizal partners for healthy growth and some cannot survive without them; however, there are fungi and fungi. Some are essential; others are of marginal value; and a few are downright dreadful, but very difficult if not impossible to eradicate.

A fine display of azaleas or rhododendrons can be blighted by the wrong kind of fungus, and one of the worst is *Seifertia azaleae*, which causes what horticulturalists call 'bud blast'. Find this one attacking your azaleas and 'blast' is likely to be the mildest of your verbal outbursts.

Rivers and Streams have Margins, too

Fungi need moisture, and so you might expect that bogs, swamps, fens, lakes, rivers and streams would be fungal hotspots. Rarely is this the case, unfortunately, although in desert regions the few trees and fungi likely to be encountered are nearly always by the waterside or at least where the water table remains close to the surface. In temperate zones, chalkstreams and culverted watercourses excepted, the water's edge is not a fixed location. Rivers don't really 'burst their banks', it's simply that we have built on the high-flow riverbed. What we call a flood is simply the river rolling over restlessly and making full use of its king-size bed. 'Flood plain' is just a euphemistic term for riverbed.

Most fungi do not cope well with long-term inundation, and so only a limited number of fungal species thrive in waterside soils, and in general those that do are equally at home in most other kinds of grasslands or woodlands that are good for fungi. There are some exceptions, however, particularly within the Ascomycota. Most are tiny and require microscopic examination to determine their identities, but here is a notable exception:

Mitrula paludosa (*Incertae sedis*: Helotiales) – Bog Beacon

In the margins of slow-flowing rivers, shallow bogs and ditches, this matchstick-like ascomycete grows in groups, the stems attached to rotting leaves and other plant debris. Look for these colourful fungi also in sphagnum moss, where the stems are partly submerged in water. Bog Beacon fruits in spring and early summer.

Head: 7 to 12mm across; irregularly egg-shaped or clavate, tapering sharply towards stem; bright yellow, sometimes with an orange tinge; smooth; gelatinous.
Stem: 2 to 5cm long and 1 to 3mm dia.; white or pale buff; covered in fine woolly fibrils.
Spores: white or pale yellow.

Waxcaps on riverbanks

Just above the regular high-water line of many lowland rivers, waxcaps are a common sight. Perhaps the river purges the soil of excess fertiliser, making the area suitable for waxcaps while the grassland further from the water's edge retains too high a nutrient load for these sensitive mushrooms to survive. It's not just the common, more tolerant waxcap species that you find in such places. For example on the banks of the River Teme, a tributary of Britain's River Severn, I have seen eight waxcap species fruiting together; that makes it a grassland fungi site richer than most country churchyards.

Chapter 10 – Fungi Forays, Photos and Food

Parting Shots, some with a Party Focus

If foraying for fungi either for fun, photography or food is something relatively new to you, this chapter could save you a lot of time and trouble. It is built on forty years' of getting things wrong and gradually learning (from others and from bitter experience) things that can make life easier. I should add that there are some mistakes that I have *not* made. I have never eaten a poisonous mushroom or even a hallucinogenic one. The earlier chapters of this book should help you to avoid that mistake, too, but the fact that there are some seriously toxic toadstools out there is not a bad thing to emphasise yet again. But let's be positive. Fungi are fun; they are quite as photogenic as flowers, birds or butterflies; and the finest of them provide food that is not only free but absolutely delicious. Have you met The Magnificent Seven? No? Well later in this chapter not only will you meet them but, thanks to my Sue, you will be able to eat them cooked in ways that I'm sure you will enjoy as much as we do. But first the when, where, what and how of fungus forays...

When? (A Mushroom is not just for Christmas)

Although more fungi fruit in summer and autumn than at other times of the year, there is always something of interest, and once you know where to look and what to look out for, you will be able to enjoy fungus forays during every month of the year. So the answer to *When?* is any time. Here is a colourful 'Fungus for all Seasons' calendar that may even convince you go for a foray to work off (or to work up an appetite for) that Christmas lunch.

January	**February**	**March**	**April**
Jelly Ear	**Scarlet Elf Cup**	**Black Morel**	**St George's Mushroom**
May	**June**	**July**	**August**
Parasol	**Field Mushroom**	**Chanterelle**	**Wood Hedgehog**
September	**October**	**November**	**December**
Cep	**Wood Blewit**	**Trumpet Chanterelle**	**Velvet Shank**

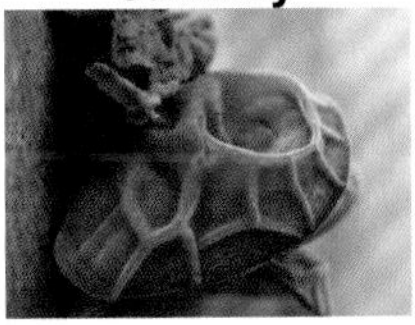

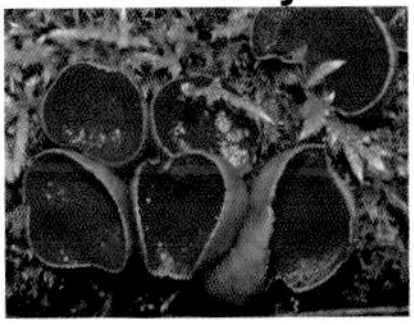

How? Tips on preparing for a foray

There are lots of things you can do when out on a foray to help make it a success... provided you have done a few important things well before setting off. For example finding fungi is a lot easier if you go to where there are fungi. I've tried the alternative and it's not a good strategy. There are also things that you will need to have when out in the wild, and of course the trick is to take them along with you. You might want to include most if not all of the following:

- Basket or compartmented plastic box
- Paper bags (not plastic) to wrap fungi
- Camera, tripod, spare batteries
- Penknife (on a lanyard)
- Field guide (in backpack)
- Pocket magnifying glass
- Notebook and pencil
- Food and drink (lightweight packaging)
- Basic first aid kit
- Watch, whistle, mobile phone
- Map and compass or handheld SatNav

You may have noticed that I haven't included hiking boots, knee pads or a walking stick. (A telescopic ski pole is light and can be stored in a backpack until required.) If you are even more forgetful than I am, you could add these to the checklist so you don't end up in a pine forest or on a mountainside wearing swimsuit and flippers. I'm quite absentminded enough, and because anything that I can put down and forget eventually gets put down and forgotten, I attach things such as my penknife and magnifying glass to my clothing via lanyards, or I hang them on neck cords. (If you, too, have never grown out of the 'gloves on elastic threaded through coat sleeves' phase you will know why I press this point.)

Some people bring along small phials of testing chemicals to help identify fungi based on colour changes; others carry gardening tools and seem bent on turning rough woodland tracks into highways. Be minimalist. Less is more - more time looking, finding and learning. If like me you like travelling light, everything in your fungus foray kit will be essential. Keeping all your kit together in one place when you are not on forays makes things easier, but somehow removing all risk seems like cheating. Hence the checklist. And in any case who keeps one camera especially for fungi forays and another for bird watching etc? Oh, do you? In that case let's move on quickly...

Perhaps it is stating the obvious, but if you are going on a foray with a group of people it is a good idea to make sure everyone has a written note of the date, time and venue and a mobile phone number to ring if they get lost on the way, have a tyre blow out, or decide en-route to take up bog snorkelling instead of fungi hunting. You can waste a lot of time waiting for 'late arrivals' who never make it, but it's also sad when a member of the group is left behind because they reached the rendezvous two minutes late and had no idea which direction the group had set off in and no way of finding out.

Where?

Many of the best fungus sites are well known. They are publicised in books and on the Web. Visit one of these hotspots at the right time of year and you are unlikely to be seriously disappointed with the diversity and abundance of fungi there. You are also unlikely to be alone. If solitude is something you value, then why not find venues that are off the beaten track (or at least if on it then with other tracks running off it that are rarely if ever visited by other fungi fanciers)? Some of the best woodland sites that I know have public access that the public simply don't use - perhaps because they just don't know about them. In some woods and forests there are rules about staying on footpaths. Even if that is the case there is no need to feel that you will necessarily be missing out on the best opportunities: often the majority of fruitbodies spring up beside paths, where the mycelia come up against hard compacted soil and simply spread along the path edge.

It is a lot harder to find level lowland grassland venues that are good for fungi but are not much visited by people; that's because these are not truly natural habitats, and they would scrub over if they weren't either mown or munched. By looking on a contour map it's not difficult to find grassy slopes that are too steep for farm machinery, and with the landowner's permission you can check out these areas for fungi. Even in intensively farmed areas I have found some good fungi sites on precipice land that is lightly grazed but never receives fertiliser or herbicides. In the uplands there are plenty of unexplored areas, and if you don't mind the occasional 'blank' it can be fun to pioneer far from the madding crowd. Thanks to the CRoW (Countryside and Rights of Way) Act 2000 there is a lot more open access in the uplands of Wales and England than there was beforehand; and similar provisions are contained in the Land Reform (Scotland) Act 2003, which has formalised the Scottish tradition of unhindered access to open countryside.

What to do (and a few things not to do)

Irrespective of the vagaries of the laws of trespass and its interpretation, it is wrong to go wandering on to private land without the owner's permission. Having asked permission of several farmers and other landowners to look for fungi on their land, I have never once been refused. I do recall getting a *'You're very welcome, of course, but Angus the Bull can be a bit temperamental. He had one of the farmhands up a tree for two hours last week'* – and on second thoughts that field didn't seem at all promising as a fungi site.

It is impossible even to look at fungi without having some impact on their habitat - that's a basic law of physics. What every responsible fungi forayer wants to do is to minimise their impact to a level that is sustainable; however, conservation is not simply a matter of ensuring that the fungi themselves are not significantly affected by what we do. Many other plants, animals and other fungi are affected when fungal fruitbodies that they depend upon are removed in great quantities, even if there is no impact on the mycelium that produced the fruitbodies. There are certainly concerns about commercial-scale mushroom picking that deprives so many other creatures of the fungal food or habitat that they depend on.

On the other hand, a reasonable amount of picking, whether it be blackberries or blewits, is okay as long as we consider the needs of others – including other organisms that share the ecosystems in which edible fungi fruit. Whether careless trampling puts common fungi species at risk is debatable, but one thing is certain: a trampled immature mushroom will not develop to brighten the countryside and give joy to other walkers. On that basis alone it is important to tread carefully.

Where can you safely tread?

Here, then, are some basic guidelines for ecologically-sensitive fungus forays:

- Look before you leap. Many beautiful fungi nestle in amongst grass or in forest leaf litter, and they can easily be destroyed by trampling feet.
- Take photographs home rather than taking fungi (unless you need samples for study and identification or when you are collecting wild mushrooms that you intend to eat).
- Collect only those edible fungi you have identified with certainty, and then leave those that are immature (they may not yet have released any spores) and any very old ones.
- Don't pick an area clean; leave the majority of the fruitbodies to spread spores, to feed animals, and to act as homes for bugs and other tiny creatures.
- Pick only sufficient common edible mushrooms for your own needs, and where there are very few consider foregoing your mushroom supper for the sake of the future.
- Never rake over leaf litter in search of immature fruitbodies, or you are certain to destroy many immature ones and perhaps even kill their mycelium.
- In many nature reserves picking fungi is prohibited or is allowed for scientific purpose only when you have applied for and been granted a permit.
- Rare species must not be picked. In many countries there is a Red Data List of vulnerable and threatened fungi species that have special legal protection.

To study a rare mushroom without damaging it or disturbing the surrounding habitat, lay a small mirror on the ground beside the fruitbody. This will enable you to look at the stem and gills (and even photograph them). Some mycologists have a hinged mirror that can be attached to a walking stick for just this very purpose. Perhaps you could make an adaptor for a telescopic skiing pole; it could all be stowed in your backpack until required.

Photographing fungi

Having taken thousands of really bad photographs of fungi over the past 40 years, I feel well qualified to advise others on how to get the same results. Some of my pictures are good, though, and I know a bit about how such accidents can become more frequent events. But if I pass on just one tip that can make a real difference it is this: use a tripod!

Camera shake is one of the biggest problems when photographing fungi in low-light conditions – and forests in particular can be dark and gloomy places. Even when out in the open there are very good reasons for not relying on a steady hand to hold the camera still: to obtain sufficient depth of field you may have to use a small aperture and therefore a correspondingly long exposure time.

Is all that gobbledygook? Don't worry, in this brief introduction to fungi photography I will explain those terms and why they matter. In short, it's all to do with image quality, which sounds simple enough but is actually determined by many factors, including personal preference. (We know what we like, even if others take a different view.)

Digital Image Terminology

Unless you use your digital camera in the Preset mode only - okay for holiday snaps, perhaps, but not likely to give best results when you need a close-up shot of a tiny ascomycete or a picture of a group of Sulphur Tufts tucked down inside a hollow tree - you will need to know a bit about white balance, the difference between optical zoom and digital zoom, pixels, file compression, and the advantages and disadvantages of the various digital file formats that most modern cameras offer as user-selectable options. Let's start and finish with just the basic essentials, leaving the optional extras to specialist books.

Pixel. This word is derived from **PIX** (**PI**cture) and **EL** (**EL**ement). Digital images are made up of a mosaic of small squares, called pixels, each being uniformly a particular colour. Although a digital photograph may look as though the colour gradations are smooth and continuous, it is actually an array of millions of tiny tiles, as shown below.

On the left is a complete digital image, while on the right the area in the red rectangle has been magnified to show the individual pixels.

A picture made up from a greater number of pixels can be magnified more before the individual pixels become discernable, and not surprisingly they are most intrusive on sharp edges where the transition from one colour to another follows a staircase rather than a smooth line. This effect is sometimes referred to as pixelation.

It seems obvious, therefore, that if digital images are to be displayed on a large screen or printed out as large pictures then a camera with a large number of pixels should give better results than one with a much smaller pixel count. This figure, often stated in millions of pixels (or megapixels), is sometimes referred to as the digital resolution of a camera. It matters…but only up to a point. There are other factors that often have a far greater influence on how good the pictures look, and we will consider the main ones shortly. In the meantime let's see how colours are represented in digital images.

Each individual pixel has a numerical value that defines the amount of red, green and blue light it must display on a scale from 0 to 255. Light is additive, so when each of the colour channels is set to 255 (maximum red, maximum blue and maximum green) the pixel displays as white. Similarly, R-G-B values of 0, 0 and 0 mean that no light is emitted and the pixel displays as a black tile. Here are a few colours and their RGB values:

Red	**Green**	**Blue**	**Colour**
255	0	0	
255	255	0	
227	108	10	
200	200	200	

Each channel has 256 possible values (Including zero) and so the number of different colours that can be displayed is 256 x 256 x 256 = 16,777,216 (more than 16 million colours). Techies reading this will realise that numbers 0 to 255 can be represented by eight bits (sequences such as 00110110). An 8-bit number is referred to as one Byte, and so all three channels can be represented by three 8-bit numbers or three bytes. Pictures stored in this way are sometimes referred to as 24-bit colour images.

Although 16 million colours sounds like more than enough, some images are produced as 16-bit numbers for each of the three channels, and they are known as 48-bit colour images. Can anyone tell the difference between 24-bit and 48-bit images? Maybe not, but beware of storing digital images in anything less than 24-bit colour. Here's why…

The file on the left, above, is saved with a depth of 24-bit colour (an available range of 16 million colours), while the 8-bit version on the right is restricted to only 256 colours. Look closely at the caps of the Fly Agarics on the right; in this lower colour-depth image you can see that colour banding mars the picture quality, most noticeably near the tops of the caps.

File Formats

Most digital cameras allow you to choose the format in which your pictures will be saved on the internal memory card. JPEG (standing for Joint Photo Experts Group – the organisation that defined this standard) is the default option on many cameras, and in this mode there is a facility for altering the level of compression, a space-saving technique that increases the number of pictures a memory card can hold, at the expense of some reduction in picture quality. Other common file formats are TIFF (Tagged Image File Format) and RAW, the latter being simply the unprocessed output from the camera's array of light-sensitive cells that turn the optical image into data. TIFF and RAW files take up more memory space than JPEG files but the picture quality is as good as the camera is capable of; that is not so with JPEG files, and the main reason is that JPEGs are usually compressed.

JPEG compression

In most pictures there are blocks of unchanging colour – a green fence rail, an area of blue sky and so on. In a digital image each pixel in such solid blocks requires 24 bits of digital data storage... unless we can store information like 'the 47 pixels to the right of this one are all the same colour'. Now the total data storage requirement is much reduced. Of course, pictures where there are few areas of constant colour will not reduce much in file size, but a JPEG file is invariably smaller than RAW data or a TIFF. In highly compressed JPEGs adjacent cells of nearly the same colour are recorded as being identical.

The maximum size of the digital file that a camera produces depends on the pixel count of the image sensor. If the camera is saving in 24-bit colour, each pixel requires 24 bits (3 bytes) of storage space. A 10MP camera can therefore produce a 30 megabyte (30MB) data file. You could store just 33 of these image files on a 1 gigabyte (1GB) memory card. This is rather limiting, although some cameras can accommodate much larger memory cards, and the trend is ever upwards. Even so, a small amount of JPEG compression can reduce the file size dramatically with no discernable degradation in picture quality, as these pictures of a Blusher (*Amanita rubescens*) show:

Uncompressed JPEG, file size 6MB

Moderately compressed JPEG, file size 0.7MB

Highly compressed JPEG, file size 0.25MB

The degradation in picture quality with increasing amounts of JPEG compression is more noticeable when you look closely at the cap warts and the gill edges of this mushroom.

Compressing a picture by a factor of ten means that your camera memory card can store ten times as many pictures, and the loss in quality is often acceptable; however, some cameras allow much greater levels of compression, but quality is more seriously degraded. JPEG compression is 'lossy', and information that is lost can never be recovered.

Image size

Another setting on a digital camera allows you to reduce the physical size of the pictures. All this does is capture an image using just part of the sensor, so a 10MP camera can act as a 2MP camera. Beware: the size at which images can be displayed or printed without jaggy pixelation becoming evident is much reduced, but of course the file size is also much smaller. What's the point in buying an expensive camera and then set it to behave like a cheaper model? Unless you are running out of storage space in the field and unable to swap memory cards or download images to a computer or tablet, it's advisable to leave the camera set to its largest picture size and its highest JPEG quality.

If your camera has a TIFF setting, the image files will be larger than JPEGs but they will be stored using a lossless form of compression that retains maximum image quality. RAW files are also large, but the storage formats are proprietary, set by the camera manufacturer. Special software is needed to convert RAW files into TIFFs or JPEGs that can be displayed on a computer screen or printed out. RAW is the storage format preferred by most professional photographers (and many keen amateurs), because adjustments to compensate for poor lighting etc can be made without losing picture quality. For most purposes, the highest quality JPEG setting is fine; it produces files with names of the form IMG1763.JPG and when you transfer the file to your computer you will probably want to change the name to something more informative.

The image manipulation software on your computer can also degrade picture quality if you use it with inappropriate settings. The format known as GIF (**G**raphics **I**nterchange **F**ormat) stores pictures in just 256 colours, for example. Compared with a low-compression JPEG file, the GIF file size is sometimes smaller; however, the reduced colour depth can have a devastating effect on image quality. Converting a GIF file back into a TIFF or a JPEG will not restore the lost quality; it is truly lost forever.

Sensor Size and Lens Quality

Many people are misled into believing that a camera with a higher pixel count will give a corresponding increase in picture quality. Apart from printing out pictures on poster-sized paper, to most people's eyes any increase above about 8MP is indiscernible – certainly on a computer screen. So why buy an expensive camera when a basic 8MP compact costs a tenth of the price? The answer is mainly to do with quality of the optics in the lens system and the size of the sensor that captures the digital image. The size of the sensor in a cheap camera is smaller than a fingernail. Compare that to a 35 x 24mm film frame and you can see how accurate the focussing must be to get a sharp image. A mid-range digital SLR (single lens reflex, where a tilting mirror allows focussing via the camera lens) such as a Canon 10D has a 22 x 15mm sensor – an area less than half that of its 35mm film equivalent but five times larger than the sensor in a cheap 8MB compact camera.

The relationship between sensor size and image quality is complex, but for a given pixel count the larger the sensor (and hence the larger the individual photo-sensitive cells) the better the image quality and the lower the noise level. It's exactly the same reason that professional photographers used large or medium format film cameras rather than tiny 110 cartridge film cameras. Cameras with large sensors can operate in low-light situations or when subjects are moving rapidly because they can be set to a 'fast film' equivalent such as ISO 3200; basic cameras with tiny sensors tend to produce 'noisy' (equivalent in film language to 'grainy') images when set above ISO 400. (For most purposes ISO 100 should give good results; use a higher setting only when necessary.) There is more to it than this. Digital SLRs use sensors that store full-frame picture data all at once, transferring it shortly afterwards to the memory card, whereas compact cameras transfer the data to the memory card as a stream of data in real time, because they have no actual shutter mechanism.

Cameras with small sensors require a lens with short focal length in order to obtain the same field of view as a cameras using a larger sensor or using 35mm film. A result of this is that compact digital cameras have a large depth of field. What this means is that when you focus on an object, anything else for quite some distance in front of or behind the focus of attention will also be sharply outlined. This is invaluable when you want not only that mushroom but also the surrounding habitat in sharp focus, but it's not so good when you want a sharp picture of the mushroom without background distractions, as getting a blurred background is virtually (or actually) impossible with some compacts.

As long as your camera has the facility to adjust manually the settings of the aperture (equivalent to dilating and contracting the pupil of a human eye) and shutter speed (how long the eye remains open), you can produce pictures with different depths of field to suit your purpose. Aperture settings are adjusted in steps, known as f-stops, each numerical step upwards halving the area of the aperture (yes, it just had to be a backwards scale!). Aperture settings typically range between f/1.4 and f/22, but in general only large lenses can accommodate the widest aperture settings.

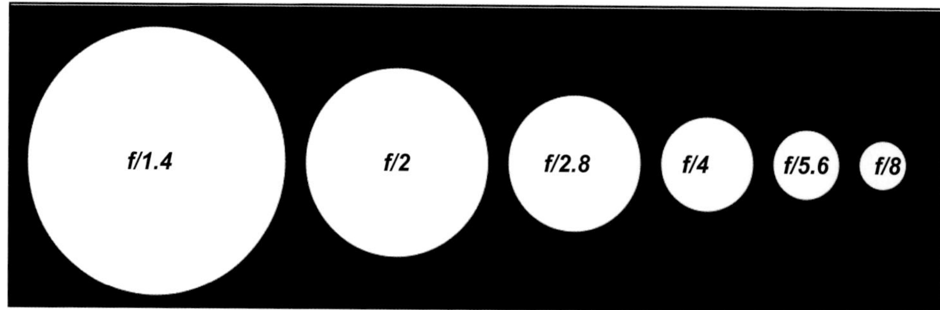

For example a lens of 50mm focal length (giving a field of view similar to that of the human eye), when set at *f/2* would have an aperture diameter of 25mm. Such a large iris would not fit in most compact cameras, but a digital SLR would accommodate it easily. At the other end of the scale, the same lens would have an iris diameter of little more than 2mm when set to *f/22*, and so to receive the same amount of total light (for the same exposure, in other words) the shutter would have to be open for more than 100 times as long.

In short, compared with a large aperture, a small aperture lets very little light through to the sensor, and so the camera has to be held still for a long time; however, the depth of field will be greater, with much more of the foreground and background in focus. In all but very dull conditions a large aperture setting may allow you to take pictures without using a tripod, but the depth of field will be limited. And one final reminder: for the same aperture setting, a compact camera with its tiny sensor always gives a greater depth of field than an SLR with a much larger sensor, but that alone does not guarantee a clear image.

14MB Compact Digital, ISO 160, Aperture f/4, exposure 1/250 sec

10MB Digital SLR, ISO400, Aperture f/3.2, exposure 1/1600 sec

Colour temperature and white balance

In the days of film photography, you would load your camera with either 'daylight balanced' film for shooting outdoors or 'tungsten balanced' film for shooting indoors under incandescent (but not fluorescent) lighting. Use daylight film indoors and the pictures came out with a yellow colour cast, just as indoor film produced a blue cast when used in outdoor light (daylight). Choosing the right film was termed using the correct 'temperature'.

With digital cameras you can set the white balance to suit whatever kind of light source is available, so that white objects really are stored as white rather than yellow or blue. There is generally an automatic setting that lets the camera decide what white balance setting to use, but it does this by guesswork based on the range of colours presented by a scene. There are usually other preset settings for sunlight, shade, flash and so on, but if your camera has a manual setting you can point the camera at a white card and an inbuilt program will work out the setting necessary to make white objects appear white.

Colour casts can always be removed afterwards using computer software such as Adobe Photoshop, of course, and for minor corrections the finished result can be excellent. Poorly balanced images can be improved substantially, but inevitably compromises are involved when large colour corrections have to be made. The closer the original image is to a perfect white balance the better any colour-corrected version will be.

Digital Zoom and Optical Zoom

Optical zoom on a compact digital camera works exactly the same way as a zoom lens on a digital SLR or a film camera, altering the focal length and the magnification as it is zoomed in and out. Provided the focus remains sharp throughout the zoom range, the image quality is unaffected. Unfortunately no zoom lens is perfect at all focal lengths, and particularly near minimum and maximum focal lengths a certain amount of 'softness' (slightly out of focus) is to be expected. In this respect you get no more than you pay for, and cheap cameras do not come complete with top-quality zoom lenses.

Digital zoom is quite different and it always degrades picture quality. All that the digital zoom feature does is to crop the image and then enlarge the portion remaining so that it fills the frame again. Don't bother with digital zoom: if necessary you can always achieve the same effect simply by cropping and resizing a picture using almost any kind of image editing software. To illustrate this point, here are two close-up pictures of my portable *Amanita ceramica*. They were both taken using the same compact digital camera.

Close-up of cap rim taken from 2 metres with x10 optical zoom. Fine details are quite clear.

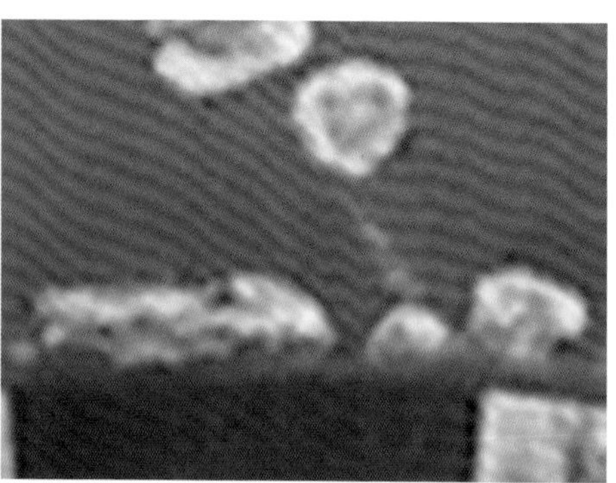

Close-up of cap rim with zero optical zoom and x10 digital zoom. The fine detail is lost.

Downsampling

Store your pictures safely at their original size. You can make smaller versions using image-processing software – for example to send copies via email to friends or to include in a Web page or a blog - but *never* resize your originals. Once downsized from say 3648 x 2736 pixels (10MP) to say 1024 x 768 pixels (0.8MP), if you later upscale an image to its original pixel dimensions it will appear blurred. Once the fine detail has been lost the picture can never be restored to its original higher definition.

One other control that you have on stored image files is to change the PPI, which stands for 'pixels per inch'. This is a feature of relevance only when you are going to print your pictures. At 360 PPI a 3648 x 2736 pixel image file would produce a picture 10" x 7.6" or 25cm x 19cm. At 72PPI the size when printed would be 125cm x 95cm – quite a large poster, but if you were to look at it closely it would appear blurred, with jaggy staircases where there should be straight edges. (Of course, posters are not usually intended for close-up viewing.) Printers also have a **D**PI setting, and that defines the number of dots per inch that they print. It's a measure of how finely spaced the individual droplets of ink or toner will be, and so you might think that a higher DPI would give a better result. To an extent it can, but printing an image file set at say 72PPI on a printer set to say 1440DPI would not produce a picture noticeably better than if the printer had been set to say 360DPI. In summary then, for a particular image file the PPI setting determines the picture size, while increasing the printer's DPI setting may improve the appearance of a printed picture but only up to a point, after which resolution is limited by the original image rather than the printer.

Camera-to-computer Interface

Images stored in a camera's memory card of your computer can be transferred to a computer in any of several ways including:

- **Cable Transfer**. By connecting a USB (Universal Serial Bus) cable between the camera and a USB 2.00 port on your computer, files can be transferred at up to 480megabits per second (60MB/s). Another cable system known as IEEE 1394 or Firewire works at much the same kind of speed.

- **Wireless transfer**. Many cameras now have a built in wireless facility, which can transfer files without the need for a cable connection between camera and computer. Typical transfer rates are (at the time of writing) slower than can be achieved by cable transfer, and so the choice is between speed and convenience.
- **Memory card reader**. Most computers can read at least one or two memory card types. All you have to do is unplug the card from your camera and plug it into the appropriate slot in the computer to transfer files across to your hard drive. Universal card readers accept many memory card types and connect to the computer via a USB socket. This can be a very convenient way of transferring files… or of leaving your memory card back at home tucked away in your computer's card slot and unavailable when you most need it.

Organising a fungi photo library

If like most people nowadays you use a digital camera, there are two fundamental options for storage. The first, which to my mind loses most of the benefits of digital photography, is to have prints made from your best pictures and store them in a traditional photo album. Fine as mementos they may be, but once you have wiped clean the camera's memory card you are pretty much stuck with that single printed copy. (Copies of digital prints are always inferior to the originals.)

Saving the pictures in digital form allows you to retrieve, resize, edit, make collages – even take prints for a photo album if you think your Auntie Elsie might like a copy. Whether stored in your computer or in an online photo library such as Flickr or Picasa Web Albums one big folder called My Fungi Pictures only works if you have a few dozen mushroom mugshots. When the number rises to hundreds, thousands, tens of thousands (and with fungi it can easily do so as there are more species out there than you could even count never mind photograph in one lifetime) you really do need an organised filing system.

As with any kind of storage system, think about how you will put the information in but even more how you will want to retrieve it. You will get sudden flashes of insight such as 'that weird bracket fungus I saw in the Hundred Acre Wood… or was in Thingum Forest? Anyway, it was last September… or was it the year before? Did you file it under *Unidentified Bracket Fungi*, or *Fungi Pictures 17th September 2010* (or *2011*), or *Thingum Forest*, or *Hundred Acre Wood*? My way is to make a DVD of all pictures from a foray. I mark it *Fungi, Hundred Acre Wood, 17th September 2011* (or whatever) and store it in my *in extremis* archive drawer somewhere secure and well away from the office where I keep my computer. I hope never to see that DVD again; if I do it's because something awful has happened. The same images are also transferred to my Fungi Filing System, which is stored on my computer's hard drive and backed up frequently onto an external drive.

Camera data

Inside each digital image is a set of metadata that is not part of the picture file; it records the date and time (assuming that you entered these into the setup when you bought the camera), the camera make and model, its settings (RAW, or JPEG with the compression settings), ISO setting (the equivalent of film speed), lens details etc. Modern digital cameras usually store metadata in EXIF format, which stands for **EX**changeable **I**mage **F**ile format. Some image-processing software can read this kind of information, but to edit it easily on a computer you will probably need special EXIF software. Other types of metadata allow you to insert descriptive information within a digital image file – for example a caption, keywords, location and so on. Two of the most commonly used metadata formats for image files are IPTC and XMP.

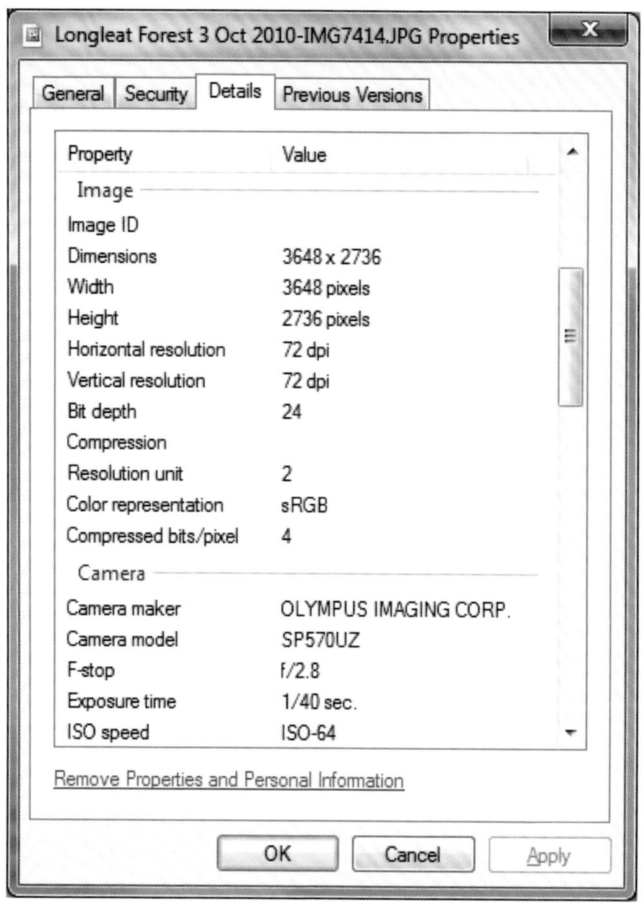

An image's basic metadata can be displayed and edited on a PC by right clicking on a file icon and selecting the 'Properties' option in the dialog box. Then select the 'Details' tab and scroll down to view the stored image information (see example, left).

An alternative solution is to build your own personal information into the file name. This may be fine for helping you to find a particular picture within your filing system, but someone else could copy the picture and alter its file name very easily. (Be aware also that some image processing software simply discards the metadata and stores only the image data.) Let's concentrate on being able to find the pictures that you want from among the many hundreds or thousands that you have stored on your computer.

Folder and File names

Giving a folder a long name is not a bad idea. In my storage system I include the scientific name, common name and family name of each species plus a unique numerical identifier. This way if I can't remember (or remember the spelling of) a scientific name for a species that has an accepted common name I can still search electronically. Synonyms can be a problem, of course, and one way to cope with this is to keep a list of common synonyms as a separate file that you can refer to if necessary. The synonyms listed in many field guides are helpful to a degree, but because there are a dozen or more out-of-date synonyms for most of the common fungi such lists cannot be made comprehensive without at least doubling the size of the books. (Field guides are for carrying in the field, and if you take two or three such tomes with you their weight will not go unnoticed!)

How many levels?

Despite the fact that ascomycetes greatly outnumber basidiomycetes, I have very few ascomycetes images that I need to file and lots more basidiomycetes. If your main interest is in macrofungi too, then you might decide to make your ascomycetes filing structure just as primitive as mine, with only species folders.

My Fungi Pictures – Folder Hierarchy		
Ascomycetes		
		Morchella esculenta (Morchellaceae)
		Morchella elata (Morchellaceae) etc
		Peziza badia (Pezizaceae)
		Species folder 4, etc
Basidiomycetes		
	Amanita	
		Amanita fulva (Amanitaceae)
		Amanita muscaria (Amanitaceae)
		Amanita phalloides (Amanitaceae)
		Amanita spissa (Amanitaceae), etc
	Genus folder 2	
		Species folder 1
		Species folder 2
		Species folder 3, etc
	Genus folder 3	
		Species folder 1, etc

Including the mycological family name within each species folder name is of course optional, but it does enable you to search for all Pluteaceae, all Strophariaceae etc should you need to. Individual basidiomycetes pictures are stored within the Species Folders, and in the filenames you can include the original image number allocated by the camera, the date and time, and the location as well as the species name.

Folder name	**File names (examples)**
Amanita muscaria (Amanitaceae) - Fly Agaric	2186 Amanita muscaria New Forest 12 Aug 2004.jpg 3187 Amanita muscaria New Forest 12 Aug 2004.jpg 5332 Amanita phalloides Algarve 17 Jul 2008.jpg
Boletus edulis (Boletaceae) - Penny Bun or Cep	1426 Boletus edulis Cenarth Woods 28 Jul 1998.jpg 2867 Boletus edulis Sweden 23 Aug 2002.jpg 7156 Boletus edulis Longleate Forest 3 Sep 2010.jpg
Coprinus comatus (Agaricaceae) - Shaggy Inkcap	4726 Coprinus comatus Newtown 12 Aug 2007.jpg 4728 Coprinus comatus Newtown 12 Aug 2007.jpg
Coprinellus disseminatus (Psathyrellaceae) - Fairy Inkcap	Etc
Coprinellus micaceus (Psathyrellaceae) – Glistening Inkcap	Etc
Coprinopsis picacea (Psathyrellaceae) - Magpie Inkcap	Etc

Parting Shots

Before leaving the subject of photographing fungi there are a couple of practical aspects worth mentioning. First, a word about using flash – or better still not using it. Unless you are really in the dark, it's nearly always possible to take pictures using natural light. The built-in flash on cameras points straight ahead, and this invariably produces rather flat-looking pictures. At short range the light intensity is far from even, and all too often at the bottom of the picture there is an oval shadow cast by the top of the lens, when shooting in landscape, or at one side when using the camera in portrait style. Of course, if you have a remote flash then you have the option of front, back or side lighting the main subject. Side lighting can make an object appear to stand out from its background.

I began this section with a plea for using a tripod to avoid the inevitable blurring associated with hand-held images. To get down really low, you will need a botanical tripod. I don't own such a gadget, and in any case who wants to carry more than one tripod with them on their rambles? A simple answer is to modify an ordinary tripod so that the legs can splay out widely. Then cut the central stem short so that the camera can be lowered almost to ground level. Here's one I made earlier:

A cut-down central stem makes this tripod ideal for photographing grassland and forest-floor fungi – not to mention any that might spring up overnight in the lounge carpet!

So that I can continue to use it for general photography, I have made a second central stem for my tripod. The spare stem is lightweight and takes up very little space in a backpack. This means that I don't have to stoop while waiting for a bird to turn its head or for the wind to relent so that I can take a picture of a tall, spindly plant and actually have its flower in the frame.

A bean bag is a practical alternative to a tripod when photographing grassland or forest-floor fungi. Neither option – tripod or bean bag – solves the problem entirely, because it is virtually impossible to press a camera shutter without causing the camera to move slightly - yes, even on the sturdiest of tripods.

An infrared remote shutter control is one answer, but these things can be quite expensive and not all cameras have such optional accessories available.

But fear not; all is not lost. Use the camera's timer, so that the picture is taken a few seconds after you press the shutter; this way all the camera movement is over before the image capture process even begins. It works equally well whether your camera is mounted on a tripod or perched on a bean bag.

One other special item needed for photographing fungi is a pair of carpet-layer's kneepads. Gardening knee pads are almost as good unless the habitat is dominated by plants with extremely long thorns, in which case stick with carpet-layer's kneepads. A plastic sheet for lying down in wet grass or mud is a luxury worth considering, too. And finally, a fold-up photography reflector/diffuser with one side silver for reflecting light onto the shaded side of your subject and the other white for a softer fill-in when required. That's it!

Making a start with microscopy

When you can't identify a fungus in the field you might want to bring a specimen home for more detailed investigation. Microscopy is the way to look at fine details, and the good news is that you can do so indoors, when the time suits you. I won't pretend that getting to grips with fungus microscopy is easy, but it is fascinating and can be very rewarding. Here are a few tips to help you get started.

Toy microscopes are great for introducing youngsters to the intricacies of animal and plant structures, but for mycology you really do need a good microscope. That's because some of the fine structures of fungi are close to the limit of what can be resolved using visible light. (X-ray wavelengths are much shorter than those of light waves, and hence a lot more detail can be observed using x-ray microscopy, but don't even contemplate remortgaging your house to buy a bottom-of-the-range x-ray microscope.) Some very usable microscopes are now available from around £150, while £500 will buy you a very good compound microscope built to last a lifetime.

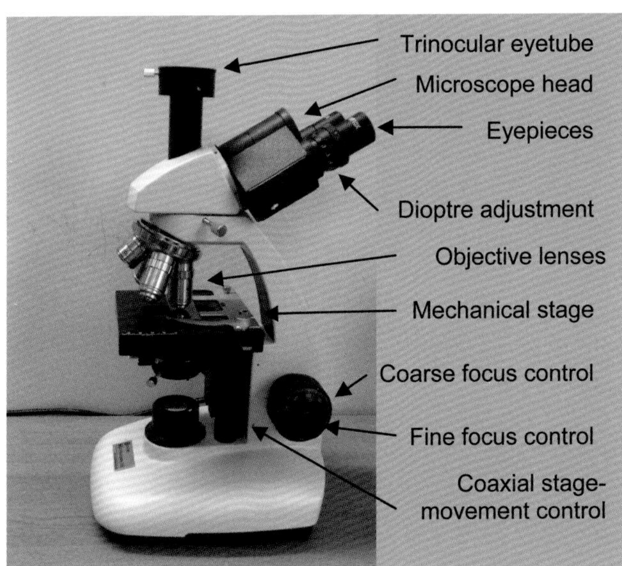

To study fungal spores, basidia, cystidia and other tiny features you will need a microscope capable of at least x400 magnification. Ideally, go for a microscope with a maximum of x1000, but to obtain reasonably clear images at such high magnification it should have an oil immersion lens.

Dimensions, shapes and ornamentation (warts, grooves etc) of spores are key identifying features for most kinds of basidiomycete fungi and for many of the ascomycetes. Spore shapes have their own 'jargon' names, including these:

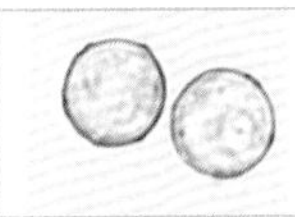		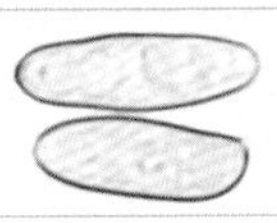		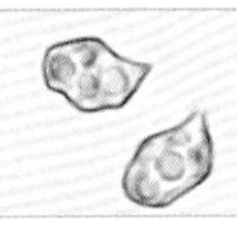	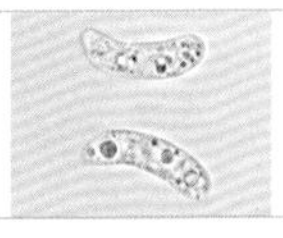
Globose	**Ellipsoidal**	**Fusiform**	**Stellate**	**Polygonal**	**Allantoid**

Spore vary considerably in other respects, too. Features to look out for include:

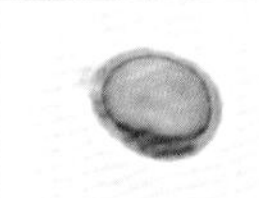				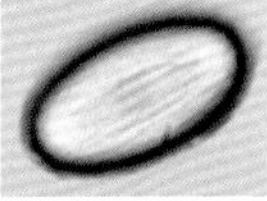	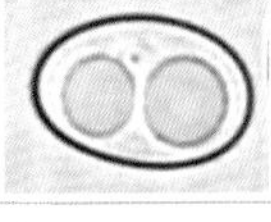
Thick walls	**Fine warts**	**Coarse warts**	**Reticulum**	**Grooves**	**Oil drops**

So that you can measure the dimensions of things that you are looking at you will need a calibrated scale that is visible with the image. It is possible to obtain an eyepiece that has an ocular micrometer scale, but because you can use a range of objective lenses with different amounts of magnification (x10, x40, x60 and x100 for example) the scale cannot be used directly to take measurements. You will have to recalibrate for each of your objective lenses, and to do that you need to view something of a known size. A 'stage micrometer' is ideal for this purpose; this is a glass slide with finely engraved lines spaced for example 10µm (ten microns) apart. Stage micrometer slides are usually made with glass that is rather thicker than ordinary microscope slides, so before using this kind of slide you will need to move the microscope stage further away from the objective lens to avoid risking damage to the lens.

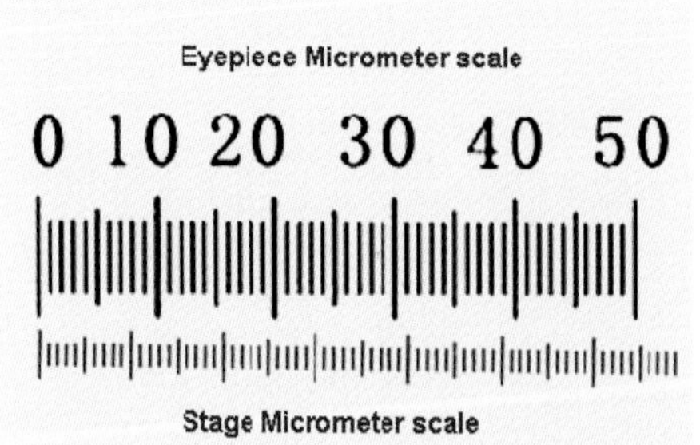

When focussed on the stage micrometer slide you will see its graticule lines as well as the lines of the ocular micrometer – two scales, which you should position one above the other. Align the two zero lines as shown on the left. Now look along the scales until you find a point where lines on the two scales are aligned vertically. In this example the major divisions on the stage micrometer represent steps of 100µm, with subdivisions of 10µm.

You will see here that 43 on the eyepiece micrometer scale aligns precisely with 550µm on the stage micrometer scale, and 550 divided by 43 gives 12.8µm per small division on the eyepiece scale. How does that help? Well, suppose the feature you want to measure spans 17 divisions on the eyepiece scale, then its actual size is 17 x 12.8 = 217.6µm. Keep a note of the scaling factor for each of your objective lenses, as they will all be different.

As with everything to do with microscopy, the calibration process gets easier with practice. If you find the instructions provided with your microscope and lens set confusing (or if you have picked up a second-hand bargain without a handbook), almost certainly someone in your local fungus group will be willing to help you set up and calibrate your system.

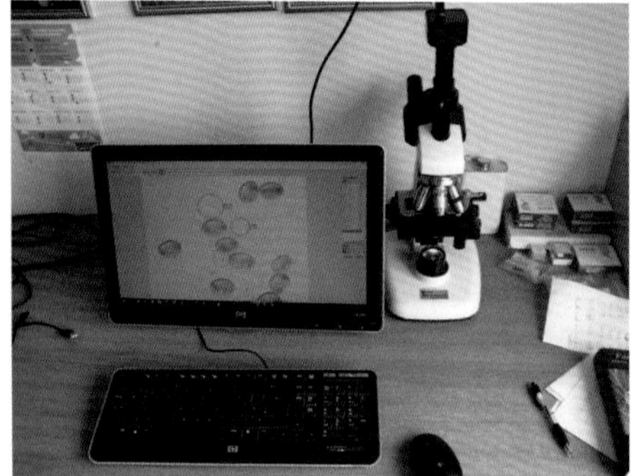

Connecting a microscope to a computer
To view on a computer screen and store as a digital image what you see via your microscope, you will need an image capture device such as a digital camera or a webcam with an adaptor to attach it to an eyepiece tube of the microscope. (A trinocular microscope allows you to use a camera even while looking through the eyepieces; this can be a useful facility but it is far from essential.) The camera connects to the computer via a USB cable.

A cheap webcam adapted via a cardboard tube held in place with tape or glue can work reasonably well, but for best results the camera and microscope need to be solidly attached so that vibration doesn't degrade the captured image. Low-cost webcams capable of one megapixel image resolution or better are available and are ideal for most purposes.

Once you have clipped a slide to the stage of your microscope, features of interest are centred in the field of view by adjusting a pair of control knobs. One of the knobs moves the mechanical stage to the left or to the right while the other moves the stage towards or away from you. Two other crucial control knobs are the coarse and fine focus controls. Finding a tiny specimen is best done initially via a lens of low magnification – say x10; then switch to a more powerful lens and readjust the fine focus to obtain a sharp image. There is also a control knob for the brightness of the illumination, which is usually via a filament lamp or a light-emitting diode most often sited directly below the objective lens, providing what is termed brightfield illumination. Darkfield illumination is also from below the specimen but at an angle so that direct light doesn't enter the objective; this requires either a special darkfield condenser or, for low magnification, a black stop inserted in the light path; it enhances contrast and provides a bright image against a dark background. For most purposes, fungi can be studied and their microscopic characters measured quite adequately using a brightfield setup.

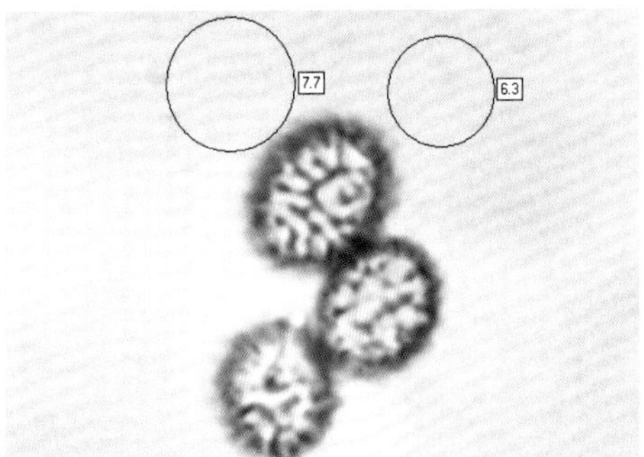

Lactarius **spores using brightfield illumination**

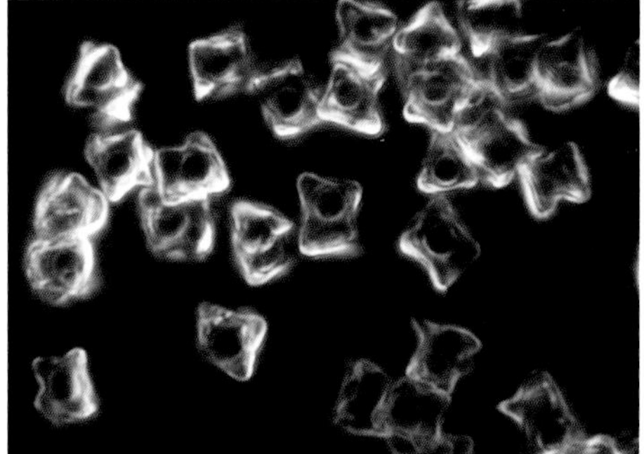

Entoloma **spores using darkfield illumination**

Calibration of your microscope is made much more straightforward if you use one of the image capturing programs designed for mycology. My favourite is MycoCam4, designed by Richard Shotbolt and available free of chanre via his website http://www.shotbolt.com . You still need a specimen of known dimensions (such as a stage micrometer slide, but once you have calibrated your system for each of your objective lenses in turn, MycoCam remembers the scaling and all your on-screen results are recorded actual size: the computer does the sums for you and saves the results for later recall when required.

Right: MycoCam4 being used to calibrate a x60 objective lens. You simply hold the left mouse button and drag a circle so that it exactly spans two major divisions on a stage micrometer slide. In this instance the major divisions are 100µm apart. Type 100 into a 'set scale' box, and then save this as a lens file with a name that you can call up again whenever you want to use that particular lens.

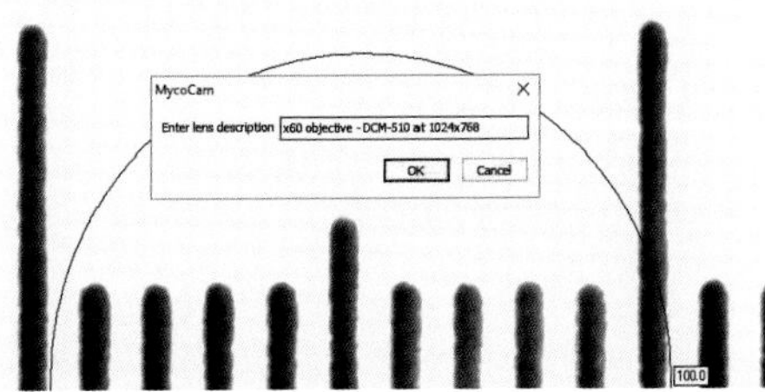

Other essential equipment
Once your microscope is set up and calibrated, all you need are slides, cover slips, a scalpel with many spare blades (some people prefer to use razor blades) and a small selection of chemicals.

Staining and testing chemicals

The fine structure of some spores and many of the other tiny parts of fungi that you will want to look at under the microscope are often almost completely translucent. They can only be seen clearly when they have been stained. Many fungi produce spores that change colour when in contact with certain chemicals, referred to as reagents (because of the reaction when spores come in contact with them). Here are some of the chemicals, stains and other reagents most commonly used in mycological microscopy:

Distilled water. (You *know* the chemical formula!) If you want to view tiny subjects in their natural colouring, water is the ideal wetting agent. Whenever possible it is best to measure spores in water initially, because their dimensions can be altered by some of the staining chemicals commonly used by mycologists. Tap water contains all sorts of additives and impurities that could limit the lifetime of a slide, and rainwater is acidic and equally problematic, but distilled water (sometimes labelled 'demineralised water') is inexpensive and readily available.

Wetting agent. You might need to add a drop of photographic wetting agent to avoid image distortion due to tiny air bubbles attached to spores or other subject material – washing-up liquid works okay! Adding about 10% of glycerine will ensure that slides last a lot longer before drying out.

Ammonia (NH_3). This useful but potentially dangerous chemical gives off an extremely pungent vapour, and so the bottle needs to be securely capped at all times except during use. (Household ammonia from any hardware shop is fine.) As well as a reagent causing colour change in some kinds of fungi, ammonia is a component of certain other reagents. Pure ammonia is a gas at normal room temperature, and for mycological use a 10% solution in distilled water is the normal concentration. That is strong, and if it gets into eyes it will cause serious damage.

Ferrous sulphate ($FeSO_4$). Many fungi fanciers and mycologists carry in their field kit a crystal of ferrous sulphate, known colloquially as Iron Salts, for rubbing on fungi (brittlegills in particular) to check for a colour reaction. Don't go to the expense of buying pharmaceutical grade crystals; the stuff sold in garden centres as a moss killer and for lowering the alkalinity of soil is dirt cheap (oops!) and works just as well.

Potassium hydroxide (KOH). This is used both as a mounting medium (usually together with a staining chemical) and as a reagent, either in the field or back at base. Cap or gill surfaces of some mushrooms change colour dramatically when contacted by KOH; they can turn yellow, red, magenta, olive or black, for example, depending on the species. So when you make a microscope slide using KOH not only is it preserved against decay but you may also elicit a diagnostic colour reaction that can sometimes contribute as much to the identification process as do the size and shape data obtained via the microscope.

PlaqSearch. Designed to highlight dental plaque, this good general-purpose stain turns chrysocystidia (yellowish cells found in the gills of some mushrooms) deep blue.

A drop of KOH on the cap of an Ugly Milkcap *Lactarius turpis*...

...and the dingy olive-brown cap cuticle instantly turns bright purple.

Melzer's Reagent. This cocktail of chemicals is difficult to obtain because one of the crucial components is the potentially dangerous substance chloral hydrate (a date-rape drug). The other components are easy to acquire – iodine crystals, potassium iodide and distilled water. Iodine reacts with starchy substances to produce an intense blue-black colour, and fungal spores that contain starch are referred to a 'amyloid'. Some specialist suppliers are able to provide this reagent for bona fide mycologists. (If you join a fungus group in the UK, you may be able to obtain Melzer's Reagent via the Fungus Conservation Trust). Spores or other features of many fungi species may undergo diagnostic colour changes when stained with Melzer's Reagent. Spores are termed:

- **Amyloid** if they turn a blue-black colour.
- **Dextrinoid** if they turn a reddish-brown colour.
- **Inamyloid (or non-amyloid)** if they merely turn yellowish or do not change at all.

These terms are used in field guides that list the chemical test characters for each species.

Other stains

The main reasons for using stains when making microscope slides are to enhance the contrast in a microscopic image and to highlight particular tissue structures. Often stains are used in combination with other chemicals that help to prevent decay or drying out of the subject material. Examples of staining agents include:

- Congo Red - an excellent general-purpose stain for looking at the fine details of hyphal structures. It is supplied as powder and is best dissolved in a 10% ammonia solution.
- Safranin - another stain that turns cell nuclei red.
- Lactophenol Cotton Blue (often referred to as simply Cotton Blue) – this stains chitin, highlighting such structures as spore ornamentation in ascomycetes.

Another parting shot - well, this one is more to do with avoiding an early departure. The chemicals mentioned above include some seriously caustic, acidic and toxic substances, and so they really must be stored where children can't get hold of them. The fumes from ammonia, for example, can burn eyes – in fact some tests merely require ammonia vapour to pass over fungal tissue to invoke a colour change. A secure safe could save a life. I have one bolted to the wall next to the bench where I keep my microscope, and it is ideal for storing chemicals, razorblades, glass slides etc.

Let's now move on to using a microscope for examining and measuring features of fungi.

Microscopy of spores

The easiest slides to make are of spores. All you have to do is to place a mature mushroom, bracket, cup fungus or whatever fertile side downwards on a microscope slide and wait a while for ripe spores to drop. Unlike when trying to make a nice spore print you don't even need to cover everything over, although I generally do so just as a reminder that there is a sharp-edged piece of glass underneath. Because you want to be able to see separate spores rather than determine the colour of spores when piled layer upon layer, you don't need a dense print and so you mustn't leave it too long.

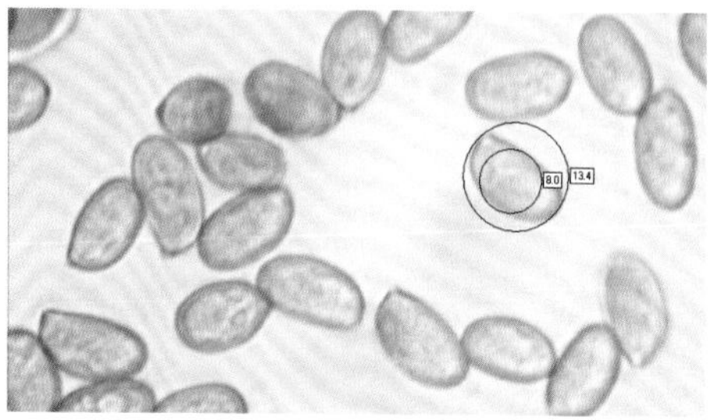

Spores of Stubble Rosegill *Volvopluteus gloiocephalus* stained with Congo Red

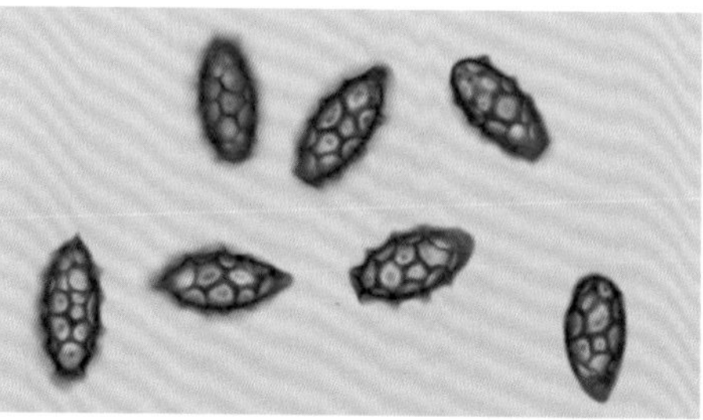

Spores of Orange Peel Fungus *Aleuria aurantia* stained with Cotton Blue

Once you have some spore dust on the slide, use a scalpel to scrape it into a tiny pile. Add a drop of stain and place a cover slip on top. Note that cover slips come in different thicknesses, and while most biological microscope objective lenses will give crisp images with No. 1 cover slips (0.13 to 0.16mm thick), should you ever decide to lash out on a x200 oil objective you may find that it requires No.0 cover slips (0.085 to 0.13.. thick). What will definitely degrade the quality (and at high magnification make focussing impossible) is if you don't notice that you have two cover slips stuck together. It can happen all to easily!

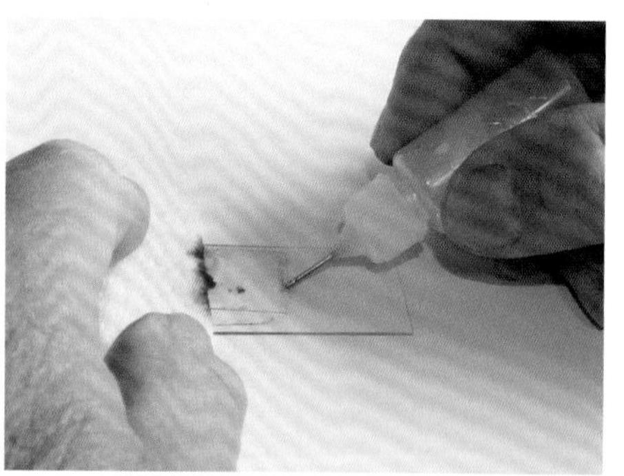

By capillary action water is drawn beneath the cover slip and washes out excess stain.

After a few minutes wash out unused stain by placing a drop of water on the edge of the cover slip while holding a piece of tissue against the opposite edge to draw out and soak up the excess. Repeat if necessary so as to maximise spore edge contrast.

For *Russula* and *Lactarius* fungi Melzer's reagent is a good first choice, as it stains the warts and ridges with which such spores are ornamented. As well as improving contrast, Melzer's can help with identification: hold the slide up to the light and you will see whether the spores are strongly amyloid or dextrinoid.

If there is only a weak reaction to Melzer's reagent, the colour change should still be visible via the microscope. Similarly, when examining asci – the spore-bearing structures within ascomycetes such as cup and flask fungi - knowing whether the tips of the asci turn blue in Melzer's is a test that can help determine species identification.

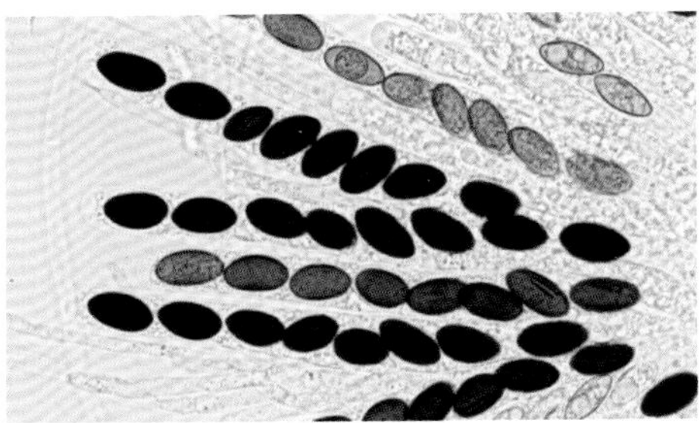

Asci and spores of Nail Fungus *Poronia punctata*, a rare ascomycete that grows on pony dung. The sterile structures between the asci are known as paraphyses, and without a suitable stain they are difficult to see.

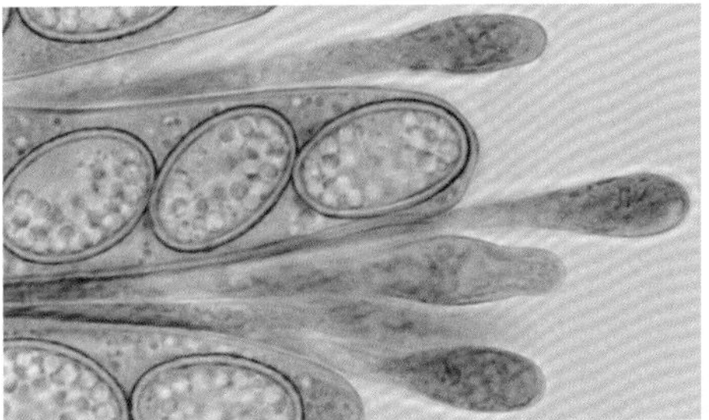

Spores, asci and paraphyses of the cup fungus *Scutellinia subhirtella* are brightly coloured. The dimensions and shapes of paraphyses are often crucial in separating similar ascomycete fungi species.

Basidiomycetes: examining the basidia and cystidia

When studying basidiomycetes under a microscope you are not limited to spore size, shape and ornamentation; you can also examine the basidia and several kinds of cystidia - hyphal cells that stand out from various surfaces. Depending on where they occur, cystidia are given different names. Pleurocystidia occur on gill faces, cheilocystidia are those on the gill edges, pileocystidia occur on the cap surface, and caulocystidia are found on the stem of the mushroom. The sizes and shapes of cystidia in these locations may be different, and these differences can help you to, er... differentiate between species. In each instance you need to make a slide containing a tiny piece of gill, cap or stem material.

Making slides from very thin slices of fungal tissue is difficult, and initially you can expect more failures than successes. Having cut off a thin sliver of material place just the tiniest piece of it on a slide, add a drop of stain and then a cover slip, applying slight pressure to flatten the section. Be gentle: cover slips are little more than one tenth of a millimetre in thickness, and they break very easily. After a minute or so wash out any excess stain; you are now ready to examine microscopically the basidia and/or any cystidia.

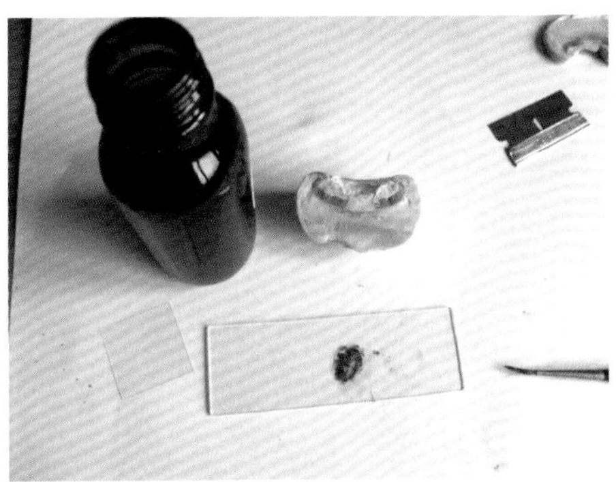

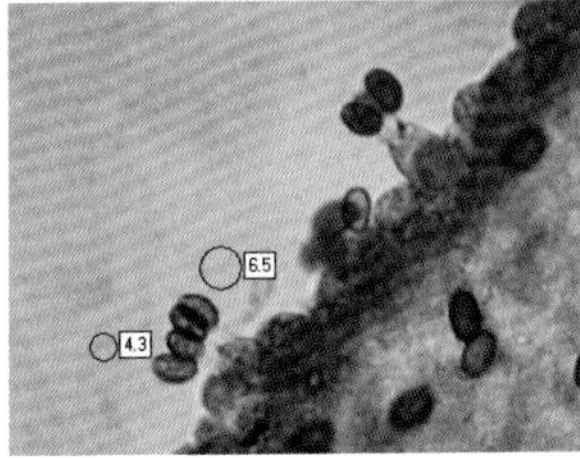

Four-spored clavate basidia on gills of Pale Brittlestem *Psathyrella candolleana*

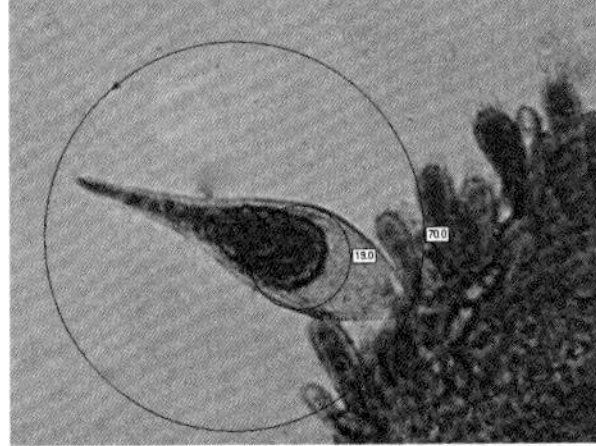

A cheilocystidium of the Cucumber Cap mushroom *Macrocystidia cucumis*.

The Deer Shield *Pluteus cervinus* has horned cystidia on gill edges and gill faces.

Hyphal structures of fruitbodies

Fungi can vary markedly in the structure of hyphae within their fruitbodies, and examining these structures can help with identification. For example the fruitbodies of basidiomycete fungi always contain generative hyphae, but they may also contain skeletal hyphae and binding hyphae. Generative hyphae are branched and usually thin walled with frequent septa (dividing walls); often they have clamp connections. Skeletal hyphae are generally long, branched, thick walled, and usually have very few or no septa (and no clamp connections). Binding hyphae are thick-walled and branch repeatedly, with outlines like deciduous trees in winter.

Hyphal structure (HS in field guides) is particularly important when studying polypores, which may be monomitic (consisting only of generative hyphae), dimitic (containing generative and skeletal hyphae) or trimitic (containing all three types). Cap surface structure can also help reveal a mushroom's identity and is determined by examining a tiny piece of the 'scalp', or pileipellis. For example a pileipellis consisting of hyphae that run parallel to the cap surface is termed a cutis, while one in which the outermost hyphae emerge more or less perpendicular to the cap surface is termed a trichoderm (hairy skin!)

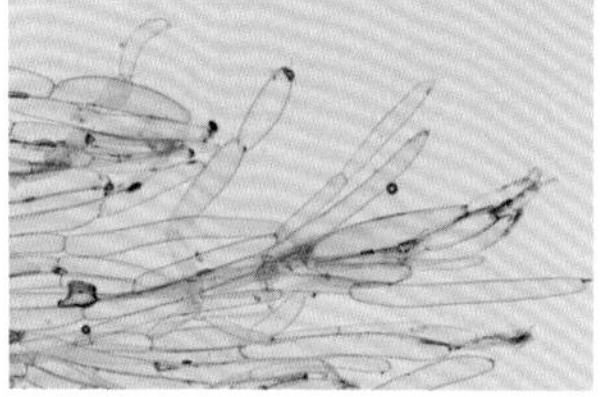

Septate hyphae in the cap of the Hare's-foot Inkcap *Coprinopsis lagopus*

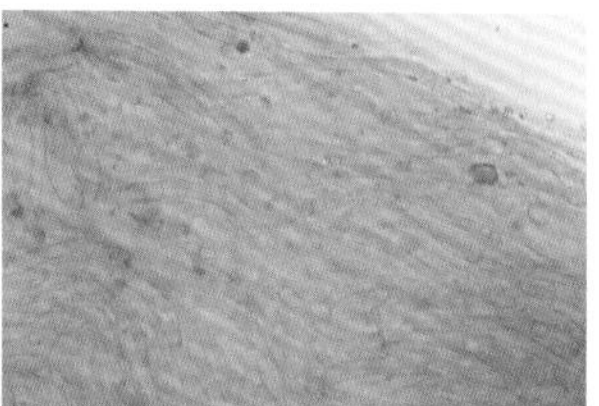

In *Arrhenia onisca* the cap hyphae run parallel to the cap surface, forming a cutis.

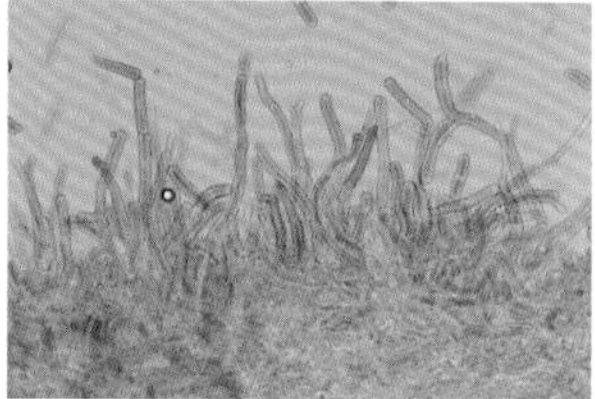

Trichoderm hyphal structure of the pileipellis of *Leccinum cyaneobasileucum*

Searching for clamp connections – the problem of proving a negative

In 1887 American scientists Albert Michelson and Edward Morley devised an experiment to measure the drift speed of the 'luminiferous aether' – an invisible substance via which light waves were assumed to travel. Within the limits of their measuring system, they found that light travelled at the same speed both against and across the direction of drift, concluding that there was no drift. From this 'failure' they further concluded that there was no aether.

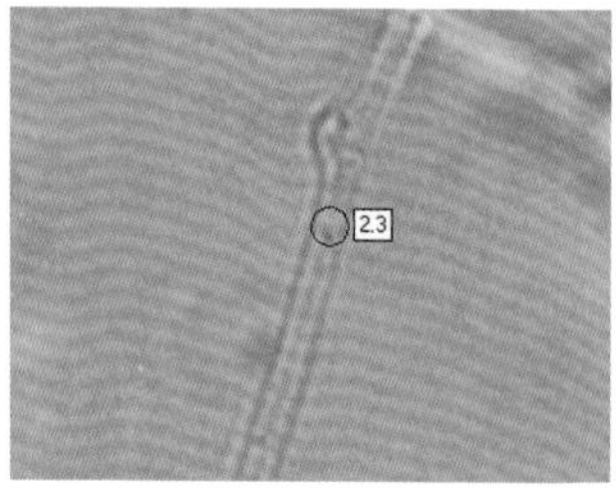

Successfully searching for clamp connections (left) among the hyphae in a fungus squash is very easy when there are plenty of clamps present; however, proving a negative can take forever. When your key or field guide says 'clamps absent' how long should you search before concluding that your specimen has no clamps? There is no right answer, but after searching for a few minutes you, like me, may begin to care a lot less about clamps and decide to move on and look for something else.

Image stacking

If you have ever tried to take a photograph of spores or other pieces of fungal tissue under a microscope, you will know how difficult it is to get everything in focus. You get one part sharp and the rest is blurred. The problem is caused by the very limited depth of field available at high magnification. Specialist but inexpensive software can come to your rescue. You take several images focussing at different depths into the tissue sample, and the software constructs a picture using the in-focus parts of your various images. Remarkably good results can be obtained using the basic image-stacking facility built in to MycoCam4; however, programs using more advanced mathematical techniques are also available. One such example is CombineZP, which can even correct for any slight movements of the specimen between one frame and another before creating a composite image with much sharper focus than any of the original frames.

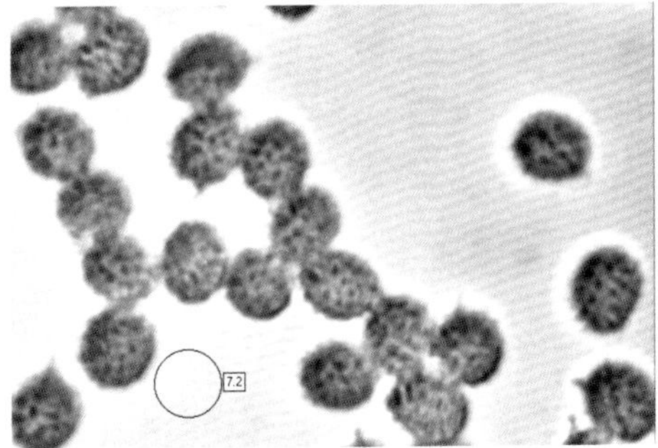

***Russula* spores, without image stacking**

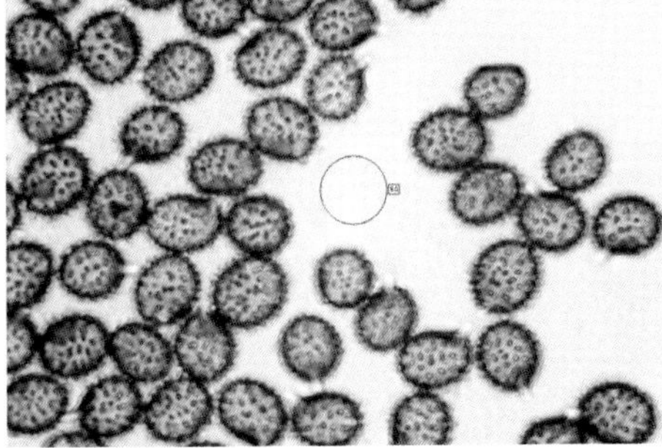

***Russula* spores, 5-frame stacked image**

When photographing tiny fungi, slime moulds, insects etc image stacking can help achieve a good depth of field. I use a x4 objective lens from my microscope attached via a connecting tube (100mm in length to suit the microscope lens) to a digital SLR camera body. The camera has a 'live view' facility, and a set of images is transferred to a computer. The lens is moved back and forth via a milling slide, which allows very fine adjustment between frames in the stack.

Simple setup for stacked macro photography

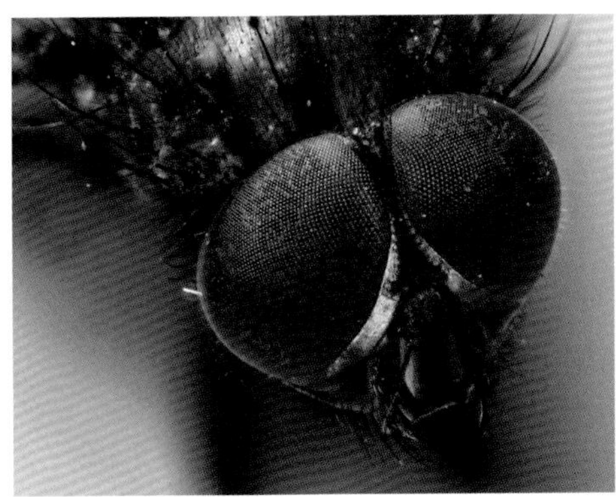

A stacked image produced via this setup

Microscopy is a complex subject and not something that everyone interested in fungi wants to get involved in; however, only a minority of species can be identified from their macroscopic characters alone, so for serious study of this subject becoming competent with a microscope is essential. For much more information on this matter there are specialist texts, and for help in choosing and setting up a microscope the websites of respected suppliers such a Brunel Microscopes are a good starting point. It's usually possible to arrange a visit to discuss your precise needs and to try out a few alternatives.

Fungi as Food for the Future

When gathering wild mushrooms, it's nice to save some for special occasions at times when there may be no opportunity to pick fresh mushrooms. When stored, mushrooms go off very quickly unless they are first preserved in some way.

Chanterelles and Trumpet Chanterelles (also known as Yellowlegs) cleaned, dried on paper kitchen towelling, and ready for use or for preserving by drying or freezing

However you intend preserving your mushrooms, the first thing to do is to clean them. In the field you may have removed as much earth and other debris and you could, but it's a sad truth that a few grains of grit can ruin an otherwise wonderful mushroom meal, and so thorough cleaning is a crucial step towards culinary excellence.

Mushrooms absorb water almost as well as blotting paper does, and if you have dry, perfectly clean mushrooms why wash them? The trouble is that rarely do we find grit-free fungi in the wild. Sometimes a soft brush will remove all traces of soil and other debris, but if it won't then I suggest you ignore all those exhortations never to wash mushrooms. If like me you don't want to eat mushrooms with bits of dead leaves stuck to their caps and grit and gremlins between their gills, washing can get rid of those aliens. When you get down to the nitty gritty, just do it. (In any case, if you gather fungi on a rainy day there is no difference whatsoever in the water content before and after washing.) Reconstituted dried mushrooms are no different from washed fresh ones in terms of water content.

After washing the mushrooms, dry off any surplus water using paper kitchen towel.

Fresh mushrooms don't stay fresh for very long, and mouldy mushrooms are not very appetising. Fortunately, there are ways of preserving fungi for future use, and the two easiest and most popular of these are drying and freezing. Most kinds of mushrooms taste just as good (and sometimes even better) when reconstituted after drying; others are better stored frozen. Here are brief details of each of these methods:

Drying

Like us, mushrooms are mainly water; unlike us, by removing all of the water you can prevent them from decaying. Drying works well for morels, boletes, blewits and oysters. (Ceps are widely considered to improve in flavour after drying and rehydration.) Any edible mushroom that is preserved in dried form will be at least reasonably good to eat once rehydrated and cooked well. (The 'well' bit is the crux of matter, as I shall explain later.)

Thick-fleshed mushrooms need to be cut into slices about 0.5 to 1cm thick. Thin-fleshed fungi can be dried whole once you have evicted any bugs that were using them as lodgings. There are several options for the drying process itself. You can for example.

1. Use a needle and strong cotton thread to make a string of mushrooms that you can hang up in an airing cupboard or in a warm, well-ventilated room – in direct sunlight is fine - until they are crisp and dry.
2. Spread them on a wire screen over a radiator, turning them periodically until dry.
3. Lay them on a tray lined with paper kitchen towel in a lukewarm, fan-assisted oven, leaving the door ajar to let the water vapour escape. Although it is very effective, this must be the worst method environmentally and economically, but in late autumn it may be the only practical option. A word of warning: if the oven is anything more than just warm the mushrooms can become extremely hard and almost impossible to rehydrate.

Mushrooms picked on a wet day, or those that had to be washed, will contain more moisture and so they will take a bit longer to dry. When the mushrooms are completely dry, store them in airtight jars. It's a good idea to label the jars right away. It's a funny thing, but no matter how good you are at identifying fungi in the wild, apart from Morels and Chanterelles once they are sliced and dried they all tend to look much the same.

Because high temperatures are not involved, any microscopic bugs left on the fungi will not necessarily be killed during the drying process. If you are at all worried about this possibility you can fix the little perrishers by placing your dried mushrooms in tightly-sealed containers and treating them to an overnight trip to -20°C in your deep freeze.

Morels are ideal candidates for preserving. They fruit in springtime and make the most wonderful sauces for barbecued steak on a warm summer evening. It's almost impossible to tell reconstituted dried morels from a fresh ones without referring to a calendar.

Reconstituting dried mushrooms when you are ready to use them is very straightforward. If you have not washed and prepared the dried mushrooms yourself, it is important to clean them as part of the reconstituting process.

Place the dried mushrooms in a bowl and cover them with boiling water. After about ten minutes stir thoroughly to dislodge any gritty debris. Remove the mushrooms with a slotted spoon and allow the soaking water to settle so that any grit particles sink to the bottom. If you intend making a risotto or a sauce dish from the mushrooms, do use the water as stock. Gently pour most of the water into a jug, discarding just the gritty dregs at the bottom of the bowl. You can use reconstituted mushrooms in any menu in exactly the same way and in the quantities specified in the recipe for fresh mushrooms.

Freezing

The first stage in this process involves *raising* the temperature rather than lowering it. When they are raw, most mushrooms do not freeze well (or if they do they cannot be kept for very long without deterioration), and so some form of cooking before freezing is generally necessary. Here's one way, and my Sue says it is definitely the best. I have checked out this claim very carefully and repeatedly – well, somebody had to do it – and I can confirm that it is entirely justified. This method is very good with Chanterelles. It works okay with Ceps, too, although the flavour is not intensified as it is when they are dried.

Leave any small mushrooms whole, but slice the larger ones. Then sauté the mushrooms in olive oil or butter and season with black pepper. Cool the resulting somewhat condensed mushroomy sauce, divide it into small portions and pack each into a separate (labelled!) freezer bag or plastic container. Stored in a deep freeze, they will keep for months... but only if you have the willpower to resist temptation.

Making a meal of it

In the section that follows, the culinary competence on which the mushroom meals depend is in no way my own; I am reliant on one of the world's unsung catering queens, my wife Sue. My only contribution, apart from extensive testing of each of the dishes, are these four pieces of important advice:

1. Most kinds of mushrooms can cause tummy upsets unless they are properly cooked, and some contain toxins that are only destroyed during the cooking process. (Those white button mushrooms from the supermarket are exceptions that prove the rule.)
2. Just as nuts, gluten and so on are wholesome foods for most people but potentially disastrous for a minority, so also with fungi. You may have eaten button mushrooms for decades with no adverse reaction, but when trying a new species it is still advisable to start with a small portion to make sure that you don't have an allergy to or intolerance of that particular mushroom.
3. Fungi whose mycelia live for many years can accumulate heavy metals and other toxins – just as slow-growing fish can. Eat wild mushroom meals as special treats now and then, as you would sea bass for example, and they are a valuable part of a balanced diet. Seven mushroom meals per week would be an *unbalanced* diet.
4. Any plants or fungi growing beside busy roads are likely to be contaminated by the exhaust fumes from vehicles as well as tyre fragments and other debris thrown onto verges during wet weather. Roadside fungi are only for looking at.

The Magnificent Seven

Thumb through a mushroom field guide, especially one of the many written by authors who live in eastern European countries, and you may be surprised at just how many 'edible' species there are - quite the majority, in fact. Having tried a lot of the recommended species – mushrooms, bracket fungi and puffballs – I have never had any problems with tummy upsets. Unless we are starving, we don't eat things just because they do not make us ill; we want to enjoy our food. It's a luxury not available to everyone, I know, but if you have a choice why settle for second best? If you gather your own wild fungi then the choice really is yours. Of course, taste is a matter of opinion, and in my opinion the following seven species – I call them The Magnificent Seven – make the best mushroom meals in the whole universe. At least they do when my Sue cooks them, and so I will end by extolling the virtues of The Magnificent Seven:

1. Wood Hedgehogs
2. Chanterelles
3. Parasol Mushrooms
4. Ceps
5. Field Mushrooms
6. Trumpet Chanterelles
7. Morels

What now follows are Sue's recipes and cooking tips for seven supper meals that you can make from one or more of these magnificent mushrooms.

Hedgehogs on Toast

Don't be nervous about trying this recipe. We are not talking about those spiky discs that were once so common on motorways when small snuffling and shambling nocturnal mammals (flatly) refused to budge and were wiped out by their natural predators, Ford Escorts and their allies. A much less grisly but just as bristly ingredient goes into this splendid lunchtime dish: the Wood Hedgehog, *Hydnum repandum*. An equally appropriate alternative is the Terracotta Hedgehog, *Hydnum rufescens*.

You have to turn these hedgehogs over if you want to see their spines.

Some years these chunky edible toothed mushrooms appear in Britain and Ireland as early as June, and in mild autumns there are often plenty still around in October and even into November. If you are able to visit woodlands in southern Europe at Christmastime and into January, keep a look out for these excellent edibles, as they seem to get a 'second wind' at the turn of the year.

This recipe will serve two as a light lunch or four as a starter dish.

- 250 grams of Wood Hedgehogs or Terracotta Hedgehogs, roughly chopped - you could substitute Chanterelles or Ceps if the Hedgehogs are playing hard to get
- 50 grams of unsalted butter
- 50 ml of dry vermouth
- I shallot – finely chopped
- a small bunch of parsley – chopped
- a squeeze of lemon juice
- salt and pepper
- 2 slices of thick buttered toast

Melt the butter in a small pan, add the chopped shallot and fry gently until softened. Add the chopped mushrooms and fry until they start to release moisture, at which point add the vermouth. Continue to cook until the liquid is reduced and syrupy. Season well with salt and pepper, add the parsley and the lemon juice and then serve immediately on hot buttered toast. (If serving as a starter, allow half a slice of toast per person.)

Chanterelle Quiche

In warm summer sunshine Sue is showing off a basket of glorious golden Chanterelles that took no more than ten minute to gather. This recipe takes rather longer than that to prepare and cook, but I promise you that without a great deal of self control Sue's Chanterelle Quiche can disappear in a flash.

Made in a 23cm flan tin with removable base, the ingredients listed provide six generous portions.

300g of Chanterelles – washed thoroughly, dried and roughly chopped. (Trumpet Chanterelles would do, although they are somewhat tougher; and if you fancy a change mixed mushrooms also work very well in this recipe.)

The Walnut Pastry	The Filling
• 200 grams of plain flour • a pinch of salt • 100 grams of unsalted butter • 100 grams of ground walnuts • 1 egg – beaten • a little milk to bind if necessary	• 2 tbsp of good quality olive oil • a clove of garlic, crushed • 2 shallots or 1 small onion, chopped finely • 2 large eggs • 200 grams of soft goat's cheese • 100 ml of single cream • a small bunch parsley – chopped • a squeeze of lemon juice

First, make the pastry by combining the flour, salt, walnuts and butter in a food mixer. Add the egg and continue mixing until you have a firm dough, adding a little milk if necessary. Chill until required.

Next make the filling. Heat the olive oil in a large frying pan; add the shallots and garlic and fry for 3-4 minutes until they are soft. Add the mushrooms and season with salt and pepper. Fry over a high heat until the moisture released by the mushrooms boils off. Add the lemon juice and parsley and set aside to cool. Beat together the eggs, goat's cheese and cream in a bowl until smooth and then season well with salt and pepper.

Line the flan tin with the rolled-out pastry and bake blind in the oven at 190°C for 20 minutes or until the edges are tinged golden brown. Remove from the oven and turn the temperature down to 170°C.

Pour the goat's cheese mix into the flan case and then scatter the mushroom mix over the top. Bake in the oven for around 25 minutes until the filling is just set. Cool slightly, remove from the flan tin and serve.

Parasol Schnitzel

Parasols are large, fleshy and very common if you know where to look. They are also very tasty, and if you are trying to cut down on your red meat consumption without feeling deprived of flavoursome food, this dish is just what the doctor ordered... or what he would have ordered if he had known how delicious it is.

Parasols (above left) are best if you pick them when the caps are just opening, as shown here. By the time you get them home they will have expanded to become the size of a small frying pan (or sometimes a large one). If you are unlucky in your hunt for Parasols, pop in to the supermarket on the way home and buy a couple of large Portobello Mushrooms – or, of course, large Wood Mushrooms (above right) or Horse Mushrooms will do as a substitute until the real thing pops up. Allow half a Parasol cap per person. (Keep the stems to chop up and add to other dishes such as soups or risottos.)

- seasoned flour
- 2 eggs beaten
- fresh or dried breadcrumbs
- olive oil or a mixture of olive oil and butter for frying

Wash the mushroom caps and pat dry on paper kitchen towel. Coat in seasoned flour, dip into the egg mixture, and finally coat liberally with breadcrumbs. Heat the oil in a large frying pan and then fry the parasol schnitzels on both sides until they are crisp and brown on the outside and piping hot in the centre. Serve as you would with meat schnitzel, with chips and a salad.

Ceps Risotto

As you can see, I have done my bit towards this very special meal: four nice Ceps as perfect as can be. It's worth checking for occupants, though, so the first step is to cut them through vertically into 1cm thick slices; if any are infested with maggots this is the best time to find out.

Finding a maggot in your meal is not nice, but nowhere near as upsetting as spotting half a maggot when you are half-way through your meal. (With this recipe the Ceps will be chopped up further during the preparation.)

Young unexpanded caps such as those on the right of this picture are very rarely bug infested, but with larger, older specimens you may have to cut away parts that have attracted the attention of insects.

The quantities listed here serve two people.

- 250 grams of chopped Ceps. (As an alternative, of if you fancy a change now and then, a mixture of wild mushrooms - Chanterelles, Ceps, Wood Blewits, Wood Hedgehogs etc - will do. If you have to buy your mushrooms, you can economise by adding a tablespoonful of dried Ceps - reconstituted beforehand, of course - to 225 grams of button mushrooms.)
- olive oil
- 150 grams of arborio rice
- 1 small onion, finely chopped
- 1 clove garlic crushed
- 1 litre of hot chicken or vegetable stock (made with stock cubes is fine)
- half a small wine glass of dry white wine (the other half shouldn't be wasted, of course) - or you can use the same quantity of dry vermouth
- 1 tbsp of grated parmesan cheese
- chopped parsley

Heat the olive oil in a deep-sided frying pan. Add the onion and garlic and fry until softened. Add the mushrooms and fry for a few minutes; then add the rice and mix until it is coated with the moisture in the pan. Begin adding the hot stock one ladle at a time, stirring it in and allowing it to become absorbed by the rice. Repeat this until the rice is cooked 'al dente' – not too soft but with no feeling of chalkiness when you bite into it.

When the last lot of stock has almost disappeared from the rice mixture, stir through the wine and the parmesan, add the chopped parsley and serve immediately.

Mushrooms are renowned for their ability to appear suddenly; in Ceps Risotto I'm sure you will find, as I do, that they can disappear even more rapidly.

Field Mushroom Soup

Unless you have a lot of Field Mushrooms that need to be used up, even a small quantity of dried wild mushroom added to ordinary shop-bought mushrooms will greatly enhance what would otherwise be a rather ordinary mushroom soup.

- 300 grams of Field Mushrooms. Horse Mushrooms, Ceps, Wood Hedgehogs, Wood Blewits or Field Blewits are just as good. If you can't get wild mushrooms, use 300 grams of supermarket button mushrooms or chestnut mushrooms and one dessertspoon of dried wild mushrooms (reconstituted before use, of course!).
- 75 grams of butter (or a slug of olive oil)
- 1 onion, chopped
- 1 tbsp flour
- 1 bay leaf
- 1 whole Morel per person
- a small bunch of parsley tied with string
- $^{1}/_{8}$ tsp (a large pinch) of mace
- 500ml of chicken or vegetable stock
- 300ml of whole milk

Heat the butter or oil in a pan. Add the onion and mushrooms, cover and 'sweat' for around ten minutes on a low heat. Add the flour and stir it through; then add the stock, stirring until the soup comes to the boil. Add the parsley, bay leaf and mace, and simmer for about 15 to 20 minutes. Remove the bay leaf, and then liquidise the contents of the pan. Return the pan to the cooker, add the milk and reheat. Season with salt and pepper and serve with croutons or chopped chives.

For a touch of luxury, add one whole dried (reconstituted) Morel per person to the soup when the stock is added, but remove them before the soup is liquidised. When the soup is ready for serving, make sure each person has a whole Morel floating in the centre of their soup bowl.

Trumpet Chanterelle Tortellini

There's a special reason why most kinds of wild mushrooms are so good to eat: by the time you have scrambled about gathering enough to make a meal you have also worked up quite an appetite. Not so with Trumpet Chanterelles, those yellow-legged gregarious woodland fungi that spring up in their hundreds and sometimes thousands. Often it's simply a matter of finding a good place (or returning to one of your favourite haunts, because these mycorrhizal mushrooms remain loyal to their partners throughout the life of the tree). Then in a matter of a few minutes you can easily gather enough for a meal for two without moving from the spot.

Trumpet Chanterelles dry very well indeed, and in sealed jars they will keep more or less indefinitely if you have the willpower to ignore them.

Whether or not you make your own pasta, or buy sheets of fresh lasagne pasta instead, the recipe below makes enough filling for pasta for four people. If any is left over it can be spread on a piece of warm, buttered toast and popped under the grill to brown for a delicious light lunch or snack.

- 100 grams very finely chopped Trumpet Chanterelles (or other wild mushrooms)
- 125 grams of brie (after rind has been removed) or soft goats cheese
- olive oil (used for frying the mushrooms and for drizzling over finished dish)
- 350 grams fresh pasta dough or lasagne sheets
- a little salt and ground black pepper to season

Heat the oil and fry the chopped mushrooms gently until all the liquor from the chanterelles has evaporated. Cool.

Beat the cheese until it forms a soft paste. Add the finely chopped mushrooms and a little salt (some cheeses are much saltier than others so be careful) and pepper and mix until the cheese and mushrooms are combined.

Roll out and cut the pasta into rings about 7cm in diameter. Place a small amount of mushroom filling in the centre of each disc of pasta, moisten the edges with a little water and then fold over and seal tightly so that the filling cannot escape during cooking.

Drop the tortellini into boiling, lightly salted water and cook for a couple of minutes or until the pasta is cooked but not too soft.

Serve the pasta with a little olive oil drizzled over, or with a simple creamy sauce. A mixed salad is an ideal accompaniment to this dish. Serve freshly grated parmesan on the side.

This recipe is based on an idea from Ashburton Cookery School.

Morel Sauce

If you are lucky enough to get a reasonable quantity of these magnificent mushrooms (any kind of morels will do other than the False Morel!), make Morel Sauce. Only the best beef, pork or venison fillet or a meaty fish such as turbot will do as an accompaniment to it!

If Black Morels spring up from the woodchip mulch in your flowerbeds or herbaceous border, they are telling you something: make Morel Sauce and freeze it for future use!

The ingredients listed here make sufficient sauce to serve four.

- 250 grams of Morels, roughly chopped. (Dried and reconstituted morels will do just as well, of course.)
- a shallot or a small onion
- a clove of garlic (crushed)
- a knob of butter for frying
- half a wine glass of cognac
- 100ml of double cream

Heat the butter and fry the shallot until it is soft. Add the chopped Morels and fry gently for about five minutes. Taste the cognac to make sure it is all right – you can't afford to take risks when something as precious as Morels is involved.

Add the cognac, cover the pan tightly and simmer for around 10 minutes. Remove the saucepan lid and continue simmering until you have reduced the liquid down to about half its original quantity. Add the double cream, warm through (but do not re-boil once the cream has been added), season and serve over the cooked steaks or fish.

After the meal, don't be in too much of a hurry to do the washing up. Check that the cognac is still okay before putting the bottle away for next time.

Appendix I – Glossary of Mycological Terms
Uncovering the meaning behind scientific short-hand

From abseiling to zoology, every specialist subject has its own jargon, a short-hand language that is clear to those involved and opaque to 'outsiders' (unless they have a key to unlock the hidden meanings). Mycology is no exception. As you get more involved with fungi, and in particular when talking with fellow enthusiasts or reading around the subject, the jargon will eventually become your own short-hand. In the meantime, here is a key to help with some terms that are frequently used in mycological circles. Compare the width of the two columns in the table and you will see why the experts talk this way: it saves a lot of time and paper (and therefore a lot of trees, and fungi too!).

Term	Meaning
acrid	with a peppery, burning taste
acute	(referring to physical shape) sharp
adnate	(gills) attached to the stem over all or most of their total depth
adnexed	(gills) tapering in depth toward stem so that the attachment is narrow
amyloid	turning blue, grey or black when stained with Melzer's reagent
annulus	ring of tissue on a mushroom stem left by a torn partial veil
apiculus	tiny projection on a spore where it is attached to the sterigma
apothecium	cup-shaped fruitbody of certain ascomycetous fungi
appendiculate	(describing a cap margin) fringed with veil fragments
appressed	(often used to describe scales) flattened down onto a surface
arbuscular mycorrhiza (AM)	(a mycorrhiza) where fungi from the Glomeromycota penetrate the roots of a (usually herbaceous) plant and provide the plant with water and nutrients while the plant supplies sugars to the fungus
ascending	(describing a ring) flaring upwards and out
ascocarp	fruitbody of an ascomycete fungus
ascomycetes	a class of fungi that produce their spores in sac-like cells called asci
ascospores	sexual spores produced in the asci of ascomycetous fungi
ascus	(pl., asci) the spore-producing cell of an ascomycete fruitbody
autodigestion	self digesting or liquefying – a characteristic of the inkcap fungi
basidiocarp	fruitbody of a basidiomycete fungus
basidiomycetes	a class of fungi that produce their spores on basidia
basidiospores	sexual spores produced on the basidia of basidiomycetous fungi
basidium	(pl., basidia) spore-producing cell of a basidiomycetous fungus
biotrophic	feeding on living cells of other organisms
bulbous	(describing a stem) with a swollen base
caespitose	crowded together in a tuft or a cluster but not attached to each other
campanulate	(describing a cap) bell shaped
cap	top part of a basidiomycete mushroom that carries the fertile tissue
carpophore	fungal fruitbody comprising stem, cap and gills
caulocystidium	a cystidium on the stem of a mushroom
cellulose	component of plant cell walls and of wood composed of glucose units
cheilocystidium	a cystidium on the edge of a mushroom gill

chlamydospores	asexual spores formed by the breaking up of fungal hyphae
cinereous	ash grey in colour
clamp connection	swollen area formed around septum in a hypha during cell division
clavate	(usually describing a mushroom stem) club-shaped
concolorous	(when comparing parts of a fruitbody) being of the same colour
context	the flesh of a fungal fruitbody
convex	(describing a cap) domed without either a hump or a depression
coprophilous	growing on dung
coriaceous	leathery
cortina	a cobweb-like partial veil consisting of fine silky fibres
crustose	(describing a lichen) forming a crust on a substrate (tree, rock etc)
cuticle	the surface layer of the cap or stem of a fruitbody
cystidium	special sterile cell among the basidia on some fungi
decurrent	(describing gills) running down the stem - as with Chanterelles
depressed	(describing a cap) where the central region is lower than the margin
descending	(describing a ring) flaring downwards and out, like a skirt
deuteromycetes	obsolete term for a group fungi not known to reproduce sexually (Molecular analysis can now determine their appropriate groups)
dextrinoid	staining brick red or brown with Melzer's reagent
dichotomous	forking/divided into pairs – as in logical decision-making trees
dikaryon	a pair of closely associated, sexually compatible nuclei
distant	(describing gills) widely spaced
eccentric	(describing stem attachment to cap) offset to one side.
ectomycorrhiza (EM)	(a mycorrhiza) where the fungus forms sheathes around plant rootlets (often of a tree), growing between but not penetrating the cells of the plant root, and providing the plant with water and nutrients while the plant supplies sugars to the fungus
emarginate	(describing gills) conspicuously notched near to the stem
endomycorrhiza	mycorrhiza in which fungal hyphae penetrate cell walls of host plant
endophyte	fungus living within a plant without causing visible symptoms of harm
floccose	with a covering of loose cotton-like scales
foetid	with a strong and offensive odour
foliose	(describing a lichen) shaped like a leaf
free	(describing gills) not attached to the stem
fruticose	(describing a lichen) shaped like a shrub
furfuraceous	(describing a surface) covered in bran-like or dandruff-like particles
fusiform	(describing a stem) spindle-shaped, tapering at top and bottom
germ pore	thin region of spore wall via which spores can germinate
gills	plates of tissue bearing the hymenium in an agaricoid fungus
glabrous	(describing a surface) bald
gleba	spore-bearing tissue enclosed within fruitbodies of gasteromycetes
glutinous	(describing a cap surface) covered with a slimy gelatinous layer
granulose	(describing a cap or stem surface) covered with small granules
hemicellulose	amorphous (non-crystalline) polysaccharides in plant cell walls

hirsute	hairy
hispid	covered with stiff bristle-like hairs
homogeneous	being the same throughout
hyaline	clear (colourless) when viewed under a microscope
hygrophanous	appearing translucent when wet, paler and more opaque when dry
hymenium	fertile spore-bearing tissue (e.g. on mushroom gill or pore surfaces)
hypha	(pl., hyphae) filamentous thread of fungal mycelium
inferior	(describing a ring) located near the base of the stem
infundibuliform	funnel-shaped
involute	(describing a cap) rolled inwards at the margin
lamellae	gills
latex	milky fluid that oozes from cut surfaces of *Lactarius* species
lichen	organism comprising a fungus and an alga or a cyanobacterium
lignicolous	growing on wood
mucilaginous	(often describing a mushroom cap) covered with slime
mycelium	body of a fungus, most of which is underground or hidden within wood
mycobiont	the fungal component of a lichen or of a mycorrhizal partnership
mycology	the study of fungi
mycophagy	the eating of fungi
mycophile	a person who loves fungi
mycophobe	a person who fears or loathes fungi
mycorrhiza	structure by which a fungus and a plant exchange nutrients mutually
myxomycetes	a large and commonly encountered group within the slime moulds
necrotrophic	feeding by killing and consuming (part of) another organism
organelle	a differentiated (separate) structure within a cell
parasitism	process whereby an organism feeds at the expense of another (host)
partial veil	protective membrane covering gills during development of a fruitbody
peridioles	egg-like spore capsules in bird's-nest fungi (Nidulariaceae)
peridium	outer wall of a fungus, especially a gasteromycete (e.g. a puffball)
perithecium	flask-shaped chambers containing asci within pyrenomycetes fungi
photobiont	photosynthesizing component (alga or cyanobacterium) of a lichen
photosynthesis	process by which plants convert carbon dioxide and water to sugars
pileus	(pl., pilei) the umbrella-shaped cap on the top of a mushroom stem
pleurocystidium	a cystidium on a gill surface
pores	the orifices of the tubes of polypore fungi via which spores emerge
pruinose	covered with a bloom (often pale, like a fine layer of chalk dust)
pseudorhiza	a tap-root-like extension at the base of a mushroom stem
pubescent	(describing a surface) covered with fine short hairs
resupinate	fruitbody that lies flat on the substrate with its hymenium outermost
reticulate	(describing a stem, notably of a bolete) marked with a net-like pattern
rhizomorph	a root-like mycelial strand comprising bunched parallel hyphae
ring	membranous remains of the partial veil attached to a stem
rufous	brownish red

saprophyte	an organism that obtains its nutrients from dead organic material
scabrous	(describing a stem or cap surface) rough with scale-like projections
septate	(describing hyphae) partitioned by cross-walls known as septa
septum	(pl., septa) a cross wall separating cells of a hyphal thread
serrate	(describing gill margins) with saw-toothed edges
sessile	without a stalk
sinuate	(describing gills) with a notch near the point of attachment to the stem
slime moulds	a group of fungus-like organisms that use spores to reproduce
sphaerocysts	globose hyphal cells in the Russulaceae and certain other fungi
spore	reproductive structure of a fungus, usually a single cell
sporophore	fungal fruitbody
squamose	(describing the surface of a cap or a stem) covered with scales
squamulose	(describing the surface of a cap or a stem) covered with tiny scales
stellate	star-shaped
sterigma	(pl., sterigmata) prong at top of basidium on which a spore develops
stipe	stem of a mushroom
stipitate	(describing a fruitbody) having a stem
striate	(describing a cap) with fine radiating lines or furrows around margin
subdecurrent	(describing gills) running just a short distance down the stem
subglobose	almost spherical
subtomentose	(describing a surface) somewhat or finely woolly
sulcate	deeply furrowed
superior	(describing a ring) located near the top of the stem
taxonomy	the classification of organisms based on their natural relationships
thallus	(pl., thalli) the body of a fungus or a lichen
tomentose	densely woolly, velvety, or thickly covered with soft hairs
trama	the flesh or context of a fungal fruitbody's cap, gills or stem
truncate	ending abruptly as if chopped off
tubes	spore-bearing cylindrical structures of boletes and polypores
umbilicate	(describing a cap) having a navel-like central depression
umbo	a raised central mound (often conical with a rounded top)
umbonate	(describing a cap) having a raised central mound
universal veil	a protective membrane that initially surrounds an entire fruitbody
Uredinales	rust fungi (an order within the Basidiomycota)
ustilaginomycetes	smut fungi (a class within the Basidiomycota)
ventricose	(describing a stem) swollen at or near to the middle
verrucose	(describing spores) covered with small rounded warts
vinaceous	the colour of pale red wine
viscid	slimy or sticky (at least when moist)
volva	remains of the universal veil found at stem base of some fungi
zonate	(usually describing a cap) marked with concentric colour bands
Zygomycota	a class of simple fungi whose hyphae generally lack cross walls

Appendix II - What's in a Name

How to find meaning in the scientific names of fungi

You are unique, the one and only you. And yet whether you are John or Jean, Pam or Paul, or pretty much anything else, you probably share your name with at least thousands and possibly millions of other people. There is one name that we all share: *Homo sapiens*, the name of our species. Fungal fruitbodies don't warrant individual names (or so we have decided!) but over the years people have found that it helps when telling other people about their finds or failures if they have names for each of the different kinds of mushroom. Unfortunately some common names refer to as many as a dozen different fungi species, often from different genera. To complicate matters further, some mushrooms species have several common names. Using common names is okay if you don't mind being misunderstood occasionally, but when getting your message across really matters using common names is far too risky. Scientific names, sometimes referred to as Latin names, refer to one and only one fungus species.

Strictly speaking there is nothing particularly scientific about the 'scientific' names of fungi. They arose via botany, and botanical names are based on an archaic language no longer spoken but serving merely as notation. (Arguments about pronunciation do seem rather pointless, therefore.) The advantage, however, is that a botanical name means the same to botanists (and mycologists) throughout the world; it avoids ambiguity. Well, that's the idea, at least – but see Appendix III for more details on this tricky issue.

A genus name is given to a group of fungi with similar physical characteristics that are confined essentially to that group. The name, usually derived from either medieval or classical Latin or as a latinized version of a Greek word, may be chosen in honour of a person, as a reference to a place or a kind of habitat, or to denote a prominent characteristic of the group of fungi. (There are also a few scientific names that have no real meaning – perhaps as a result of an initial misidentification.)

The second part of a botanical binomial is known as the specific epithet. Whereas a genus name is (generally!) a noun, a specific epithet may be either a noun or an adjective. Again it can be a reference to a person (for example *queletii*, in honour of the pioneering French mycologist Lucien Quélet) or it might refer to size (*giganteus*), or colour (*rubellus*) or to the typical habitat (such as *palustris*, meaning swamp) in which the fungus usually grows.

Genera

The origins/bases of common genus names are indicated in the table below.

Agaricus	of the country
Agrocybe	field cap/head
Aleuria	wheat flour
Amanita	Mount Amanus
Armillaria	like a bracelet
Asterophora	star-shaped spores
Astraeus	star
Auricularia	ear
Bankera	Howard J Banker
Bjerkandera	Clas Bjerkander
Bolbitius	cow pat
Boletus	a clod

Bulgaria	leather bag
Calocera	beautiful horn
Calocybe	beautiful head
Calvatia	bald/hairless
Camarophyllus	vaulted gills
Cantharellus	chalice/cup
Chlorociboria	green-yellow chalice
Clathrus	iron grid/lattice
Clavaria	like a club
Clitocybe	sloping head
Clitopilus	sloping cap

Collybia	like a small coin
Coprinus	dung
Cordyceps	swollen head
Coriolus	leathery
Cortinarius	with a curtain
Crepidotus	slipper
Cystoderma	blistered skin
Daedalea	labyrinthine
Daldinia	charred wood
Dermocybe	skin-head
Entoloma	(margin) inrolled
Exidia	staining/exuding
Fistulina	tube or pipe
Flammulina	flame
Fomes	tinder
Galerina	helmet
Ganoderma	lustrous skin
Geastrum	earth star
Geoglossum	earth tongue
Gomphidius	peg, stake or nail
Grifola	braided hair of griffin
Gymnopilus	naked head
Hebeloma	blunt
Helvella	aromatic herb
Hericium	hedgehog
Heterobasidion	irregular base
Hydnum	mushroom
Hygrocybe	moist head
Hygrophorus	water carrier
Hypholoma	fringed with tissue
Inocybe	fibre head
Inonotus	fibrous
Kuehneromyces	Robert Kühner
Laccaria	painted
Lacrymaria	tears (as in crying)
Lactarius	milk
Laetiporus	bright/abundant
Leccinum	fungus
Lentinus	pliable, or sticky
Lenzites	Harald Othmar Lenz
Leotia	smooth mushroom
Lepiota	scaly mushroom
Lepista	wine goblet
Leucoagaricus	white *Agaricus*
Lycoperdon	wolf's flatulence
Lyophyllum	loose or free gills
Macrocystidia	large cystidia
Macrolepiota	large and scaly

Marasmius	withered
Melanoleuca	black and white
Meripilus	partitioned cap
Morchella	morel
Mutinus	phallic deity
Mycena	mushroom
Neobulgaria	new leather bag
Nidularia	little nest
Omphalina	little navel
Otidea	ear
Oudemansiella	Corneille Oudemans
Panaeolus	variegated
Panellus	ragged
Paxillus	small stake/stick/peg
Peziza	stalkless mushroom
Phaeolepiota	dusky and scaly
Phaeolus	dusky
Phallus	phallus
Phellinus	corky
Pholiota	scaly
Piptoporus	detachable pores
Pisolithus	pea in stone
Pleurotus	side ear
Polyporus	many pores
Psathyrella	brittle/fragile
Psilocybe	bare/smooth head
Ramaria	branching
Russula	reddish
Sarcodon	fleshy with teeth
Schizophyllum	split gills
Scleroderma	hard skin
Serpula	snake
Stereum	hard
Strobilomyces	pine cones
Stropharia	belt
Suillus	swine (pigs)
Thelephora	having nipples
Trametes	thin
Tremella	trembling, like a jelly
Tricholoma	hairy/fibrous
Tubaria	trumpet
Tulostoma	knob on a club
Tylopilus	lumpy cap
Volvariella	volva or bag
Xerocomus	dry
Xylaria	woody

Specific epithets

The bases of specific epithets of some common fungi are indicated in the table below. (Variable endings such as *lucida, lucidus, lucidum* have not been given multiple entries.)

abietus	fir trees
acaulis	stemless
acerbum	bitter
acerrimus	very sharp
acris	acrid
acuminatus, acutus	with a sharp point
adiposa	fat
adspersum	scattered
adusta	scorched, swarthy
aegeritus	poplar trees
aeruginosa	blue-green
aestivus	summer
alba	white
alnicola	alder trees
ammophila	sand loving
amoenolens	pleasant smelling
anthracina	charcoal or coal
apiculatus	with a small point
appendiculatus	small appendage
applanatum	flattened
arborescens	tree-like
argenteus	silvery
aspera	rough
asterospora	star-shaped spores
ater, atra, atro	dark, blackish
atramentaria	inky
aurantiaca	orange
aurata, aurea	gilded/golden
auricula	ear
australis	southern
azonites	not zoned
azurea	azure, sky blue
badius	reddish-brown
betula, betulina	birch trees
bisporus	two-spored basidia
blanda	pleasant
bolaris	lumps of paint
bombycina	silky
borealis	northern
brevipes	short foot
brumalis	winter
butyracea	buttery
caerulea	deep blue
caesius	blue-grey

caespitosus	clustered/tufted
campestris	fields
canadensis	of Canada/America
candicans	shining white
candidus	pure white
caninus	dog
capillaris	hair
carnea	flesh coloured
castaneus	chestnut
cavipes	hollow foot
ceracea	waxy
cervinus	deer/fawn coloured
chlorophana	pale green
chrysorrheus	gold flowing
cibarius	food/edible
ciliata	fringed with hair
cinerea	ashen
cingulatum	girdled
cinnamomeus	cinnamon coloured
cirrhatus	curled
citrina	lemon yellow
claroflava	bright yellow
clavipes	club foot
coccineus	scarlet
cochleatus	snail shell
collinitus	covered in slime
comatus	covered in hair
communis	common
confluens	running together
confragosa	rough/scaly
cordata	heart
cornuta	horn
coronaria	crown
cortina	curtain
crispa	finely waved, curled
cristata	crested
croceus	saffron (yellow)
cruentus	bloody
cuspidata	pointed
dealbata	whitewashed
decolorans	fading
decora	beautiful
delibutus	greasy
dulcis	sweet
eburneus	ivory

echinocephalus	spiny head
edulis	edible
elata	tall
elegans	elegant, slender
epipterygia	small wing on top
erythropus	reddish foot
esculenta	good to eat
fascicularia	bundled
ferruginosa	rusty
fimbriata	fringed
flammula	flame
flava	yellow
floccopus	woolly foot
foenisecii	haymaking
foetens	stinking
fornicatus	arched/vaulted
fragrans	fragrant
fragrantissima	very fragrant
fruticosa	shrub-like
fuliginosa	soot
fulva	tawny (fox coloured)
fusca	dark/dusky
fusiformis	spindle shaped
gambosa	swollen base
geotropa	erect above earth
gibba	humped/rounded
glaucus	grey bloom
gracilis	graceful
grandis	big
griseum	grey
hepatica	of liver
hirsuta	hairy
hispidus	bristly
humilis	low
hybridus	hybrid
illota	dirty/unwashed
imbricata	covered in scales
impolitus	rough/matt
incarnata	flesh coloured
infundibuliformis	funnel shaped
integra	whole/entire
inversa	upside down
involutus	in-rolled
junonius	Juno
laccata	painted
lactea	milky
laeta	bright or abundant
lateritium	colour of bricks
leoninus	lion

littoralis	seashore
livida	lead grey
lucida	clear/glossy
luridus	lurid/unclean/dingy
luteus	yellow
maculata	spotted/blotchy
maxima	largest
mellea	honey coloured
miniata	painted with red lead
minor	smaller
mollis	soft and/or hairy
montana	mountains
mucosus	slime/mucus
muscaria	fly
nigra	black
nitida	shining
odorata	scented
ovata	egg shaped
paludosa	swamp/marsh/bog
palustris	marshes
panaeolus	variegated
peronata	booted/sheathed
personata	masked
piperatus	peppery
polymorpha	many shapes/forms
plicatilis	pleated
praecox	early/premature
psittacina	parrot
pubescens	downy
pulchella	pretty
pulverulentus	powdery
pumilis	low
punctata	spotted
purpurea	purple
rosea	rosy red
ruber, rubra	red
rubescens	becoming red
rufus	ruddy
sanguinea	blood
sardonia	very bitter
silvaticus	woodland
speciosa	showy
spectabilis	spectacular
tabescens	decomposing
tomentosa	hairy
variegata	variegated
vellereus	woolly
viridis	green
vulgaris	common

Appendix III – Citation of Mycology Authorities

How fungi father figures are cited in the scientific naming convention

In accordance with the International Code of Botanical Nomenclature (ICBN), the complete scientific name of a fungus consists of a Latinised binomial (*Genus* name followed by *species* name, using the system introduced by Linnaeus in his *Species Plantarum* of 1753). The binomial, written in italics, is followed by the name of the authority who applied that binomial to it. The names of famous fungi pioneers who described numerous species are, by tradition, abbreviated often to just the surname - sometimes in truncated form.

Most introductory texts (including this one) and even some field guides omit the names of authorities on the basis that few amateurs have much interest in the matter of who first described a species and gave it its specific epithet. Professionals need full citations for several reasons. One species may have been named and described by two or more authorities unaware of one another's work or not realising that the fungi were actually the same species. Even when a species was uniquely described and named by an authority in the distant past, during the intervening years its binomial name may have been altered. The full authority citation states who allocated the original species epithet and who later moved it into a different genus. (Some species have been through many such changes.) Full citations allow us to search the technical literature in order to find the original descriptions of species.

Some citations are very straightforward. For example, it was the Swedish botanist Elias Fries, in his *Systema Mycologium* published in 1821, who first described the Chanterelle and named it *Cantharellus cibarius*. There have been no changes to this name, and so it has always been simply cited as:

Cantharellus cibarius Fries

or, more commonly, using an abbreviated form of the author's name:

Cantharellus cibarius Fr.

You won't find Pliny or Caesar cited as naming authorities, because the ICBN rule is that (with the exception of rusts, smuts and gasteromycetes fungi, where C H Persoon's 1801 *Synopsis Methodica Fungorum* takes precedence) the starting point for fungi taxonomy is Elias Fries' *Systema Mycologium* of 1821. Names sanctioned (meaning that they were retained without change) by Fries in his 1821 publication still stand today, albeit with genus amendments in many instances. This applies not only to species that Fries himself named but also to species named by others, including Linneaus, before these dates. (This rule applies equally to species named by Persoon other than in categories mentioned above.)

So, for example, in 1821 the white edible agaric that we know as St George's Mushroom was named by Fries as *Agaricus gambosus*. In fact this species had already been described by Linnaeus, in his *Species Plantarum* published in 1753, in which he called it *Agaricus georgii*. Fries chose not to accept Linnaeus's epithet, and he renamed it *Agaricus gambosus*. Under the ICBN rules, the specific epithet given by Fries is retained today. This mushroom was later moved by Paul Kummer to the genus *Tricholoma*, and more recently Rolf Singer moved it to the genus *Calocybe*. As a result, St George's Mushroom can be identified as either:

Agaricus gambosus Fr.
Tricholoma gambosum (Fr.) Kummer
Calocybe gambosa (Fr.) Sing.

You will note that Rolf Singer's surname has been abbreviated in the third of these citations, which is the scientific name by which this mushroom is generally known today.

Currently accepted binomial names of fungi therefore include many that were first named by authors prior to the 1821 publication by Fries or the 1801 publication by Persoon, where those names were sanctioned (retained) by Fries or Persoon. They are cited showing the original authority and the sanctioning authority. For example:

Agaricus campestris L.: Fr.

shows that Linnaeus named the Field Mushroom as *Agaricus campestris* and that Fries retained that name in his 1821 publication. An alternative form of writing this name, again acknowledging the original contribution by Linnaeus, is:

Agaricus campestris L. ex Fr.

In principle, therefore, there is no reason why a fungus species might not still have a name given to it by Pliny (who would have coped well with the Latin)... except that the binomial system had not been devised in Pliny's day. That's why there are common names but no scientific names predating those assigned by Linnaeus.

Fries with everything

You will also see the authority reference Fr.: Fr. It is used where Fries named a species prior to 1821 and retained the original name in his *Systema Mycologium.* Species first named by Fries in his 1821 publication and unaltered since then are written in the form:

Agaricus augustus Fr.

All of the species named by authorities subsequent to these founders of fungi taxonomy and unchanged since are written in the form:

Russula violacea Quél.

The authority referenced in this case is the great French mycologist Lucien Quélet, who first described this brittlegill mushroom in 1882.

If people investigating fungi had all worked together, perhaps that would be the end of the matter. Unfortunately, occasionally by chance different authorities applied the same binomial name to two or more different species – in which case the names are known as homonyms and the ICBN rule is that the name remains with the fungus to which it was applied earliest; once the mistake is recognised, the other species must be renamed.

Sometimes the same species was named separately by two or more people, and then the various names are known as synonyms. Many of the fungi illustrated in this book have several synonyms, and they are all valid names under the ICBN rules. In quoting binomials I have been guided by the checklists published by the British Mycological Society.

Standard abbreviations of authorities' names

The following selected list of mycological authorities is taken mainly from the database of authorities for plant (and fungi) names maintained by the Royal Botanic Gardens, Kew. Standard abbreviations are listed in the first column and highlighted in bold in the authors' full names in the second column.

Abbreviation	Authority	Born	Died
Afzel.	Adam **Afzel**ius	1750	1837
Alb.	Johannes Baptista von **Alb**ertini	1769	1831
Atk.	George Francis **Atk**inson	1854	1918
Badham	Charles David **Badham**	1806	1857
Bataille	Frederic **Bataille**	1850	1946
Batsch	August Johann Georg Karl **Batsch**	1761	1802
Battarra	Giovanni Antonio **Battarra**	1714	1789
Berk.	Miles Joseph **Berk**eley	1803	1889
Bolton	James **Bolton**	1758	1799
Bondarzew	Appolonaris Semyonovich **Bondartse**v	1857	1968
Bonord.	Hermann Friedrich **Bonord**en	1801	1884
Boud.	Jean Louis Emile **Boud**ier	1828	1920
Bref.	Julius Oscar **Bref**eld	1839	1925
Bres.	Giacopo **Bres**adola	1847	1929
F Brig.	**F**rancesco **Brig**anti	1802	1865
V Brig.	**V**incenzo **Brig**anti	1766	1836
Brond.	Louis de **Brond**eau	1794	1859
Broome	Christopher Edmund **Broome**	1812	1866
Bull.	Jean Baptiste Francois **Bull**iard	1752	1793
Cooke	Mordecai Cubitt **Cooke**	1825	1914
Coker	William Chambers **Coker**	1872	1953
Curtis	Moses Ashley **Curtis**	1808	1872
D C	Augustin Pyramus **D**e **C**andolle	1778	1841
Desm.	John Baptiste Henri Joseph **Desm**azieres	1786	1862
Desv.	Nicaise Auguste **Desv**aux	1784	1856
Dicks.	James J. **Dicks**on	1738	1822
Dill.	Johann Jacob **Dill**enius	1684	1747
Ditmar	Fr. L P **Ditmar** [dates of publications]	[1806]	[1817]
Earle	Franklin Sumner **Earle**	1856	1929
Ellis	Job Bicknell **Ellis**	1829	1905
Fr.	Elias Magnus **Fr**ies	1794	1878
Fuckel	Karl Wilhelm Gottlieb Leopold **Fuckel**	1821	1876
Genev.	Leon Gaston **Genev**ier	1830	1880
Gillet	Claude-Casimir **Gillet**	1806	1896
Grev.	Robert Kaye **Grev**ille	1794	1866
Gray	Samuel Frederick **Gray**	1766	1828
Harkn.	Harvey Wilson **Harkn**ess	1821	1901
Henn.	Paul Christoph **Henn**ings	1841	1908
Hohenbühel	Ludwig Samuel Joseph David Alexander von **Hohenbühel** Heufler	1817	1885
Holmsk.	Theodor **Holmsk**jold	1732	1794
Hudson	William **Hudson**	1730	1793
Jacq.	Nicolaus Joseph von **Jacq**uin	1727	1817

Jungh.	Franz Wilhelm **Jungh**uhn	1809	1864
Kalchbr.	Karoly **Kalchbr**enner	1807	1886
Karsten	Gustav Karl Wilhelm **H**ermann **Karsten**	1817	1908
P Karst.	**P**etter Adolf **Karsten**	1834	1917
Kauffmann	Calvin Henry **Kauffmann**	1869	1931
Klotzsch	Johann Friedrich **Klotzsch**	1805	1860
Krombh.	Julius Vincenz von **Krombh**olz	1782	1843
Kühner	Robert **Kühner**	1903	1996
Kummer	Paul **Kummer**	1834	1912
Lasch	Wilhelm Gottfried **Lasch**	1787	1863
Lenz	Harald Othmar **Lenz**	1798	1870
Letellier	Jean Baptiste Louis **Letellier**	1817	1898
Lév.	Joseph-Henri **Lév**eillé	1796	1870
Leysser	Friedrich Wilhelm von **Leysser**	1731	1815
L.	Karl von **L**inné (Carl **L**innaeus)	1707	1778
Lloyd	Curtis Gates **Lloyd**	1859	1926
Massee	George Edward **Massee**	1850	1917
P Micheli	**P**ier Antonio **Micheli**	1679	1737
Mont.	Jean Pierre Francois Camille **Mont**agne	1784	1866
Morgan	Andrew Price **Morgan**	1836	1907
Murrill	William Alphonso **Murrill**	1869	1957
Nees	Christian Gottfried Daniel **Nees** von Esenbeck	1776	1858
Opat.	Wilhelm **Opat**owski	1810	1838
Pat.	Narcisse Theophile **Pat**ouillard	1854	1926
Paulet	Jean Jacques **Paulet**	1740	1826
Peck	Charles Horton **Peck**	1833	1917
Pers.	Christiaan Hendrik **Pers**oon	1761	1837
Quél.	Lucien **Quél**et	1832	1899
Rabenh.	Gottlob Ludwig **Rabenh**orst	1806	1881
Ravenel	Henry William **Ravenel**	1814	1887
Relhan	Richard **Relhan**	1754	1823
Retz.	Anders Jahan **Retz**ius	1724	1821
Richon	Charles Eduard **Richon**	1820	1893
Rostk.	Friedrich Wilhelm Gottfried Theophil **Rostk**ovius	1770	1848
Romagn.	Henri Charles Louis **Romagn**esi	1912	1999
Roze	Ernest **Roze**	1833	1900
Sacc.	Pier Andrea **Sacc**ardo	1845	1920
Schaeff.	Jacob Christian **Schaeff**er	1718	1790
Schröt.	**J**oseph **Schröt**er	1837	1894
Schumacher	Heinrich Christian Friedrich **Schumacher**	1757	1830
Schw.	Lewis David von **Schw**einitz	1780	1834
Scop.	Joannes Antonius **Scop**oli	1723	1788
Secr.	Louis **Secr**etan	1758	1839
Sing.	Rolf **Singer**	1906	1994
A H Smith	**A**lexander **H**anchett **Smith**	1904	1986
Sommerf.	Soren Christian **Sommerf**elt	1794	1838
Sowerby	James **Sowerby**	1757	1822
Thax.	Roland **Thax**ter	1857	1932
Tul.	Louis Rene **Tul**asne	1815	1885
Underw.	Lucien Marcus **Underw**ood	1853	1907

Velen.	Josef **Velen**ovský	1858	1949
A Venturi	**A**ntonio **Venturi**	1805	1864
Vitadd.	Carlo **Vittad**ini	1800	1865
Viv.	Domenico **Viv**iani	1772	1840
Wall.	Carl Friedrich Wilhelm **Wallr**oth	1792	1857
Weinm.	Johann Anton **Weinm**ann	1782	1858
Willd.	Carl Ludwig von **Willd**enow	1765	1812
Wulfen	Franz Xavier von **Wulfen**	1728	1805

A January display of Velvet Shank mushrooms *Flammulina velutipes*

Appendix IV – Other Fungi Information Sources
Organisations, books, multimedia and Web resources

For anyone interested in learning more about the fascinating kingdom of fungi and how the rest of Life on Earth critically depends on fungal organisms, there is now a wealth of information available. Here is a very limited selection of organisations and user-friendly information sources that aim to help newcomers to the subject.

Organisations with specialist expertise in fungi

British Mycological Society
City View House, 5 Union Street, Ardwick, Manchester, England M12 4JD
www.britmycolsoc.org.uk

Department of Agriculture, Environment and Rural Affairs (DAERA), Northern Ireland
Dundonald House, Upper Newtownards Road, Ballymiscaw, Belfast BT4 3SB
www.daera-ni.gov.uk

Natural Resources Wales
Ty Cambria, 29 Newport Rd., Cardiff, Wales CF24 0TP
https://naturalresources.wales

Department of the Environment, Heritage and Local Government, Ireland
Newtown Road, Wexford Y35 AP90 Ireland
www.environ.ie

Natural England
4th Floor, Foss House, Kings Pool, 1-2 Peasholme Green, York, England YO1 7PX
www.gov.uk/government/organisations/natural-england

Plantlife
14 Rollestone Street, Salisbury, Wiltshire, England SP1 1DX
www.plantlife.org.uk

Royal Botanic Gardens
Kew, Richmond, Surrey, England TW9 3AE
http://www.kew.org/science-conservation/plants-fungi

Scottish Natural Heritage
Great Glen House, Leachkin Road, Inverness, Scotland IV3 8NW
www.snh.gov.uk

The Fungus Conservation Trust (formerly Association of British Fungus Groups)
Harveys, Alston, Axminster, Devon, England EX13 7LG
www.abfg.org

Introductory books about fungi

John Webster and Roland W S Weber, *Introduction to Fungi*, Cambridge University Press, 3rd edition 2007, ISBN-13: 978-0-521-01483-0

Brian Spooner and Peter Roberts, *Fungi*, Collins, 2005, ISBN 0-00-220153-4

Roy Watling, *Fungi*, The Natural History Museum, London, 2003, ISBN-10: 0-565-09182-4

Patrick Harding, *Mushroom Miscellany*, Collins, 2008, ISBN: 978-0-00-728464-1

George McCarthy, *Photographing Fungi in the Field*, Guild of Master Craftsmen, 2001, ISBN 1-86108-236-3

Steven L Stephenson, *The Fungal Kingdom*, Timber Press, 2010, ISBN: 9780881928914

John Wright, *Mushrooms*, Bloomsbury Press, 2007, ISBN: 978-0-7475-8932-7

Paul Sterry and Barry Hughes, *Collins Complete Guide to Mushrooms and Toadstools*, Collins, 2009, ISBN: 978-0-00-723224-6

Michael Jordan, *The Encyclopedia of Fungi of Britain and Europe*, Frances Lincoln, 2004, ISBN: 978-0711223790

Roger Phillips, *Mushrooms*, Macmillan Reference, 2nd Edition 2006, ISBN: 978-0-33044-237-4

Jens H Petersen, *The Kingdom of Fungi*, PPrinceton University Press, 2033, ISBN: 9780691157542

CDs and DVDs about Fungi

Bryce Kendrick, *The Fifth Kingdom*, www.mycolog.com/fungicd.htm

E.A. Dauncey et al, *Poisonous Plants and Fungi in Britain and Ireland*, Kew Publishing, 2002, ISBN 1-900347-92-X

Fungi websites

First Nature (UK): www.first-nature.com/fungi

Index Fungorum (UK): www.indexfungorum.org

Scottish Fungi (UK): sites.google.com/site/scottishfungi

Fungi Online (UK): www.fungionline.org.uk

Northern Ireland Fungus Group (UK): www.nifg.org.uk

European Mycological Association (EU): http://www.euromould.org

Mycological Society of America (USA): msafungi.org

Tom Volk's Fungi (USA): botit.botany.wisc.edu/toms_fungi

Michael Kuo (USA): www.mushroomexpert.com

Mykoweb - Michael Wood (USA): www.mykoweb.com

Australian National Botanic Gardens (AU): www.anbg.gov.au/fungi

Species Index – Scientific Names

Page numbers in **bold** denote main entries.

Species Index – Common Names

Page numbers in **bold** denote main entries.

Plums and Custard *Tricholomopsis rutilans* grows on dead conifer stumps and sometimes on the bases of fence posts; it is a common sight in mature spruce plantations.

The Dark Fieldcap *Cyclocybe erebia*, is a woodland fungus; its cap colour is very variable, sometimes with a centre so dark that it appears to be almost jet black.

General Index

Topics other than those referring to particular fungus groups or species.

Picture Credits

The author and publishers gratefully acknowledge the following generous picture contributions (identified by page numbers and positions on the page):

David Adamson	13 top, 227 bottom, 238 top, 265 top, 288 bottom, 325 bottom right, 329 bottom, 446 right
Patrea Andersen	303 top
Vaisey Bramley	296 top (insert)
Zoran Bozovic	5
Brian Broad	374
Doug Collins	380 bottom
Jochen Dahle	195 top
Paul Digard	38
Sigisfredo Garnica	49 bottom, 50 top, 52 top
Simon Harding	222 middle, 287 top, 305 bottom, 310 bottom 3 pictures, 446 right
David Harries	328 bottom right, 357 top, 348 bottom, 336 top right
Richard Haynes	261 bottom, 299 middle, 386
Sue Impey/Cranfield University	34
David Kelly	71, 79, 154 middle, 175 bottom, 192 middle, 310 bottom x 3, 360 bottom, 372 bottom left, 385 top, 403 top right, 406 top right, 407 top, 408 top, 440
Nigel Kent	39 bottom, 89 bottom, 108 bottom, 162 top, 235 bottom
Andreas Kunze/ Wikipedia	123 bottom
James Langiewicz	233 bottom
James Lindsey	332 bottom
Mark Mackie	135 middle
Plantin.com	136
Mike & Hilary Rose	306 bottom, 307 top
VincEnzo Ricceri	157 top
Shane Templeton	448
Penny Turner	240 bottom, 303 bottom
Greg Whitear	80

Subject to any accidental errors or omissions in the above (in which case please accept our apologies), all other pictures and diagrams are by Pat and Sue O'Reilly.

Shaggy Scalycaps *Pholiota squarrosa*...

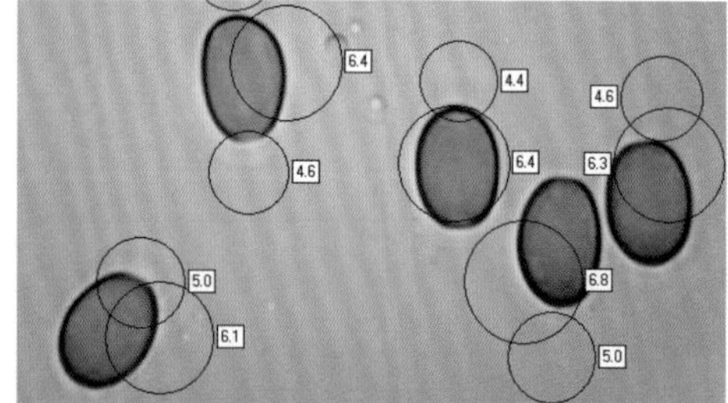

...and the spores via photomicroscopy

About the Author

Pat O'Reilly is a naturalist whose fascination with fungi stretches back more than 45years. His pursuit of mushrooms, toadstools and other fungal fruitbodies has taken him to many countries; but, as he says, there is a special satisfaction in finding and identifying beautiful fungi close to home. (And with many thousands of species in Britain and Ireland, most of which occur throughout Europe and elsewhere in the world, fungus forays can be fun even on a shoestring budget.)

Writing and broadcasting on wildlife and countryside topics for the past 35 years, Pat is the author of more than 20 books and several hundred articles. With his wife Sue he developed and maintains the *First Nature* website, which receives more than a million visits per year. Many of the hundreds of enquiries received through the website each year come via the extensive Fungi section.

Pat is an active conservationist. He established and for 14 years led the Young Conservationists Initiative both in Wales and overseas, via which up to 140 young people each year took part in habitat monitoring and restoration projects. As an appointed advisor to the UK and Welsh Assembly Governments on environmental issues, he has chaired and served on several advisory committees and special commissions. Pat also served on the Council of CCW (the Countryside Council for Wales), making good use of his special interest in fungi conservation (he is a Member of the British Mycological Society) and the management of National Nature Reserves in Wales. For his work in this field Pat O'Reilly was awarded an MBE in 2003.

Fairy Inkcaps *Coprinellus disseminatus*, Slovenia

And finally...

A beautiful veiled stinkhorn *Dictyophora multicolor*, Yalong Bay Golf Club, Sanya, China

For more information about the fascinating kingdom of fungi, details and several thousand pictures of many more species, please keep in touch via **www.first-nature.com/fungi**